KT-529-699

INTRODUCTION

Practice for Advanced Mathematics: Mechanics provides an extensive bank of practice questions for the aspiring A or AS level mathematics student.

It is assumed that the book will be used in support of taught lessons, or as a revision guide, and thus the development or proof of results from first principles has been kept to a minimum. Each topic is introduced with a brief overview of key points, followed by one or more worked examples.

The main exercises contain questions of two kinds. **A** questions are straightforward questions intended to practise one simple skill, such as finding the resultant of two vectors. **B** questions are slightly longer; they usually involve two or more stages in their solution, and are beginning to approach the standard of many A level questions.

At the end of each chapter is a set of **C** questions: these are set at A level standard, and are generally longer than **B** questions.

In order to solve many of the questions you will need a calculator. The worked answers and those to the exercises have generally been constructed using a Casio fx–7700GH calculator, although the use of such a graphics calculator is not necessary.

We would like to thank Mr D C Taylor who greatly assisted us with the proof reading.

Peter Nunn and David Simmons
August 1998

PRACTICE
FOR
ADVANCED

MECHANICS

MATHEMATICS DIVISION
THE HENLEY COLLEGE
DEANFIELD AVENUE
HENLEY-ON-THAMES
RG9 1UH

PETER NUNN & DAVID SIMMONS

Hodder & Stoughton

047921

THE HENLEY COLLEGE LIBRARY

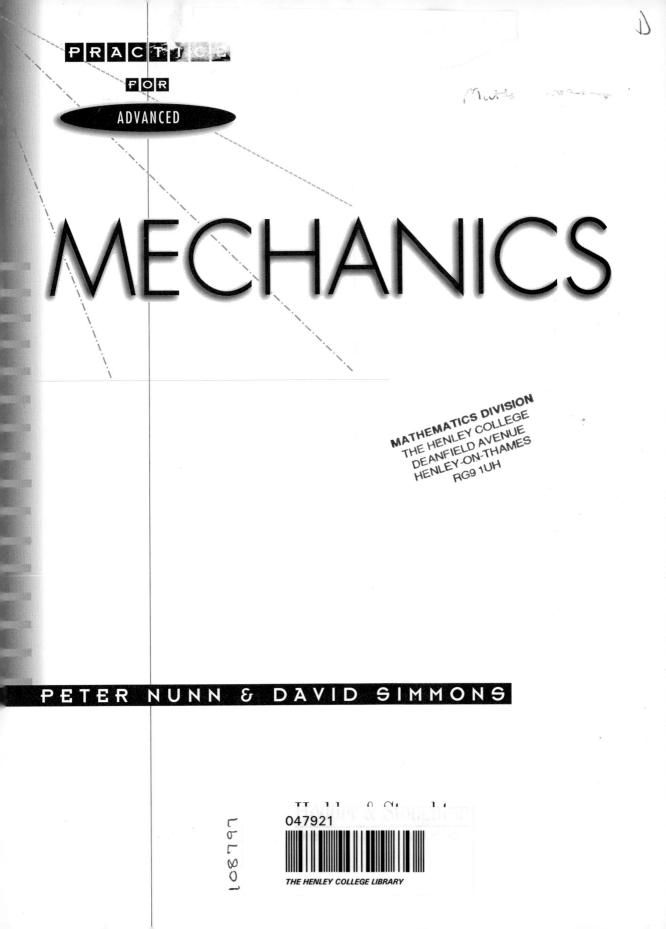

Orders: please contact Bookpoint Ltd, 39 Milton Park, Abingdon, Oxon OX14 4TD. Telephone: (44) 01235 400414, Fax: (44) 01235 400454. Lines are open from 9.00–6.00, Monday to Saturday, with a 24 hour message answering service. Email address: orders@bookpoint.co.uk

British Library Cataloguing in Publication Data
A catalogue record for this title is available from The British Library

ISBN 0 340 701 668

First published 1998
Impression number   10 9 8 7 6 5 4 3 2 1
Year   2004 2003 2002 2001 2000 1999 1998

Copyright © 1998 Peter Nunn, David Simmons

All rights reserved. No part of this publication may be reproduced or transmitted in any form or by any means, electronic or mechanical, including photocopy, recording, or any information storage and retrieval system, without permission in writing from the publisher or under licence from the Copyright Licensing Agency Limited. Further details of such licences (for reprographic reproduction) may be obtained from the Copyright Licensing Agency Limited, of 90 Tottenham Court Road, London W1P 9HE.

Cover photo from Tony Stone Images

Cover design by Lis Rowe.
Page design by Lynda King.
Illustrations by Jeff Edwards

Typeset by Wearset, Boldon, Tyne and Wear.
Printed in Great Britain for Hodder & Stoughton Educational, a division of Hodder Headline Plc, 338 Euston Road, London NW1 3BH by Scotprint Ltd, Musselburgh, Scotland.

CONTENTS

Chapter 1

KINEMATICS (1): MOTION IN A STRAIGHT LINE

1.1 Displacement, velocity and acceleration

Key points

Displacement and distance

In Figure 1.1 points C and D are a distance of 3 units from point O. However, C has a displacement of +3 from O, whereas D has a displacement of −3 from O.

Distance is a scalar quantity (it has magnitude only).

Displacement is a vector quantity (it has both magnitude and direction).

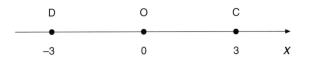

Figure 1.1

Speed and velocity

The following results are familiar from GCSE work.

If the speed is constant

$$\text{speed} = \frac{\text{distance}}{\text{time}}$$

If the speed varies

$$\text{average speed} = \frac{\text{total distance}}{\text{time}}$$

The most common units of speed are m s^{-1} and km h^{-1}.

It is worth remembering the conversion factor: 1 m s^{-1} = 3.6 km h^{-1}.

Figure 1.2

In Figure 1.2, two cars A and B are moving along a straight road relative to a fixed point O.

The speed of both cars is 30 m s^{-1}. However, the displacement of A from O is increasing, and the displacement of B from O is decreasing.

A has a velocity of $+30$ m s^{-1}, while B has a velocity of -30 m s^{-1}.

In general, if velocity is constant

$$\text{velocity} = \frac{\text{displacement}}{\text{time}}$$

if velocity varies

$$\text{average velocity} = \frac{\text{total displacement}}{\text{time}}$$

A particle with uniform velocity is one whose speed is constant and whose direction does not change.

Time–displacement (t,x) graphs

Time–displacement graphs often help us to analyse motion in one dimension.

The gradient at any point of the (t,x) graph gives the velocity at that point.

Acceleration

Acceleration is the rate of change of velocity:

$$\text{average acceleration} = \frac{\text{change in velocity}}{\text{time}}$$

The units of acceleration are m s^{-2}.

When the velocity is decreasing the acceleration will be negative. A negative acceleration is often called a deceleration or retardation.

Time–velocity (t,v) graphs

Time–velocity graphs help us to analyse the motion in a similar way to time–displacement graphs.

In general, on a (t,v) graph the gradient at any point gives the acceleration at that point and the area under the graph gives the displacement.

Example 1

A boy starts from a bus stop, A, on a long straight road and walks 270 m towards the next stop, reaching point B in 1.5 minutes. He waits 1 minute between stops when he sees a bus arriving. He decides that A is the closest stop and begins to run back to A. He covers a distance of 150 m in 30 seconds to a point, C, when he realises he has missed the bus and gives up!

(a) Draw a (t, x) graph for the boy's motion.

(b) Calculate his average velocity for the journey.

(c) Calculate his average speed for the journey.

Solution

(a) Figure 1.3 shows a graph of the boy's journey, plotting the distance covered against the time taken for the several stages of his journey, where x measures the distance from A in metres.

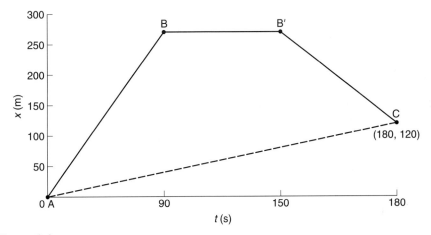

Figure 1.3

In the first section, his velocity is uniform and is given by the ratio displacement/time, which is the gradient of the line AB, i.e. $270/90 = 3$ and his velocity is 3 m s^{-1}.

In the section labelled BB', his velocity is 0 m s^{-1}.

Over the final section B'C the gradient is $-150/30 = -5$. His speed is 5 m s^{-1} and the negative sign of his velocity shows that he is moving back towards A.

(b) From the graph we can calculate the average velocity over the whole journey, which is defined as

$$\frac{\text{total displacement}}{\text{time}} = \frac{120}{180} \approx 0.67$$

which is the gradient of the dotted line AC in Figure 1.3. His average velocity for the journey is 0.67 m s^{-1}.

(c) The average speed is

$$\frac{\text{total distance travelled}}{\text{time}} = \frac{420}{180} \approx 2.33$$

2.33 m s^{-1} is the constant speed the boy would need in order to cover the whole distance non-stop.

Note: the total displacement is given by the vector **AC**, which is the resultant of the separate displacements. The total distance travelled is the actual distance walked by the boy.

Example 2

A cyclist is moving with a velocity of 4 m s^{-1} when she comes to a downhill slope along which she freewheels and her velocity increases at a constant rate to 12 m s^{-1} after 10 s. The road then levels out and she decides to keep her speed steady at 12 m s^{-1} for a further 5 s, after which there is an incline in the road. She allows herself to slow down at a constant rate to rest after a further 5 s.

(a) Draw a (t,v) graph for the motion.

(b) Calculate the average acceleration.

(c) Calculate the total distance travelled by the cyclist.

Solution

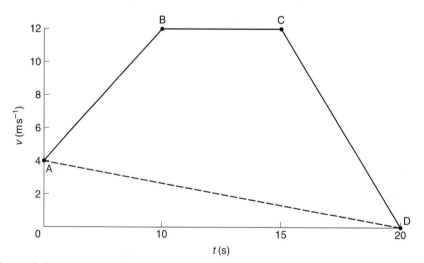

Figure 1.4

(a) We look at the motion at various stages.

From A to B the acceleration is uniform

$$\text{acceleration} = \frac{\text{change in velocity}}{\text{time}} = \text{gradient of AB} = \frac{8}{10}$$

The acceleration is 0.8 m s^{-2}.

(Since the speed is increasing the slope of the (t,v) graph is positive even though the cyclist is travelling downhill.)

From B to C acceleration is zero.

From C to D acceleration = gradient of CD (negative) = 12/5.

The acceleration is -2.4 m s^{-2}.

(b)　Average acceleration = $\dfrac{\text{change in velocity over the whole path}}{\text{time taken}}$

$\qquad\qquad$ = gradient of AD

$\qquad\qquad$ = $-5/20$.

The acceleration is 0.25 m s^{-2}.

(c)　For the first part of the journey, the graph is in the shape of a trapezium whose area is given by:

$0.5(4 + 12) \times 10 = 80$

so the distance travelled is 80 m.

Alternatively, since her average speed from A to B is 8 m s^{-1}, over 10 s the cyclist travels a distance of 80 m.

In section BC she is travelling at a steady 12 m s^{-1} for 5 s, so she covers a distance of 60 m, which is the area under that section of the graph.

From C to D, her average speed is $\frac{1}{2}(12 + 0) = 6$ m s^{-1}, so she travels a distance of 30 m in 5 s, which again is the area under the graph, namely of the triangular shape.

The total distance over the whole journey is 170 m.

Exercise 1.1

A1　Jack and Jill take 5 minutes to walk at a constant speed 500 m up a hill. At the top they admire the view for 3 minutes, before Jack falls and rolls down the hill at a constant speed taking 2 minutes to reach the bottom. Draw a (t,x) graph and find Jack's average speed for the whole journey.

A2　A cyclist with an initial velocity of 3 m s^{-1} moves in a straight line with a constant acceleration of 0.5 m s^{-2} for 10 s. What is her final velocity and how far does she travel in that time?

A3　A girl is running at 2 m s^{-1} and 5 s later she is running at 2.5 m s^{-1}. What is her constant acceleration and how far has she gone in the 5 s?

A4　A particle moves in a straight line OAB starting from rest at O. The particle accelerates uniformly at 3 m s^{-2} from O to A, where OA = 6 m. From A to B the particle decelerates uniformly to rest for 3 seconds and comes to rest at C. Draw a (t,v) graph and use it to find:

(a)　the time taken to reach A

(b)　the speed of the particle as it reaches A

(c)　the distance OB.　　　　*continued*

Exercise 1.1 *continued*

A5 A car accelerates from rest as shown in the table

Time (s)	Gear	Acceleration (m s^{-2})
0–2	1	5
2–3	change	−1
3–5	2	4
5–6	change	−1
6–8	3	3
8–9	change	−1
9–10	4	2

Draw a (t,v) graph and use it to find the speed and the distance travelled in these 10 s.

A6 On approaching a station a tube train decelerates uniformly from 30 m s^{-1} to 20 m s^{-1} over a distance of 200 m. Find:

(a) the deceleration

(b) the total time for it to come to rest under this deceleration.

A7 A car's speed is reduced from 36 m s^{-1} to 24 m s^{-1} under a constant retardation of 2.5 m s^{-2}. Draw a (t,v) graph and use it to find:

(a) the time taken

(b) the distance covered.

B1 A cyclist travels from his home to the shops along a long straight road a distance of 300 m at a constant speed of 6 m s^{-1}. He stops for 1 minute to buy a drink and then rides back past his home a further distance of 150 m (to a friend's house) at a constant speed of 8 m s^{-1}. Draw a (t,x) graph of his journey and find:

(a) the total time taken

(b) his average speed for the whole journey

(c) his average velocity for the whole journey.

B2 A car is moving with constant acceleration in a straight line so that it covers 10 m and 12 m in two successive intervals of 1 s. What is its acceleration?

B3 Two competitors A and B race along a straight road starting from a point O. A runs with an initial velocity of 3 m s^{-1} and an acceleration of 0.5 m s^{-2}. B starts from rest with an acceleration of 1.5 m s^{-2}. By drawing a (t,v) graph, find out when B overtakes A. How far are they from O when this happens?

B4 Figure 1.5 shows the displacement of a cyclist along a long straight road where the displacement shown is from her home at the point O.

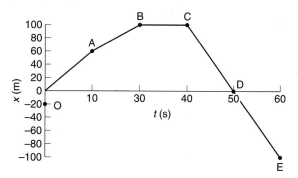

Figure 1.5

(a) Describe her motion for each part of the path, OA, AB, BC, CD, DE.

(b) What is the significance of the point E, which is below the x-axis?

(c) What is her average speed over the 60 s?

(d) What is her average velocity over the same time?

B5 A boy kicks a football towards a wall at 20 m s^{-1} from a point 10 m away. The ball rebounds at 10 m s^{-1} along the same line. The boy stops the ball at a point 8 m from the wall. Draw a (t,x) graph, where x is the distance of the ball from its starting point. Find both the average speed and the average velocity for the complete path.

B6 A billiard ball is hit at 3 m s^{-1} from a point A so that it moves off at right angles to a cushion 0.5 m away. It rebounds at a speed of 1 m s^{-1} until it hits the opposite cushion

2 m away. Draw a (t,x) graph showing the displacement from A and find the average speed of the ball over the whole journey.

B7 A car is moving along a motorway at 144 km h^{-1}. At the instant it passes a lay-by a police car leaves the lay-by starting from rest, and moves with a constant

acceleration of 3 m s^{-2} for 20 seconds and then travels at constant velocity. Use a (t,v) graph to find:

(a) how long it takes for the police car to overtake the motorist

(b) the distance travelled by the police car in this time.

1.2 Constant acceleration formulae

Key points

There are a large number of everyday examples in which motion under constant acceleration occurs. A particular example of this is when an object falls freely under gravity.

Suppose a particle starts from a point O with initial velocity u m s^{-1} and moves with constant acceleration a m s^{-2} to reach a final velocity of v m s^{-1} after time t s.

The final velocity is given by $v = u + at$ (1)

The distance travelled is given by $s = \frac{1}{2}(u + v)t$ (2)

or $s = ut + \frac{1}{2}at^2$ (3)

Rearranging equation (1) as $v + u = at$

and equation (2) as $v + u = 2s/t$

we obtain $v^2 - u^2 = 2as$ (4)

which is often rearranged as $v^2 = u^2 + 2as$

These four equations are referred to as the constant acceleration formulae

$$v = u + at \qquad (1)$$
$$s = \tfrac{1}{2}(u + v)t \qquad (2)$$
$$s = ut + \tfrac{1}{2}at^2 \qquad (3)$$
$$v^2 = u^2 + 2as \qquad (4)$$

Example 1

A man is running for a bus. He accelerates from rest at 2 m s^{-2} for the first 3 s, maintains a constant speed for 2 s, and then decelerates at 1 m s^{-2} for a further 2 s. How far does the man travel in the 7 s?

Solution

We can solve this using a (t,v) graph, as in Section 1.1, or by use of the constant acceleration formulae.

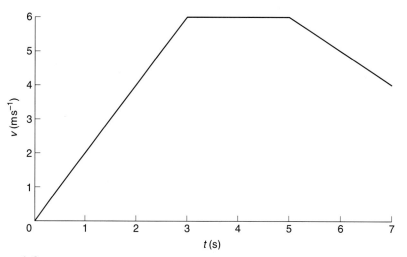

Figure 1.6

Figure 1.6 shows the (t,v) graph for the motion.

Stage 1: We have $u = 0$, $t = 3$, $a = 2$.

Using $s = ut + \frac{1}{2}at^2$ $s = 0 + \frac{1}{2} \times 2 \times 9 = 9$

Using $v = u + at$ $v = 0 + 2 \times 3 = 6$

Stage 2: We have $u = 6$, $t = 2$, $a = 0$.

Using $s = ut + \frac{1}{2}at^2$ $s = 6 \times 2 + \frac{1}{2} \times 0 \times 4 = 12$

Stage 3: We have $u = 6$, $t = 2$, $a = -1$ (deceleration).

Using $s = ut + \frac{1}{2}at^2$ $s = 6 \times 2 + \frac{1}{2} \times -1 \times 4 = 10$

The total distance is 31 m (which is equal to the area under the (t,v) graph shown).

Example 2

A tube train starts from rest with constant acceleration until it reaches a maximum speed at 20 m s^{-1}. It then travels at a constant speed of 20 m s^{-1} before it decelerates uniformly to rest. The distance from station to station is 1.5 km and the train is at maximum speed for $\frac{2}{3}$ of the total journey time.

(a)   Illustrate this information on a (t,v) graph.

(b)   Find the total time of the journey.

(c)   If the magnitude of the deceleration is twice the magnitude of the acceleration, find the magnitude of the deceleration.

Solution

(a)   If we let T be the total journey time, the (t,v) graph will be as shown in Figure 1.7.

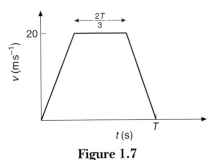

Figure 1.7

(b)   The distance travelled is given by the area under the (t,v) graph. $20(T + 2T/3) = 1500$ (using the formula for the area under a trapezium), giving $5T/3 = 150$ and T is 90 s.

(c)   If the magnitude of the deceleration is twice the magnitude of the acceleration, the magnitude of the gradient of section CD will be twice the gradient of section AB. Therefore the time decelerating will be half of the time accelerating (why?).

The time at constant speed is $(2/3) \times 90 = 60$ s.

The time decelerating is $(1/3) \times 30 = 10$ s.

The magnitude of the deceleration is 2 m s^{-2}.

Example 3

In a qualifying heat for the Womens 100 m in the Atlanta Olympics, Merlene Ottey ran approximately as follows:

0–20 m starting from rest with a constant acceleration of 3 m s^{-2}

20–90 m at constant speed

90–100 m at a constant deceleration of 0.5 m s^{-2} (she slowed down realising that she had easily won the heat).

What was her maximum speed and what was her total time for the race?

Solution

Stage 1: 0–20 m   Using $s = ut + \frac{1}{2}at^2$ $20 = 1.5t^2$

giving $t = 3.65$ s

Using $v^2 = u^2 + 2as$ $v^2 = 120$

giving $v = 10.95$ m s^{-1} (taking the positive root).

Stage 2: 20–90 m $t = 70/10.95 = 6.39$ s

Stage 3: 90–100 m   Using $s = ut + \frac{1}{2}at^2$ $10 = 10.95t - 0.25t^2$

giving $t = 0.925$ s.

Therefore her maximum speed was 10.95 m s^{-1} and her time was
$3.65 + 6.39 + 0.925 = 10.97$ s.

Exercise 1.2

Take g as 9.8 m s^{-2}, where necessary.

Use the constant acceleration formulae for questions **A1** to **A5**.

A1   A ball is thrown vertically upwards with a speed of 20 m s^{-1}. If it moves freely under gravity, how high will it rise?

A2   A tile falls off the edge of a roof 20 m high. How long does it take to hit the ground, if air resistance is neglected?

A3   A car accelerates uniformly in a straight line from rest to 30 m s^{-1} in 10 s. Calculate the acceleration and the distance travelled in that time.

A4   What acceleration in m s^{-2} is needed to increase the speed of a car from 0 to 15 km h^{-1} in 100 m?

A5   A ball is thrown vertically upwards at 15 m s^{-1} from a point A which is 12 m vertically above the horizontal ground. Given that the ball moves freely under gravity, find:

(a)   the greatest height above ground reached by the ball

(b)   the speed of the ball at the instant when it strikes the ground.

A6   A car accelerates uniformly from rest at a point O. It passes a marker A on the side of the road at 20 m s^{-1} and passes the next marker B, 1 km along the road from A after a further 40 s.

Find the acceleration of the car and the time taken to travel from O to A.

Use graphical methods for questions **A7** and **A8**.

A7   A tube train takes 40 s to travel between two stops which are 500 m apart. On starting it is uniformly accelerated up to a speed of 20 m s^{-1} and maintains this speed until it is brought to rest by a constant retardation. If the time occupied in accelerating is twice that in retarding, calculate the acceleration and distance travelled at full speed.

A8   In a heat for the 100 m in the Atlanta Olympics an athlete accelerated from rest to his maximum speed of 12 m s^{-1} in 2 s. He maintained this top speed for a further 6 s, and then seeing that he had won he 'eased off' (decelerated uniformly), crossing the line in a time of 9.95 s. What was his speed when he crossed the line? What was his deceleration?

B1   A car moving with uniform acceleration along a straight level road passed under two bridges with speeds 108 km h^{-1} and 144 km h^{-1} respectively. Find the speed of the car when it was exactly midway between the bridges.

Exercise 1.2 *continued*

B2 A man is running in a straight line and covers 6 m, 9 m and 21 m in successive intervals of 3 s, 2 s and 3 s. Show that this is consistent with constant acceleration. Find the acceleration and the speed at the end of the 8 s period.

B3 A ball is dropped from a high-rise block of flats. The distance between floors in the block is the same. The ball takes 1 s to fall from the 10th to the 9th floor and 0.5 s to fall from the 9th to the 8th. What is the distance between floors?

B4 A train starts from rest with constant acceleration until it reaches a speed v. It then travels at the constant speed v before it decelerates uniformly to rest. The average speed for the journey is $\frac{3}{4}v$. What fraction of the time is covered at constant speed? What fraction of the distance is covered at constant speed?

B5 In a rally cars are set off at intervals of two minutes. If two cars accelerate uniformly from rest to a maximum of 100 km h^{-1} in 1 minute, find how far the first car will have gone when the second car starts. How far apart will they be at top speed?

B6 At the end of a race, athlete A is 190 m from the tape and is running at a constant speed of 10 m s^{-1}. Athlete B is 200 m from the tape with a speed of 8 m s^{-1} when he accelerates uniformly at 0.5 m s^{-2} until he reaches a speed of 12 m s^{-1}. Prove that B wins the race and find how far from the tape he overtakes A.

B7 A lift descends with uniform acceleration a, followed by uniform retardation $2a$. If it begins and ends at rest, descending a distance y in time t, prove that $y = \frac{1}{3}at^2$.

B8 A driver on a motorway is travelling in a car at a constant speed of 40 m s^{-1}. In order to turn off at a junction she begins braking at the first distance marker for the exit, and the net deceleration over the next 300 m is shown in the table.

Distance after braking started (m)	Resultant deceleration (m s^{-2})
0–100	−3
100–200	−4
200–300	−0.5

What is the speed of the car at the end of the 300 m?

For how long did braking take place?

B9 A train starts from rest with constant acceleration a, until it reaches a speed w. It then travels at a constant speed w before it decelerates uniformly to rest, the retardation (deceleration) having magnitude f. The average speed for the whole journey is $(7/8)w$.

(a) Show that the train travels at a constant speed for three-quarters of the total time taken.

(b) Find what fraction of the journey is covered at constant speed.

B10 A ball is thrown vertically upwards with a speed of 29.4 m s^{-1}. At what height has the speed dropped to 19.4 m s^{-1}, and for how long is the ball above this height?

Revision questions

Take g as 10 m s^{-2}, where necessary.

C1 A particle P starting from rest at O moves in a straight line OABC. It accelerates uniformly at 2 m s^{-2} from O to A. It then travels at constant velocity to B and then decelerates at 3 m s^{-2} from B to C. Given that BC is 6 m and the total time from O to C is 12 s, find the distance AB.

continued

C2 A balloon rises vertically from rest on the ground with constant acceleration 1 m s^{-2}. A small sack of ballast is released from the balloon when it has risen to a height of 360 m.

(a) Find the speed of the balloon when the ballast is released.

(b) Find the maximum height reached by the ballast.

(c) Find the time taken by the ballast to reach the ground.

(d) Find the speed of the ballast on hitting the ground.

C3 A car accelerates uniformly from rest to a speed of 30 m s^{-1} in T s. It maintains this speed for 40 s and then decelerates to rest in a further $2T$ s. Given that the total distance travelled is 1.65 km, use a (t,v) graph to find the value of T and the magnitude of the deceleration during the final stage of the motion.

C4 A ball is thrown vertically upwards with speed u. After a time t, another ball is thrown vertically upwards from the same point with the same speed. Show the balls will collide at a height of $(4u^2 - g^2t^2)/8g$.

C5 A particle starts from rest at $t = 0$ and moves in a straight line. Its acceleration over the first 100 s is given by:

$a = 4 \qquad 0 \le t < 30$

$a = 1 \qquad 30 \le t < 50$

$a = -2.5 \quad 50 \le t < 100$

where t is in seconds and a is in m s^{-2}.

Sketch the (t,v) graph and find the total distance travelled over the interval $0 \le t < 100$.

C6 Two cyclists A and B are travelling in the same direction along a road. A is moving at 12 m s^{-1} when he passes B who is moving at 8 m s^{-1}. They continue at these speeds for 1 minute. Both decelerate at different rates and A comes to rest in a further 2 minutes. B comes to rest at the same point as A.

(a) Sketch, on the same diagram, the (t,v) graphs for A and B.

(b) Find the distance travelled by A in the 3 minutes before he stops.

(c) Find the difference in stopping times between A and B.

(d) Find the magnitude of the deceleration of B.

C7 A boy drops a ball from rest out of a window at a height of 12 m above ground. At the same instant another boy kicks a football vertically upwards from the ground with a speed of 16 m s^{-1}. How high above ground do the balls pass each other?

C8 A juggler throws an apple vertically with a speed of 12 m s^{-1} and 1 second later he throws an orange vertically in the same straight line with a speed of 6 m s^{-1}. How long after the orange is thrown do they collide? In what direction are they moving at that time?

C9 Figure 1.8 shows the (t,x) graph for a particle moving over a period of 12 seconds.

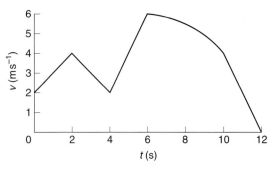

Figure 1.8

(a) Write down the velocity of the particle at times 1, 3, 5, and 11.

(b) What is the average velocity over the first 6 seconds?

(c) Describe what is happening to the particle between $t = 6$ and $t = 12$.

(d) Sketch the (t,v) graph for the motion.

Revision questions *continued*

C10 Figure 1.9 shows the (t,v) graph for a car over a period of 20 seconds.

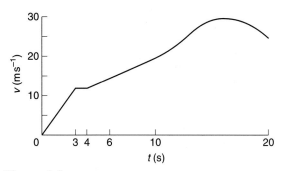

Figure 1.9

Find:

(a)   the acceleration over the first 3 s

(b)   the average acceleration over the first 20 s

(c)   the distance travelled over the first 20 s.

Sketch the (t,x) graph for the first 10 seconds.

Chapter 2

VECTORS IN MECHANICS

Key points

Vectors may be used to represent physical quantities which have both magnitude and direction, such as displacement, velocity and acceleration.

Triangle law of addition

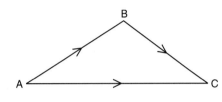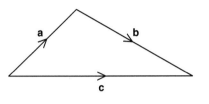

Figure 2.1

$$\mathbf{AB} + \mathbf{BC} = \mathbf{AC} \qquad \text{or} \qquad \mathbf{a} + \mathbf{b} = \mathbf{c}$$

AC is called the **resultant** of **AB** and **BC**.

Parallelogram law of addition

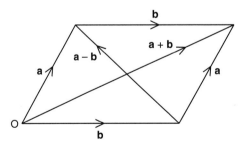

Figure 2.2

The resultant of **a** and **b**, namely **a** + **b**, is the diagonal from O of the parallelogram formed by them. The other diagonal is given by the vector **a** − **b** or **b** − **a** depending on its direction.

Resolution of vectors into components

It is often convenient to express a given vector in terms of its components in two perpendicular directions. For instance, these might be in the direction of the x and y axes, using unit base vectors $\mathbf{i} = \begin{pmatrix} 1 \\ 0 \end{pmatrix}$ and $\mathbf{j} = \begin{pmatrix} 0 \\ 1 \end{pmatrix}$,

or in the directions east and north. The vector $\mathbf{OP} = \mathbf{p}$, shown in Figure 2.3 may be resolved into components along the x and y axes.

It may be written as

$\mathbf{p} = r\cos\theta°\,\mathbf{i} + r\sin\theta°\,\mathbf{j}$

or as

$\mathbf{p} = \begin{pmatrix} r\cos\theta° \\ r\sin\theta° \end{pmatrix}.$

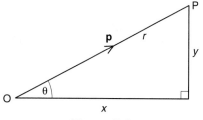

Figure 2.3

Magnitude and direction

A vector written as $\mathbf{p} = a\mathbf{i} + b\mathbf{j}$ or $\mathbf{p} = \begin{pmatrix} a \\ b \end{pmatrix}$ has magnitude $\sqrt{(a^2 + b^2)}$ and

direction with the x-axis given by $\tan^{-1}(b/a)$.

The magnitude of a vector is also known as its length or modulus and may be written $|\mathbf{p}|$.

Unit vectors

The most widely used unit vectors in mechanics are the unit base vectors along the x- and y-axes of the Cartesian coordinate system. However, a unit vector may be found in the direction of any given vector.

For example, the modulus, or length of the vector $2\mathbf{i} + 3\mathbf{j}$ is $\sqrt{(2^2 + 3^2)} = \sqrt{13}$.

To derive a vector of unit length parallel to $2\mathbf{i} + 3\mathbf{j}$ the vector is divided by $\sqrt{13}$, to give $\dfrac{2}{\sqrt{13}}\mathbf{i} + \dfrac{3}{\sqrt{13}}\mathbf{j}.$

Example 1

A light aircraft heads due north with a speed of 150 km h^{-1}, but is blown off course by the wind and actually heads on a bearing of 015° with a speed of 200 km h^{-1}. Find the speed and direction of the wind.

Solution

Method 1 – by trigonometry

The resultant velocity of the plane is the velocity of the plane plus the velocity of the wind, so that

$\mathbf{OR} = \mathbf{OP} + \mathbf{PR}$

Using the cosine rule

$PR^2 = OP^2 + OR^2 - 2\,OP\,OR\cos 15°$

$\qquad = 150^2 + 200^2 - 2 \times 150 \times 200\cos 15°$

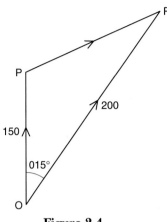

Figure 2.4

giving PR = 67.4.

The wind speed is approximately 67.4 km h^{-1}.

Its direction is found using the sine rule

$$\frac{\sin O\hat{P}R}{200} = \frac{\sin 15°}{67.4}$$

giving O$\hat{P}$R = 129.8° Hence the bearing of the wind is $(180° - 129.8°) = 50.2°$.

Method 2 – using components

The velocity of the plane, **OP** $= \begin{pmatrix} 0 \\ 150 \end{pmatrix}$

The resultant velocity, **OR** $= \begin{pmatrix} 200 \sin 15° \\ 200 \cos 15° \end{pmatrix} = \begin{pmatrix} 51.8 \\ 193 \end{pmatrix}$

The velocity of the wind, **PR** = **OR** − **OP** $= \begin{pmatrix} 51.8 - 0 \\ 193 - 150 \end{pmatrix} = \begin{pmatrix} 51.8 \\ 43 \end{pmatrix}$

Its speed PR $= \sqrt{(51.8^2 + 43^2)} = 67.4$.

Its bearing is given by $90° - \tan^{-1}(43/51.8) = 90° - 39.8° = 50.2°$.

Thus the plane flies at approximately 67 km h^{-1} on a bearing of 050°.

Example 2

A boy decides to swim across a river to reach a point on the opposite bank. The river is 36 m wide and the boy can swim at 3 m s^{-1} in still water. There is a current of 2 m s^{-1} flowing parallel to the bank.

(a) How far down the opposite bank will the boy land, if he heads at right angles to the bank?

(b) If he wants to reach the point opposite him on the far bank, in which direction should he head upstream and how long will he take to cross the river?

Solution

(a)

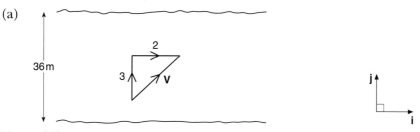

Figure 2.5

Taking base vectors **i** and **j** down and across the river, Figure 2.5 shows a vector triangle for the velocities of the boy and the river. His resultant velocity, **v**, is the sum of these two velocities.

So, $\mathbf{v} = \begin{pmatrix} 0 \\ 3 \end{pmatrix} + \begin{pmatrix} 2 \\ 0 \end{pmatrix} = \begin{pmatrix} 2 \\ 3 \end{pmatrix}$, which has magnitude $\sqrt{13}$ and direction

given by $\tan^{-1}(3/2) = 56.0°$ with the bank.

Whilst the direction of his resultant is not directly across the river, the component across the river is still 3 m s^{-1}, and so he takes $36/3 = 12 \text{ s}$ to cross.

In this time, the river has carried him downstream $2 \times 12 = 24 \text{ m}$, which is how far from the point opposite his starting point he will have drifted.

(b)

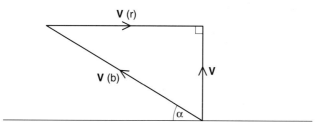

Figure 2.6

In this case, the direction of his resultant velocity is known, but not its magnitude. The magnitude of his initial velocity is known, but not its direction.

Let the velocity of the boy be $\mathbf{V}(b) = \begin{pmatrix} -3\cos\alpha \\ 3\sin\alpha \end{pmatrix}$, where α is the

angle of his velocity with the bank upstream.

The velocity of the river, $\mathbf{V}(r) = \begin{pmatrix} 2 \\ 0 \end{pmatrix}$.

Let his resultant velocity, $\mathbf{V} = \begin{pmatrix} 0 \\ V \end{pmatrix}$, which has no component in the **i** direction.

So

$$\begin{pmatrix} 0 \\ V \end{pmatrix} = \begin{pmatrix} -3\cos\alpha \\ 3\sin\alpha \end{pmatrix} + \begin{pmatrix} 2 \\ 0 \end{pmatrix}$$

Equating components, $-3 \cos \alpha + 2 = 0$, giving $\cos \alpha = 2/3$ and hence $\alpha = 48.1°$.

His resultant speed is given by $V = 3 \sin \alpha = 2.23 \text{ m s}^{-1}$.

So, he should head at an angle of $48°$ to the bank upstream.

Since his speed across the river is approximately 2.2 m s^{-1}, it will take him 14 s to cross.

Exercise 2.1

In questions **A1** to **A5** find the resultant vector by calculation, giving both its magnitude and direction.

A1 A velocity of 10 m s^{-1} north and a velocity of 2 m s^{-1} east.

A2 A displacement of 3 m due south and a displacement of 5 m due west.

A3 A velocity of 2 m s^{-1} due south and a velocity of 5 m s^{-1} in the direction north east.

A4 A displacement of 15 km due east and a displacement of 10 km south west.

A5 A velocity of 25 km h^{-1} north west and a velocity of 15 km h^{-1} on a bearing of $040°$.

A6 A ball is hit with a speed of 20 m s^{-1} at an angle of $30°$ to the horizontal ground. What are the components of its velocity parallel and perpendicular to the ground?

A7 A girl is sliding down a water slide with a speed of 3 m s^{-1}. The slide is inclined at an angle of $20°$ to the horizontal. What are the components of her velocity in the horizontal and vertical directions?

A8 A raindrop falls vertically with a speed of 5 m s^{-1} onto a road which has a slope of $10°$ with the horizontal. What are the components of its velocity down and perpendicular to the slope immediately before impact?

A9 A boy swims across a river with a speed of 2 m s^{-1} at angle of $30°$ to the bank upstream of him. What are the components of his velocity at right angles and parallel to the bank downstream of him?

A10 A plane flies 100 km on a bearing of $300°$, followed by a distance of 150 km on a bearing of $010°$. What are the total distances it flies east and north?

B1 A yacht leaves Torquay and sails at 5 knots on a bearing of $185°$ for 6 hours. As it crosses the English Channel the tide, which has a speed of 3 knots in the direction due west, takes it off course. What is the resultant speed and direction of the yacht, and how far off course will it be after 6 hours? [1 knot = 1 nautical mile per hour]

B2 In question **B1**, in which direction should the yacht sail if it is to stay on course and actually head on the bearing $185°$?

B3 A girl swims at 1.5 m s^{-1} along the length of a leisure pool which is 50 m long and 20 m wide. There is a wave machine in action which pushes the water across the pool to produce a current of 0.5 m s^{-1}. If she starts at one corner of the pool and swims in a straight line parallel to the long side, how far across the pool will she have drifted by the time she completes a length?

B4 A straight section of a river flows parallel to its banks, which are 300 m apart, with a speed of 4.2 m s^{-1}. A swimmer, who can swim with a speed of 6.3 m s^{-1} in still water, starts from a point on one bank and heads across the river at right angles to its banks. Find his resultant speed and the distance downstream he will be when he reaches the opposite bank.

Exercise 2.1   *continued*

B5   In question **B4**, at what angle with the bank upstream should the swimmer head if he is to reach the point directly opposite him on the far bank?

B6   A light aircraft sets out from London City Airport to fly to Birmingham, which is in the direction north west of London. The plane flies at 200 km h^{-1}. If there is a wind blowing at 50 km h^{-1} due north, on what bearing should the pilot fly if he is to head for Birmingham?

B7   A yacht sails on a course which involves passing three buoys at the corners, A, B and C, of an equilateral triangle of length 500 m, as shown in Figure 2.7.

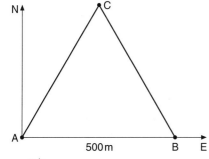

Figure 2.7

The sea is still, but there is a wind blowing at a speed of 2 m s^{-1} parallel to BC. The speed of the yacht in still water is 4 m s^{-1}. A yachtswoman starts at A and sails first to B and then to C and from C back to A.

(a)   At what angle to the line AB should she head if her resultant on the first leg takes her to B? How long does she take to reach B?

(b)   If she changes direction at B and runs parallel to the wind, how long does she take to reach C?

(c)   She changes direction again at C. At what angle to the line CA should she head to ensure that she reaches A and how long does she take to complete the last leg?

(d)   What would have been the time of the complete circuit if there had been no wind?

2.2 Forces

Key points

When the resultant of the forces acting on a particle is zero, the particle is said to be **in equilibrium**.

To solve problems involving more than three forces either

(a)   the vector polygon is divided into several vector triangles, which are solved using a combination of the sine and cosine rules, or

(b)   the fact that the components of the vectors must balance in any direction means that components in two directions may be equated.

The most commonly used unit of force is the Newton, (see Chapters 4 and 5).

Example 1

Two forces **P** and **Q** act on a particle at a point O, as shown in Figure 2.8(a). **P** has magnitude of 9 units and acts on a bearing of 070°, while **Q** acts on a bearing of 210°. It is known that the resultant **R** acts due south.

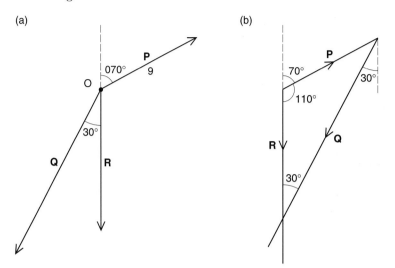

Figure 2.8

Find the magnitude of **Q** and of the resultant **R**.

Solution

Figures 2.8(b) shows the triangle of forces.

Using the sine rule

$$\frac{Q}{\sin 110°} = \frac{9}{\sin 30°} = \frac{R}{\sin 40°}.$$

Hence $Q = 16.9$ and $R = 11.6$.

Example 2

Figure 2.9(a) shows three forces in equilibrium. Find the magnitude of **F** and the angle α.

Solution

The three forces form a closed triangle as in Figure 2.9(b), where the vectors are added tip-to-tail.

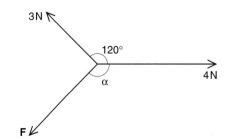

Figure 2.9a

From the cosine rule

$F^2 = 3^2 + 4^2 - 2 \times 3 \times 4 \cos 60°$,
giving $F = \sqrt{13}$ N.

From the sine rule

$$\frac{F}{\sin 60°} = \frac{3}{\sin (180 - \alpha)°}$$

$$\sin (180 - \alpha)° = 3 \sin 60°/\sqrt{13}$$

$$180 - \alpha = 46.1°$$

$$\alpha = 134°$$

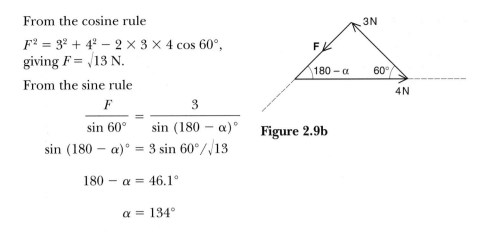

Figure 2.9b

Example 3

The forces shown in Figure 2.10 are in equilibrium. Find the magnitude of **F** and the angle α.

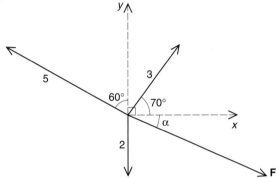

Figure 2.10

Solution

In this case each force is resolved into its components parallel to the x and y axes, using the fact that the sum of the components in each direction must be zero. Each force can be written as a column vector, but as neither the magnitude nor the direction of **F** is known, it is easier to leave it as the letter **F**.

So $\begin{pmatrix} 3 \cos 70° \\ 3 \sin 70° \end{pmatrix} + \begin{pmatrix} -5 \sin 60° \\ 5 \cos 60° \end{pmatrix} + \begin{pmatrix} 0 \\ -2 \end{pmatrix} + \mathbf{F} = \begin{pmatrix} 0 \\ 0 \end{pmatrix}$

Rearranging and evaluating gives $\mathbf{F} = \begin{pmatrix} 3.304 \\ 3.319 \end{pmatrix}$

Using the R → P conversion button on a scientific calculator, or the appropriate alternative on a graphics calculator

$F \approx 4.68$ N and $\alpha \approx 45.1°$.

Alternatively, using Pythagoras' theorem

$F^2 = 3.304^2 + 3.319^2$ giving $F \approx 4.68$ N

and from the components of **F**, $\tan \alpha = 3.319/3.304$, giving $\alpha \approx 45.1°$.

Exercise 2.2

A1 A force **S** of magnitude 5 N acts in the direction due south on a particle, and a force **T** acts in the direction north-east. Given that their resultant **R** is of magnitude 12 N, find the magnitude of **T** and the direction of **R**.

A2 Two forces **P** and **Q** act on a particle at an angle of 60° to each other. A third force **X** of magnitude 10 N acts at an angle of 130° to **P** and 170° to **Q**. If the resultant force of the system is zero, find the magnitudes of **P** and **Q**.

A3 A particle is acted upon by two forces, one of magnitude 8 N on a bearing of 030° and the other of magnitude 5 N on a bearing of 120°. Find the magnitude and direction on the resultant force on the particle.

A4 A small toy boat is in the middle of a narrow stream. Two children are on opposite sides of its banks. One is pulling forward with a force **P** at an angle of 60° to a line parallel to the bank and the other is pulling with a force **Q** at an angle of 150° to the same line, as shown in Figure 2.11. If the resultant direction of the boat is backwards parallel to the banks, show that the magnitude of the resultant force is the same as the magnitude of **P**.

A5 Three children are pulling on a school bag with forces of 15 N, 30 N and 38 N at angles of 120°, 150° and 90° with each other. Assuming the bag does not break, in which direction will it move?

A6 Two men are pulling a light truck along a railway line by ropes on each side of the track. The mass of the truck is 850 kg and they pull with forces 180 N and 250 N at angles of 15° and 27° to the track. Assuming the truck moves at a steady speed along the track, what is the resistance to motion along the track?

A7 Two forces **P** and **Q** act on a particle, where **P** = 2**i** − 3**j** and **Q** = **i** − 4**j**. Find the force **R**, which is needed to keep the particle in equilibrium. What is its magnitude and direction?

A8 A force **P** has magnitude 5 N and acts due south on a particle at a point O. A second force **Q** acts in the direction 045° and a force **R** acts in the direction 120°. If the system is in equilibrium, find the magnitudes of **Q** and **R**.

A9 Three forces **F₁**, **F₂** and **F₃** act on a particle so that it is in equilibrium. **F₁** has magnitude 4 N and acts due west. **F₂** has magnitude 6 N and acts due north. Find the magnitude and direction of **F₃**.

A10 In each case shown in Figure 2.12 find the magnitude of **F** and the angle α, if the forces are in equilibrium.

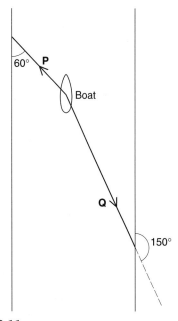

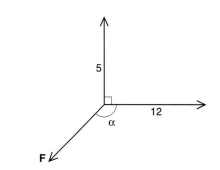

Figure 2.11

Figure 2.12a

Exercise 2.2 *continued*

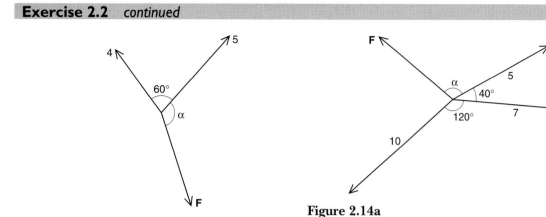

Figure 2.14a

Figure 2.12b

Figure 2.12c

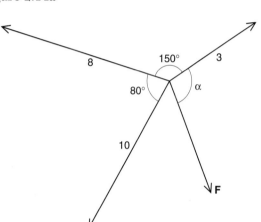

Figure 2.14b

BI Four horizontal wires are attached to a telegraph pole, as shown in Figure 2.13. The magnitudes of the tensions and the directions of three of them are shown. Find the tension F in the fourth wire and the angle α if the pole is in equilibrium.

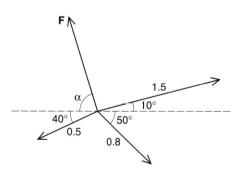

Figure 2.13

B2 In each part of Figure 2.14 find the magnitude of the unknown force **F**, and the angle α if in each case the forces are in equilibrium.

B3 Three forces **P**, **Q** and **R** act on a particle which is at the origin and which is in equilibrium. **P** has magnitude 10 N and acts along the line $y = 2x$. **Q** has magnitude 8 N and acts along the line $y = -0.5x$. Find the magnitude and direction of **R**, giving the equation of the line along which it acts.

B4 Suppose in question **B3** that the force **Q** acts along the line $y = -3x$. Find the magnitude and direction of **R**.

B5 A particle is acted upon by a force of magnitude 2 N in the direction parallel to the vector $\mathbf{i} + 2\mathbf{j}$ and by another of magnitude 3 N in the direction parallel to the vector $2\mathbf{i} + 3\mathbf{j}$. Find to two decimal places the magnitude and direction of the force **X** needed to keep the system in equilibrium.

(Hint: find unit vectors parallel to the two given vectors.)

continued **23**

Exercise 2.2 *continued*

B6 Three forces **P**, **Q** and **R** act on a particle, where **P** = 2**i** + 3**j**, **Q** = −7**i** + 5**j** and **R** = x**i** + y**j**.

Given that the particle is in equilibrium, find the values of x and y.

The force **R** is now removed and another force **S** = −**i** + 2**j** is applied to the system. What is the resultant of **P**, **Q** and **S**?

Revision questions

C1 Four boys are each pulling on a school bag, with forces of magnitudes and directions as shown in Figure 2.15. Find the magnitude and direction of the resultant force on the bag.

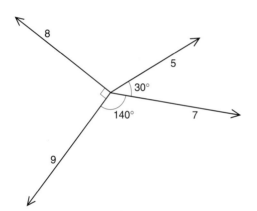

Figure 2.15

C2 Figure 2.16 shows a regular hexagon ABCDEF with forces acting along AB, BC, BD and BF as indicated. What is the magnitude and direction of the resultant force acting at B?

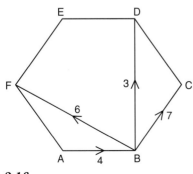

Figure 2.16

C3 ABCD is a rectangle with sides AB = 3 cm and AD = 5 cm. Forces act along its sides from the point A as shown in Figure 2.17. Find the magnitude of the resultant and the direction it makes with the side AB.

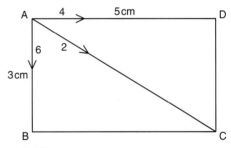

Figure 2.17

C4 Two girls are pulling a heavy trunk of mass 50 kg across a floor with forces of 25 N and 45 N respectively at an angle of 45° between them. There is a resistance force which opposes the direction of the motion of magnitude 30 N. Find the magnitude and direction of the resultant force on the trunk.

C5 Figure 2.18 shows a Scout on an aerial runway, AB. The mass of the Scout and pulley is 45 kg and the contact between the pulley and the rope offers no resistance. He is being held at rest by a rope as shown in the diagram. Find the magnitude of the tension, **P**, in the rope:

(a) by drawing a vector diagram

(b) by taking components horizontally and vertically

(c) by taking components parallel and perpendicular to the runway.

Revision questions *continued*

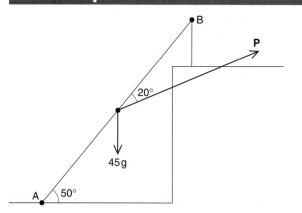

Figure 2.18

(The weight force on the boy which acts vertically downwards may be taken as 450 N.)

C6 The sea is moving at 3 knots in the direction due south. A motor boat heads at 15 knots on a bearing of 030°, but is blown off course by a wind of 6 knots blowing from the north west. The resultant velocity of the boat relative to the sea bed is the sum of the three vectors described above. Find its magnitude and direction.

(Hint: the unit of speed, the knot, is not relevant to the solution of the question.)

Chapter 3

KINEMATICS (2): POINTS MOVING IN A PLANE

3.1 Displacement, velocity and acceleration

Key points

When an object moves in a plane, its position vector relative to an origin varies with time. Suppose the object moves from point P to point Q in time t, as in Figure 3.1.

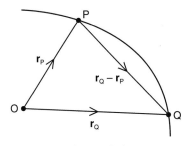

Figure 3.1

The displacement $\mathbf{PQ} = \mathbf{r}_Q - \mathbf{r}_P$

Average velocity $= \dfrac{\text{displacement}}{\text{time}} = \dfrac{\mathbf{r}_Q - \mathbf{r}_P}{t}$

Velocity at an instant, $\mathbf{v}$ is defined by: $\mathbf{v} = \dfrac{d\mathbf{r}}{dt}$

- **The velocity vector gives the direction of the motion.**
- **The velocity acts along the tangent to the path.**
- **The magnitude of the velocity vector gives the speed.**

The change in velocity as the object moves from P to Q is $\mathbf{v}_Q - \mathbf{v}_P$, as shown in Figure 3.2.

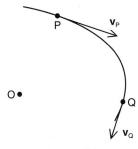

Figure 3.2

$$\text{Average acceleration} = \frac{\mathbf{v}_Q - \mathbf{v}_P}{t}$$

Acceleration at an instant, $\mathbf{a}$ is defined by $\mathbf{a} = \dfrac{d\mathbf{v}}{dt}$

Example 1

The position vector of a particle at time t relative to an origin O is given by:

$$\mathbf{r} = (2t + 3)\mathbf{i} + (t^2 - 1)\mathbf{j}$$

(a) Find the average velocity over the interval $t = 0$ to $t = 3$.

(b) Find the velocity at $t = 2$ and give the speed and the direction of motion.

(c) Find the acceleration when $t = 2$.

(d) Find the equation of the path.

(e) Sketch the path and indicate the velocity when $t = 2$.

Solution

(a)   When

$$t = 0 \quad \mathbf{r} = 3\mathbf{i} - \mathbf{j}$$
$$t = 3 \quad \mathbf{r} = 9\mathbf{i} + 8\mathbf{j}$$

The displacement from $t = 0$ to $t = 3$ is $6\mathbf{i} + 9\mathbf{j}$

The average velocity is $\dfrac{6\mathbf{i} + 9\mathbf{j}}{3} = 2\mathbf{i} + 3\mathbf{j}$

(b)
$$\mathbf{v} = \frac{d\mathbf{r}}{dt} = 2\mathbf{i} + 2t\mathbf{j}$$

> Differentiate the x and y components of $\mathbf{r}$ separately.

When $\quad t = 2, \mathbf{v} = 2\mathbf{i} + 4\mathbf{j}$

Speed $\quad = |\mathbf{v}| = \sqrt{(2^2 + 4^2)} = 4.47 \text{ m s}^{-1}$

If α is the angle the direction makes with the x-axis,

$$\tan \alpha = \frac{4}{2}$$
$$\alpha = 63.4°$$

(c) $\mathbf{a} = \dfrac{d\mathbf{v}}{dt} = 0\mathbf{i} + 2\mathbf{j} = 2\mathbf{j}$

> Differentiate the x and y components of $\mathbf{v}$ separately.

(d)
$$\mathbf{r} = (2t + 3)\mathbf{i} + (t^2 - 1)\mathbf{j} = x\mathbf{i} + y\mathbf{j}$$

Giving $\quad x = 2t + 3$ $\qquad\qquad$ (1)

and $\quad y = t^2 - 1$ 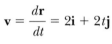 $\qquad\qquad$ (2)

From (1) $\quad t = \dfrac{(x - 3)}{2}$

> The parametric equations of the path.

Substituting in (2) $y = \left(\dfrac{x-3}{2}\right)^2 - 1$

giving $y = \tfrac{1}{4}(x-3)^2 - 1$

This is the equation of a parabola with vertex $(3,-1)$.

(e)   Figure 3.3 shows the path and the velocity vector when $t = 2$ as required.

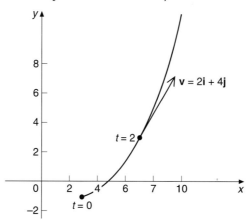

Figure 3.3

Example 2

The velocity of a particle at time t is given by $\mathbf{v} = \begin{pmatrix} -2/t^2 \\ t/4 \end{pmatrix}\ (t \geq 1)$

(a)   Find the value of t when the particle is moving in a direction making an angle of $30°$ to the x-axis.

(b)   The particle is at the point $(1,2)$ at $t = 1$. Find the equation of the path for $t > 1$.

(c)   Sketch the path.

(d)   Find the acceleration vector at time t.

(e)   What is t when the magnitude of the acceleration is $\tfrac{5}{8}$?

Solution

(a)   If the particle is moving in a direction making an angle of $30°$ to the x-axis, the gradient of the tangent to the path is $\pm \tan 30° = \pm 1/\sqrt{3}$, as shown in Figure 3.4.

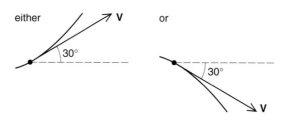

Figure 3.4

The gradient of the velocity vector is

$$\frac{t/4}{-2/t^2} = \frac{-t^3}{8}$$

Therefore $\quad \dfrac{-t^3}{8} = \dfrac{-1}{\sqrt{3}}$ giving $t = 1.67$ s

(b) $\qquad \dfrac{d\mathbf{r}}{dt} = \begin{pmatrix} t/4 \\ -2/t^2 \end{pmatrix}$

Integrate the components separately with different constants of integration.

$$\mathbf{r} = \begin{pmatrix} t^2/8 + c_1 \\ 2/t + c_2 \end{pmatrix}$$

When $\qquad t = 1, \mathbf{r} = \begin{pmatrix} 1 \\ 2 \end{pmatrix}$

therefore $\quad \begin{pmatrix} 1/8 + c_1 \\ 2 + c_2 \end{pmatrix} = \begin{pmatrix} 1 \\ 2 \end{pmatrix}$

giving $c_1 = \frac{7}{8}$ and $c_2 = 0$

$$\mathbf{r} = \begin{pmatrix} t^2/8 + 7/8 \\ 2/t \end{pmatrix} = \begin{pmatrix} x \\ y \end{pmatrix} \quad \text{therefore } x = t^2/8 + \tfrac{7}{8}, y = 2/t$$

Substituting $t = 2/y$ gives $x = \dfrac{1}{2y^2} + \dfrac{7}{8}$

This is the equation of the path.

(c) See Figure 3.5.

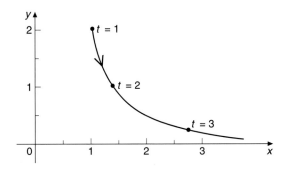

Figure 3.5

(d) $\qquad \mathbf{a} = \dfrac{d\mathbf{v}}{dt} = \begin{pmatrix} 1/4 \\ 4/t^3 \end{pmatrix}$

(e) $\qquad |\mathbf{a}|^2 = \dfrac{1}{16} + \dfrac{16}{t^6} = \left(\dfrac{5}{8}\right)^2$

giving $\qquad t^6 = \dfrac{64 \times 16}{21} \Rightarrow t = 1.91$ s

Exercise 3.1

A1 Figure 3.6 shows a car leaving a motorway. It takes 4 seconds to travel from P to Q and 5 seconds to travel from Q to R. Calculate the average acceleration from:

(a) P to Q

(b) Q to R

(c) P to R.

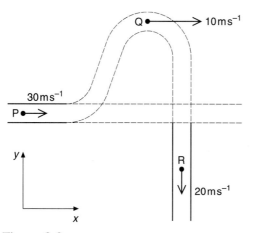

Figure 3.6

A2 The cars on a Ferris wheel in a fairground (Figure 3.7) move at a constant speed of

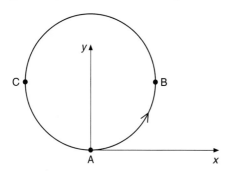

Figure 3.7

10 m s^{-1} when at full speed. It takes 20 s for a complete revolution. Calculate the average acceleration in going from:

(a) A to B

(b) B to C

(c) A to A.

A3 With respect to an origin O, the displacement of a particle P at time t seconds is given by

$$\mathbf{r} = (4t - 3)\mathbf{i} + (t^2 - 3t)\mathbf{j}$$

(a) The particle is at point A when $t = 1$. Find the position vector of A.

(b) The particle is at point B when $t = 3$. Find the position vector of B.

(c) Find the vector **AB**.

(d) Find the average velocity of the particle in moving from A to B.

(e) Find the velocity vector at time t.

(f) Find the velocity after 2 s.

A4 A particle moves so that its position vector after t s. with respect to an origin O is given by $\mathbf{r} = 2t^{3/2}\mathbf{i} + (3t - 1)\mathbf{j}$. Find:

(a) the position vector, **OA**, of the particle after 4 s

(b) the position vector, **OB**, of the particle after 9 s

(c) the distance AB

(d) the velocity vector at time t

(e) the acceleration vector at time t.

A5 The position vector of a cat with respect to an origin O t seconds after it sees a mouse is given by $\mathbf{r} = 3t\mathbf{i} + (4/t)\mathbf{j}$ $(t \geq 1)$.

(a) Find **r** when $t = 1, 2, 3, 4, 6$.

(b) Plot the path of the cat for $1 \leq t \leq 6$.

(c) Find the equation of the path of the cat.

(d) Find the velocity vector after t s.

(e) Find the acceleration vector after t s.

A6 The position vector of a particle P with respect to an origin O at time t seconds is given by $\mathbf{r} = 3t^2\mathbf{i} + 24t^{1/2}\mathbf{j}$. Find:

(a) the velocity and the speed at time t

(b) the time when the particle is moving parallel to $4\mathbf{i} + \mathbf{j}$

(c) the acceleration at time t.

B1 With respect to a fixed origin O, the velocity **v** of a particle P at time t is given by $\mathbf{v} = 3t^2\mathbf{i} - 6t^{1/2}\mathbf{j}$. The particle starts from a point A with position vector $\mathbf{i} - \mathbf{j}$ when $t = 0$. Find:

(a) the acceleration when $t = 1$

(b) the position vector after time t

(c) the position vector, **OB**, when $t = 1$

(d) the distance AB.

B2 The acceleration of a particle P at time t s is given by $\mathbf{a} = 4t\mathbf{i} - 3\mathbf{j}$. At time $t = 0$, P is at the point $(-3,-1)$, moving with velocity $\mathbf{i} + 2\mathbf{j}$. Find:

(a) the velocity vector at time t

(b) the position vector at time t

(c) the position vector and speed of the particle after 3 s.

B3 An object moves in a plane so that its position vector after t s is given by:
$$\mathbf{r} = \begin{pmatrix} 3t^2 - 4t + 1 \\ t^2 + 3 \end{pmatrix}$$

(a) Find the velocity at time t.

(b) When is the object moving parallel to $\begin{pmatrix} 2 \\ 1 \end{pmatrix}$?

(c) Show that the acceleration is constant and find its magnitude.

(d) Show that the speed is minimum when $t = \frac{3}{5}$.

B4 An object moves in a plane so that its velocity after time t is given by
$$\mathbf{v} - 2t\mathbf{i} - \frac{3}{(t+3)^2}\,\mathbf{j}.$$
It starts at $t = 0$ from the point $(0,1)$.

(a) Find $\mathbf{v}$ when $t = 0, 3, 6$.

(b) Find the position vector at time t.

(c) Find the acceleration vector at time t.

(d) What happens to $\mathbf{a}$, $\mathbf{v}$ and $\mathbf{r}$ as t gets very large?

(e) Sketch the path and mark on the vectors $\mathbf{v}$ and $\mathbf{a}$ when $t = 3$.

B5 A girl slides down a playground slide so that her position vector at time t s is given by
$$\mathbf{r} = 2t\mathbf{i} + (2/(t+1) - \tfrac{1}{2})\mathbf{j}$$

(a) Plot the path for $t = 0$ to $t = 3$.

(b) Find the velocity vector at $t = 1$. Mark this on your diagram.

(c) Find the acceleration at $t = 1$. Mark this on your diagram.

(d) Find the average velocity between $t = 0$ and $t = 3$.

B6 A particle moves so that its position vector at time t is given by:
$$\mathbf{r} = (3t^2 - 5)\mathbf{i} + (t^3 - t^2/2)\mathbf{j}$$
When is the particle moving parallel to $3\mathbf{i} + 4\mathbf{j}$?

B7 A particle moves so that its position vector at time t is given by:
$$\mathbf{r} = (t^2 - 12t + 6)\mathbf{i} + (t^3/6 - 18t)\mathbf{j}$$
Find when the particle is at rest.

Find the position vector and the acceleration of the particle at that instant.

B8 Referred to a fixed origin O the position vector of a particle P at a time t is $\mathbf{r}$ where $\mathbf{r} = 6t^2\mathbf{i} + t^{5/2}\mathbf{j}$ $(t \geq 0)$.

At the instant when $t = 4$, find:

(a) the magnitude of the speed of P

(b) the magnitude of the acceleration of P.

B9 A particle P moves so that its position vector at time t is given by
$$\mathbf{r} = (t^3 - 2t)\mathbf{i} + (4t^2 + 4t)\mathbf{j} \quad (t \geq 0).$$
When is the particle moving parallel to the vector $\mathbf{i} + \mathbf{j}$?

3.2 Uniform acceleration

Key points

If the acceleration **a** is constant: $\dfrac{d\mathbf{v}}{dt} = \mathbf{a}$. The equations of motion are:

$$\mathbf{v} = \mathbf{u} + t\mathbf{a} \tag{1}$$

$$\mathbf{r} = t\mathbf{u} + \tfrac{1}{2}t^2\mathbf{a} \tag{2}$$

$$\mathbf{r} = \frac{t(\mathbf{u} + \mathbf{v})}{2} \tag{3}$$

$$2\mathbf{a} \cdot \mathbf{r} = \mathbf{v}^2 - \mathbf{u}^2 \tag{4}$$

Notice that equations (1)–(3) are vector equations, whereas equation (4) is a scalar equation.

We can illustrate equations (1)–(3) by diagrams as shown in Figure 3.8.

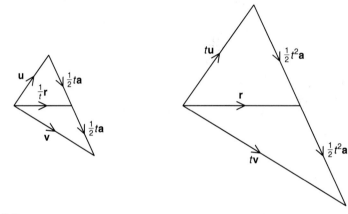

Figure 3.8

Example 1

A particle starts at the point $(2, -1)$ with velocity $(5\mathbf{i} + 3\mathbf{j})$ m s^{-1}. It is subject to a constant acceleration, and after 2 seconds its velocity is $(11\mathbf{i} - 5\mathbf{j})$ m s^{-1}. Find:

(a) the acceleration, **a**

(b) the position vector **r** at time t

(c) when the particle crosses the x-axis.

Solution

(a) Using
$$\mathbf{v} = \mathbf{u} + t\mathbf{a}$$
$$11\mathbf{i} - 5\mathbf{j} = 5\mathbf{i} + 3\mathbf{j} + 2\mathbf{a}$$
$$\Rightarrow 2\mathbf{a} = 6\mathbf{i} - 8\mathbf{j} \text{ and } \mathbf{a} = 3\mathbf{i} - 4\mathbf{j}$$

(b) $$\mathbf{r} = t\mathbf{u} + \tfrac{1}{2}t^2\mathbf{a} + (2\mathbf{i} - \mathbf{j})$$

Hint: if a particle does not start at the origin then its position vector when $t = 0$ is added to equation (2).

$$\Rightarrow \mathbf{r} = (5t\mathbf{i} + 3t\mathbf{j}) + \tfrac{1}{2}t^2(3\mathbf{i} - 4\mathbf{j}) + (2\mathbf{i} - \mathbf{j})$$

$$= (3t^2/2 + 5t + 2)\mathbf{i} + (-2t^2 + 3t - 1)\mathbf{j}$$

(c)   The path crosses the x-axis when $y = 0$.

From (b): $-2t^2 + 3t - 1 = 0$

$$2t^2 - 3t + 1 = 0$$

Factorising: $(2t - 1)(t - 1) = 0$

giving $t = \tfrac{1}{2}$ and $t = 1$ (it crosses the x-axis twice).

Example 2

At time $t = 0$ an object moving in a horizontal plane is at the origin. At that moment its velocity $\mathbf{u}$ is $\begin{pmatrix} 10 \\ 6 \end{pmatrix}$ m s^{-1} and its constant acceleration $\mathbf{a}$ is $\begin{pmatrix} -5 \\ 3 \end{pmatrix}$ m s^{-2}.

(a)   Find an expression for $\mathbf{v}$ in terms of t.

(b)   When will the object be moving at 45° to the x-axis?

(c)   When will it be moving parallel to the y-axis?

(d)   Find an expression for the position vector $\mathbf{r}$ with components in terms of t.

(e)   When does the object cross the line $y = 2x$?

Solution

(a)   Using $\mathbf{v} = \mathbf{u} + t\mathbf{a}$: $\mathbf{v} = \begin{pmatrix} 10 \\ 6 \end{pmatrix} + t\begin{pmatrix} -5 \\ 3 \end{pmatrix} = \begin{pmatrix} 10 - 5t \\ 6 + 3t \end{pmatrix}$ (1)

(b) $\tan 45° = 1$, so the object is moving at 45° to the x-axis when the gradient of $\mathbf{v}$ is 1.

Remember: the direction of a particle is given by the gradient of the velocity vector $\mathbf{v}$, *not* of its position vector.

i.e. $\dfrac{6 + 3t}{10 - 5t} = 1 \Rightarrow t = \tfrac{1}{2}$

(c)   The object is moving parallel to the y-axis when the x component of $\mathbf{v}$ is zero, i.e. $10 - 5t = 0 \Rightarrow t = 2$

(d)   Integrating (1) $\mathbf{r} = \begin{pmatrix} 10t - (5t^2/2) + c_1 \\ 6t + (3t^2/2) + c_2 \end{pmatrix}$

and since $\mathbf{r} = \mathbf{0}$ when $t = 0$, $c_1 = c_2 = 0$, and $\mathbf{r} = \begin{pmatrix} 10t - (5t^2/2) \\ 6t + (3t^2/2) \end{pmatrix}$

33

(e)   On the path: $y = 6t + 3t^2/2$, $x = 10t - 5t^2/2$

This intersects $y = 2x$ when $6t + 3t^2/2 = 20t - 5t^2$

giving $\dfrac{13t^2}{2} = 14t \;\Rightarrow t = 28/13 = 2.15$ s.

Exercise 3.2

A1   A particle moves in a horizontal plane with an acceleration $\begin{pmatrix} 4 \\ -2 \end{pmatrix}$ m s^{-2}. At time $t = 0$, it is at the origin moving with a velocity $\begin{pmatrix} 12 \\ 1 \end{pmatrix}$ m s^{-1}. Find:

(a)   the velocity **v** after 5 s

(b)   the displacement **r** after 3 s.

A2   A particle starts at the origin with velocity $(3\mathbf{i} + 5\mathbf{j})$ m s^{-1} and has constant acceleration $(-\mathbf{i} - 2\mathbf{j})$ m s^{-2}.

(a)   Find the velocity at time t.

(b)   When will the particle be moving parallel to the x-axis?

(c)   When will the particle be moving parallel to the y-axis?

A3   A particle starts from the origin with a velocity $\begin{pmatrix} 10 \\ -3 \end{pmatrix}$ m s^{-1} and has a constant acceleration $\begin{pmatrix} 2 \\ 1 \end{pmatrix}$ m s^{-2}. Find the velocity and displacement after 4 s.

A4   A particle moving with constant acceleration has an initial velocity of $\begin{pmatrix} 4 \\ 3 \end{pmatrix}$ m s^{-1} and after 6 s the velocity is $\begin{pmatrix} 7 \\ -3 \end{pmatrix}$ m s^{-1}.

(a)   Find the acceleration.

(b)   If the particle started at the origin, what was its displacement after 6 s?

A5   A particle moves in a plane so that its position vector at time t s is given by:

$\mathbf{r} = \begin{pmatrix} 5 - 2t \\ 3t^2 + 1 \end{pmatrix}$

(a)   Prove that the acceleration is constant.

(b)   Sketch the path of the particle.

B1   Two particles move in a plane. Particle A starts at the origin with a velocity $\begin{pmatrix} 3 \\ 4 \end{pmatrix}$ m s^{-1} and a constant acceleration $\begin{pmatrix} 2 \\ -1 \end{pmatrix}$ m s^{-2}.

Particle B starts at the point (12,0) with velocity $\begin{pmatrix} 6 \\ 2 \end{pmatrix}$ m s^{-1} and a constant acceleration $\begin{pmatrix} -1 \\ 0 \end{pmatrix}$ m s^{-2}. Show that the particles will collide. State where and when this will occur.

B2   A particle starts at the point (1,2) with an initial velocity $\begin{pmatrix} 4 \\ 3 \end{pmatrix}$ m s^{-1}. It moves under a constant acceleration **a** and after 2 s it is at the point (5,10).

(a)   Find **a**.

(b)   Find the velocity when $t = 2$.

(c)   When is the particle moving perpendicular to its original direction? Where is it at that time?

(d)   Sketch the path indicating clearly your answer to (c).

B3   Two particles A and B move in a horizontal plane. After t seconds A has position vector $t^2\mathbf{i} - 3t\mathbf{j}$ and B has position vector $3t\mathbf{i} + (t^2 - 2)\mathbf{j}$.

Exercise 3.2 *continued*

(a) Find the distance AB when $t = 2$.

(b) Show that A and B are always moving perpendicular to each other.

(c) Sketch the paths of A and B on the same diagram.

B4 Two particles A and B move in a plane. Particle A starts at $t = 0$ from the point $(0,3)$ with an initial velocity $\begin{pmatrix} 1 \\ 1 \end{pmatrix}$ m s^{-1} and a constant acceleration $\begin{pmatrix} 0 \\ -2 \end{pmatrix}$ m s^{-2}. B starts at the origin with an initial velocity $\begin{pmatrix} 0 \\ -1 \end{pmatrix}$ m s^{-1} and a constant acceleration $\begin{pmatrix} 2 \\ 1 \end{pmatrix}$ m s^{-2}.

(a) Find the position vectors of A and B at time t.

(b) Will the particles collide?

(c) When are they moving parallel to each other?

(d) When are they moving perpendicular to each other?

3.3 Projectiles

Key points

Assuming that air resistance can be ignored, the only force acting on a body near the surface of the Earth is its weight. This gives rise to a constant acceleration, usually referred to as the constant acceleration due to gravity. An object moving freely under gravity is called a **projectile**. Writing $\mathbf{a} = \mathbf{g}$ we can apply the constant acceleration formulae of Section 3.2:

$$\mathbf{v} = \mathbf{u} + t\mathbf{g} \qquad (1)$$
$$\mathbf{r} = t\mathbf{u} + \tfrac{1}{2}t^2\mathbf{g} \qquad (2)$$
$$2\mathbf{g} \cdot \mathbf{r} = v^2 - u^2 \qquad (3)$$

In practical problems we usually take the x and y axes horizontally and vertically. Figure 3.9 shows a particle with initial velocity $\mathbf{u}$ at an angle θ to the horizontal. θ is called the angle of projection or angle of elevation.

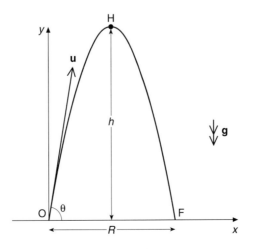

Figure 3.9

Using column vector notation we have:

$$\mathbf{u} = \begin{pmatrix} u\cos\theta \\ u\sin\theta \end{pmatrix}, \mathbf{g} = \begin{pmatrix} 0 \\ -g \end{pmatrix}, \mathbf{r} = \begin{pmatrix} x \\ y \end{pmatrix}$$

From (1), (2) and (3) we get:

$$\mathbf{v} = \begin{pmatrix} u\cos\theta \\ u\sin\theta - tg \end{pmatrix} \tag{4}$$

$$\mathbf{r} = \begin{pmatrix} ut\cos\theta \\ ut\sin\theta - \frac{1}{2}t^2 g \end{pmatrix} \tag{5}$$

$$-2gy = v^2 - u^2 \tag{6}$$

At H, where the height is maximum, the vertical component of $\mathbf{v}$ is zero.

From (4): $t = \dfrac{u\sin\theta}{g}$

Substituting this value of t in (5) we get:

$$h = u\left(\frac{u\sin\theta}{g}\right)\sin\theta - \frac{1}{2}g\,\frac{u^2\sin^2\theta}{g^2} = \frac{u^2\sin^2\theta}{2g}$$

At F: $t = 2\left(\dfrac{u\sin\theta}{g}\right)$ (from the symmetry of the motion)

Substituting this value of t in (5) we get

$$R = u\left(\frac{2u\sin\theta}{g}\right)\cos\theta = \frac{u^2\sin 2\theta}{g} \quad \text{(the horizontal range)}$$

We obtain the equation of the path by eliminating t from the equations for x and y in (5). This is $y = x\tan\theta - \dfrac{gx^2\sec^2\theta}{2u^2}$

The path of a projectile is usually called its **trajectory**.

In practical problems the value of g is taken as 10 m s^{-2} (to 1 significant figure) or 9.8 m s^{-2} (to 2 significant figures) or 9.81 m s^{-2} (to 3 significant figures).

Example I

A golf ball is hit at 40 m s^{-1} at an angle of $30°$ to the horizontal. Find:

(a)   the time of flight to the first bounce

(b)   the horizontal range

(c)   the maximum height

(d)   the equation of the trajectory

(e)   the speed when the height is 15 m.

Take g as 10 m s^{-2}.

Solution

We have $\qquad \mathbf{u} = \begin{pmatrix} 40 \cos 30° \\ 40 \sin 30° \end{pmatrix}, \mathbf{g} = \begin{pmatrix} 0 \\ -10 \end{pmatrix}$

Using $\mathbf{r} = t\mathbf{u} + \frac{1}{2}t^2\mathbf{g}$: $\begin{pmatrix} x \\ y \end{pmatrix} = \begin{pmatrix} 40t \cos 30° \\ 40t \sin 30° - 5t^2 \end{pmatrix}$

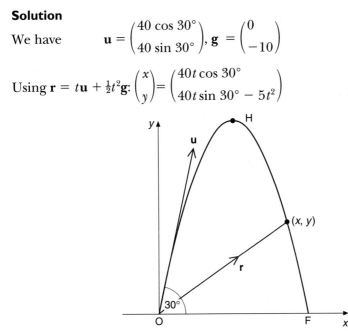

Figure 3.10

(a) At F, $y = 0$, giving $t(40 \sin 30° - 5t) = 0$

$\Rightarrow t = 8 \sin 30° = 4 \text{ s}$

(b) When $t = 4$, $x = 40 \times 4 \times \cos 30° = 80\sqrt{3} = 138.6$

The horizontal range is approximately 140 m.

(c) At H, $t = 2$ (half the time of total flight)

and $h = 80 \sin 30° - 20 = 20 \text{ m}$

(d) From the equation for $\begin{pmatrix} x \\ y \end{pmatrix}$ $\quad x = (20\sqrt{3})t$ and $y = 20t - 5t^2$

Eliminating t: $\qquad\qquad y = \dfrac{x}{\sqrt{3}} - \dfrac{x^2}{240}$

(e) When $y = 15$ we find v from the equation $-2gy = v^2 - u^2$

$-2 \times 10 \times 15 = v^2 - 40^2$

giving $v^2 = 1300 \Rightarrow v = 10\sqrt{13}$

We could find v using $\mathbf{r} = t\mathbf{u} + \frac{1}{2}t^2\mathbf{g}$ as follows.

When $y = 15$ $\qquad\qquad\qquad 15 = 40t \sin 30° - 5t^2$

giving $\qquad\qquad\qquad 5t^2 - 20t + 15 = 0$

dividing by 5 $\qquad\qquad\qquad t^2 - 4t + 3 = 0$

Factorising $\qquad\qquad\qquad (t-1)(t-3) = 0$

Hence $t = 1$ or $t = 3$ ◄

> Notice that there are two answers here: $t = 1$ when the ball is rising and $t = 3$ when the ball is falling.

When $t = 1$, $\mathbf{v} = \begin{pmatrix} 40 \cos 30° \\ 40 \sin 30° - 10 \end{pmatrix} = \begin{pmatrix} 20\sqrt{3} \\ 10 \end{pmatrix}$

and $|\mathbf{v}| = 10\sqrt{(12 + 1)} = 10\sqrt{13}$ as before.

Example 2

A diver springs off a 10 m board at 8 m s^{-1} at an angle of 65° to the horizontal.

Taking g as 9.81 m s^{-1}, find to 3 significant figures:

(a)   the time taken before she hits the water

(b)   the distance she is from the edge of the pool on impact

(c)   her speed of entry

(d)   the angle at which she enters the water.

Solution

Notice that in Figure 3.11 we take the origin at the top of the board. In this type of question we start with $\mathbf{r} = t\mathbf{u} + \frac{1}{2}t^2\mathbf{g}$: $\begin{pmatrix} x \\ y \end{pmatrix} = \begin{pmatrix} 8t \cos 65° \\ 8t \sin 65° - 4.905t^2 \end{pmatrix}$

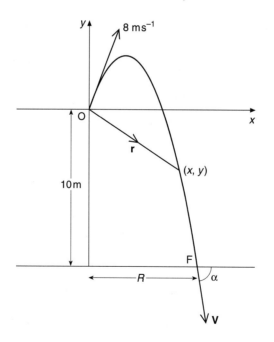

Figure 3.11

(a)   At F $\begin{pmatrix} x \\ y \end{pmatrix} = \begin{pmatrix} R \\ -10 \end{pmatrix}$

$\Rightarrow \qquad -10 = 8t \sin 65° - 4.905t^2$

giving $4.905t^2 - 7.25t - 10 = 0$

Solving this using the quadratic formula: $t = 2.35$ s (ignoring the negative root)

(b)   At F $R = 8 \times 2.35 \times \cos 65° = 7.93$ m

(c)   Using $\mathbf{v} = \mathbf{u} + t\mathbf{g}$ with $t = 2.35$:

$$\mathbf{v} = \begin{pmatrix} 8 \cos 65° \\ 8 \sin 65° - 9.81 \times 2.35 \end{pmatrix} = \begin{pmatrix} 3.38 \\ -12.37 \end{pmatrix}$$

Speed $= |\mathbf{v}| = \sqrt{(3.38^2 + 12.37^2)} = 12.8$ m s^{-1}

(d)   If she enters at an angle α downwards from the horizontal (Figure 3.12):

$$\tan \alpha = \frac{12.37}{3.38}$$

giving $\alpha = 74.7°$

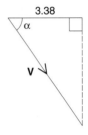

Figure 3.12

Exercise 3.3

Take g as 10 m s^{-2}, where necessary.

A1 A golf ball is hit from a point O with an initial velocity whose horizontal and vertical components are 12 m s^{-1} and 15 m s^{-1}. The highest point of the path is H and the ball hits the horizontal ground again at a point F. Find:

(a)   the time taken to reach the point F

(b)   the distance OF

(c)   the height of H above the ground.

A2 A projectile is fired at 50 m s^{-1} at an angle of 60° to the horizontal from a point O. It hits the horizontal plane through O again at a point F. Find:

(a)   the maximum height reached

(b)   the time taken to reach F

(c)   the distance OF

(d)   the speed when the height is 40 m.

A3 A footballer kicks a ball towards a goal at 20 m s^{-1} at an angle of 25° to the

horizontal, as shown in Figure 3.13. He is 30 m from the goal and the crossbar is 2.5 m high. Will the ball bounce in front of the crossbar, go into the goal without bouncing or fly over the bar?

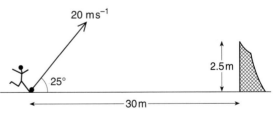

Figure 3.13

A4 A rugby player takes a penalty kick. He is 40 m from the goal line, directly in front of the posts. The crossbar is 4 m above the ground. He kicks the ball at 55° to the horizontal with a speed of 25 m s^{-1}.

(a)   Will the ball clear the crossbar?

(b)   What is the speed of the ball as it crosses the goal line?

continued   **39**

Exercise 3.3   *continued*

A5 A particle is projected with a speed u at an angle of projection α where $\tan \alpha = \frac{3}{4}$. The horizontal range is 120 m. Find:

(a) u

(b) the maximum height of the particle.

A6 Two particles are projected from the same point on horizontal ground with the same speed. Particle A has an angle of projection of 30° while particle B has an angle of projection of 60°.

(a) Which particle is in the air longest?

(b) Prove that the horizontal ranges of A and B are the same.

(c) Prove that B rises three times as high as A during its flight.

A7 A particle is projected from a point A on horizontal ground with a speed of 50 m s^{-1} at an angle α to the horizontal where $\tan \alpha = \frac{4}{3}$. Find:

(a) the maximum height reached

(b) the speed of the particle after 2 seconds

(c) for how long it is 20 m above the ground

(d) whether the particle will clear a wall 15 m high with its base 210 m from A.

A8 A projectile has an initial speed of 60 m s^{-1} and rises to a maximum height of 40 m above the horizontal ground from which it is projected. Find:

(a) the angle of projection

(b) the time of flight

(c) the horizontal range.

B1 A girl throws a stone from a tower 20 m high at an angle 50° to the horizontal. The stone lands 30 m from the base of the tower. Find:

(a) the speed with which the stone was thrown

(b) the time taken for the stone to land

(c) the maximum height above the ground reached by the stone.

B2 A projectile has an initial speed of 80 m s^{-1} and rises to a height of 30 m above the ground. Find:

(a) the angle of projection

(b) the time of flight

(c) the horizontal range.

B3 A child throws a toy from her bedroom window into the garden. The speed of projection is 8 m s^{-1} and the angle of projection is α where $\tan \alpha = 2$. The toy takes 2 s to hit the ground. Find:

(a) the height above ground from which the toy is thrown

(b) how far from the house the toy lands.

B4

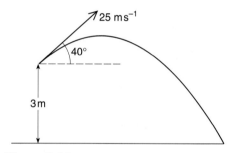

Figure 3.14

A skier travelling at 25 m s^{-1} hit a ramp and took off at an angle of 40° to the horizontal, as shown in Figure 3.14. Find:

(a) how long she was in the air

(b) her maximum height above ground

(c) her speed on landing.

B5 A shot putter can project the shot with an initial speed of 20 m s^{-1} from a height of 2.5 m.

(a) What is the horizontal range if he projects the shot with an angle of projection of 40°?

(b) Find the corresponding values if the angle of projection is:
(i) 45°
(ii) 50°.

(c) What would be his 'best' angle for maximum horizontal range? (Use trial and error.)

Exercise 3.3 *continued*

B6 An aircraft is flying with a constant velocity of 100 m s^{-1} in a straight line at a constant height of 100 m above level ground. It releases a bomb when vertically above a point A. The bomb lands at B. Find:

    (a) the time taken for the bomb to reach the ground

    (b) the distance AB

    (c) the speed of the bomb on landing

    (d) where the aircraft is relative to the bomb when the bomb lands.

B7 A boy stands on the top of a cliff 120 m above a beach, as shown in Figure 3.15. His father stands on the beach 90 m from the bottom of the cliff. At the instant the boy drops an apple his father releases an arrow aimed towards the apple with a speed u m s^{-1} at an angle of elevation α where $\tan \alpha = \frac{4}{3}$. Find:

    (a) the position vector of the arrow relative to O in terms of u and t

    (b) the height of the apple above the beach at time t

    (c) the condition on u for the arrow to hit the apple before the apple hits the beach.

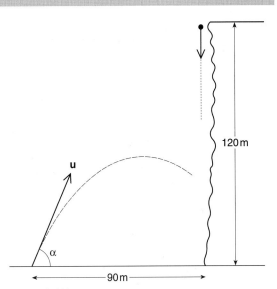

Figure 3.15

B8 A particle is projected from a point O and passes through point A 80 m horizontally and 120 m vertically from O, 4 seconds after projection. Find:

    (a) the angle of projection

    (b) the speed of projection

    (c) the speed of the particle as it passes through A.

Revision questions

Take g as 9.8 m s^{-2}, where necessary.

C1 A particle moves in a plane so that at time t its position vector is given by:

$$\mathbf{r} = \begin{pmatrix} t^2 - 1 \\ t^3 - t \end{pmatrix} \ (t \geq 0)$$

    (a) Find $\mathbf{v}$ and $\mathbf{a}$ whose components are in terms of t.

    (b) When is the particle moving parallel to the x-axis?

    (c) Sketch the path of the particle.

C2 A particle P_1 moves so that its position vector at time t is $\mathbf{r}_1 = t^2\mathbf{i} + 2t\mathbf{j}$.

A second particle P_2 moves so that its position vector is $\mathbf{r}_2 = (2 - t)\mathbf{i} + (3 - t^2)\mathbf{j}$.

    (a) Find the distance P_1P_2 when $t = 2$.

    (b) Show that there is an instant when the particles meet.

    (c) Show that the speeds of the particles are never equal.

continued **41**

C3 Two particles A and B are moving in a horizontal plane. At time t they have position vectors given by:
$\mathbf{r}_A = 2t\mathbf{i} + (t^2 + 2)\mathbf{j}, \mathbf{r}_B = t^3\mathbf{i} + 3t\mathbf{j} \ (t \geq 0)$

(a) Show that the particles never meet.

(b) Find the distance AB when $t = 3$.

(c) When are the particles moving parallel to each other? How far apart are they at this instant?

C4 A particle is projected with a speed of 40 m s^{-1} at an angle α to the horizontal where $\tan \alpha = \frac{3}{4}$. Find:

(a) the maximum height reached

(b) the time taken to reach a height of 20 m

(c) for how long the particle is above 20 m

(d) the speed of the particle after 2 s.

C5 A hockey player scoops a ball so that it hits the crossbar of the goal, as shown in Figure 3.16. Find:

(a) the maximum height of the ball

(b) the distance AB.

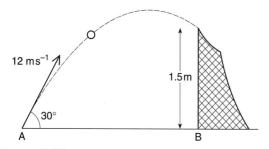

Figure 3.16

C6 A golfer at a point A needs to hit a ball over a tree of height 10 m at a horizontal distance 20 m from A. She also wants the ball to land at a distance of 80 m from A. Prove that the angle of projection must be $\tan^{-1}\left(\frac{2}{3}\right)$ and find the speed of projection.

C7 A cricket ball is hit from a height of 0.5 m above horizontal ground with a speed of 26 m s^{-1} at an angle α above the horizontal where $\tan \alpha = \frac{5}{12}$.

(a) Find the time for which the ball is at least 2.5 m above the ground.

(b) The ball is caught by a fielder who is 45 m away from the point where the batsman hit the ball. Find the height above ground at which the fielder made the catch.

You need some advanced techniques of differentiation for the last two questions.

C8 A particle P moves in a plane so that its position vector after time t s is given by
$$\mathbf{r} = \begin{pmatrix} \cos \pi t \\ \sin \pi t \end{pmatrix}.$$

Plot the positions of P in intervals of 0.25 s from $t = 0$ to $t = 2$.

(a) Find $\mathbf{v}$ with components in terms of t. Mark the velocity vectors on your sketch at points corresponding to $t = 0, 0.5, 1, 1.5$, and calculate the speeds at these times.

(b) Find $\mathbf{a}$ with components in terms of t. Mark the acceleration vectors on your sketch at the same points as in (a). What do you notice about the magnitude of the acceleration vector in each case?

Describe the motion of the particle.

C9 A particle P moves in a plane so that its position vector at time t is given by:
$$\mathbf{r} = \begin{pmatrix} e^t - e^{-t} \\ e^t + e^{-t} \end{pmatrix} (t \geq 0)$$

(a) Find column vectors for $\mathbf{v}$ and $\mathbf{a}$ with components in terms of t.

(b) Find the equation of the path.

(c) Sketch the path of the particle.

Chapter 4

STATICS (1)

Key points

In Chapter 2 we saw how forces could be represented by vectors and that their resultant may be found by vector addition or the use of components. In this chapter we examine different types of physical forces which may act on bodies, and how to determine their magnitudes and directions. We begin with the condition for equilibrium of a particle.

> **A particle remains at rest (in equilibrium) if the resultant force on the particle is zero.**

This rule is only true for particles, in which case the forces acting must pass through a single point.

In the following we will begin by treating quite 'large' objects as particles, for example, suitcases, paving stones, people or even cars.

Weight

This is the force on a body due to the gravitational attraction of the Earth. It has magnitude mg Newtons where m is the mass of the body in kilograms and g is the acceleration due to gravity in m s^{-2}.

In many practical problems it is convenient to choose x and y axes horizontally and vertically, so that the weight force acts vertically downwards.

Tension in strings/ropes/springs

Figure 4.1(a) shows a girder being supported by wires. T represents the forces exerted by the wire AB at its ends. It exerts a force T down at A and up at B.

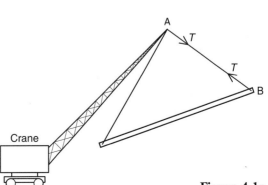

Figure 4.1a

43

The forces at a point P in the wire act away from P, as shown in Figure 4.1(b), which is why we say that the wire is under tension.

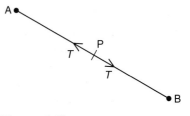

Figure 4.1b

Modelling assumptions:

(a)   We always assume that the tension in a wire is constant along its length.

(b)   We regard strings/wires, etc. as 'light', i.e. of negligible mass.

(c)   We regard strings and wires to be of fixed length or 'inextensible'.

Elastic strings and springs which may stretch are considered in Chapter 11.

Thrust in springs/rods

Figure 4.2(a) shows a TV on a tall stand. *T* represents the force exerted by the support AB which is upwards on the TV at A and downwards on the base at B. The forces on either side of P are trying to compress it (Figure 4.2(b)) and we say that the rod is under compression.

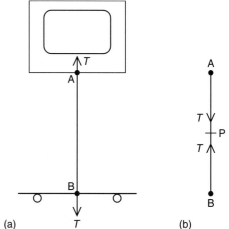

Figure 4.2   (a)   (b)

Normal contact forces

When two bodies are in contact they exert forces on each other. The magnitudes and directions of these forces are governed by Newton's third law. This states

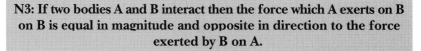

N3: If two bodies A and B interact then the force which A exerts on B on B is equal in magnitude and opposite in direction to the force exerted by B on A.

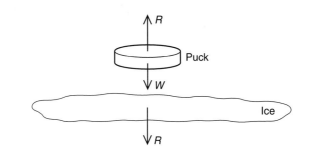

Figure 4.3

The consequences of this law are discussed further in Chapter 5.

If the bodies in contact are smooth, the contact forces will be perpendicular to the bodies. For a particle in contact with a smooth surface, the contact force will be perpendicular to the surface. In Figure 4.3, if we treat the ice puck as a particle and the contact with the ice as smooth, then the contact force will be perpendicular to the ice.

Note: never assume that the contact force between an object and the surface on which it rests is equal to the weight force. Label it with a separate letter (e.g. R) and use the condition for equilibrium to determine its magnitude.

Example 1

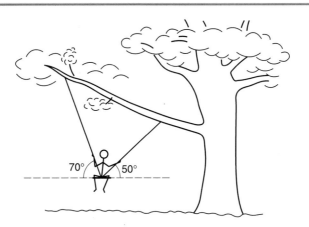

Figure 4.4

Figure 4.4 shows a child sitting on a garden swing which is suspended by two ropes from the branch of a tree. The mass of the child and the seat total 40 kg. Find the tension in the two ropes, giving your answer to 2 significant figures.

Take g as 9.8 m s^{-2}.

Solution

First we draw a simplified model of the situation in which we treat the child + seat as a particle, and label the forces acting on the 'child + seat' (Figure 4.5).

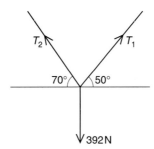

Figure 4.5

T_1 and T_2 are the tensions in the two ropes and 40 g is the (vertical) weight force.

We illustrate two ways of finding T_1 and T_2.

Method 1. Triangle of forces
The force vectors are added, and since they are in equilibrium they must form a closed triangle, as shown in Figure 4.6.

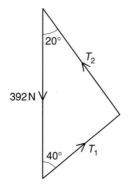

Figure 4.6

From the sine rule:

$$\frac{T_1}{\sin 20°} = \frac{392}{\sin 120°} \Rightarrow T_1 = 160 \text{ N}$$

Similarly $$\frac{T_2}{\sin 40°} = \frac{392}{\sin 120°} \Rightarrow T_2 = 290 \text{ N}$$

Method 2. Using components (see Figure 4.7)

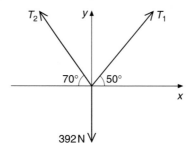

Figure 4.7

Horizontally $\quad\quad\quad T_1 \cos 50° - T_2 \cos 70° = 0$ (1)

Vertically $\quad\quad\quad\quad T_1 \sin 50° + T_2 \sin 70° = 392$ (2)

From (1), $\quad\quad\quad T_2 = T_1 \dfrac{\cos 50°}{\cos 70°} = 1.88\ T_1$

Substituting for T_2 in (2) gives

$T_1 (\sin 50° + 1.88 \sin 70°) = 392$

giving $T_1 = 160$ N as before, and $T_2 = 290$ N

Note: Method 1 in this example is equivalent to using **Lami's Theorem**.

This states that if three forces acting at a point as in Figure 4.8(a), are in equilibrium, then

$$\frac{P}{\sin \alpha} = \frac{Q}{\sin \beta} = \frac{R}{\sin \gamma}$$

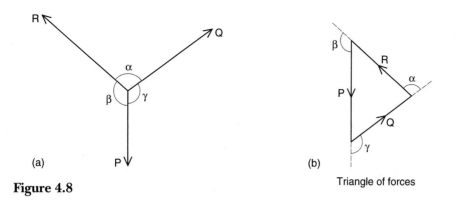

Figure 4.8

Triangle of forces

Example 2

A toboggan of mass 25 kg is held on an icy slope by a rope, as shown in Figure 4.9(a). The rope is pulling up the line of greatest slope. Find:

(a) the tension in the rope

(b) the normal contact force between the toboggan and the slope.

Take g as 9.81 m s^{-2} and give your answers to 3 significant figures.

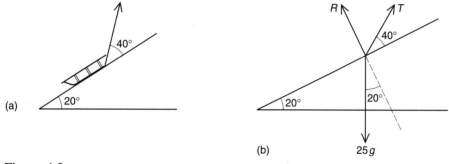

Figure 4.9

Solution

Figure 4.9(b) shows all the forces acting on the toboggan.

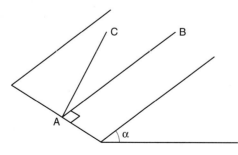

Figure 4.10

Note: a line of greatest slope is one which is drawn in the plane and is perpendicular to any horizontal line drawn in the plane. In Figure 4.10 AB is a line of greatest slope by AC is not.

In cases like this it is often useful to consider components of the forces acting in directions parallel and perpendicular to the slope.

Since the toboggan is at rest all the forces balance.

Parallel to the plane (i.e. up the line of greatest slope)

$$T \cos 40° - 25g \sin 20° = 0$$

giving $T = \dfrac{25 \times 9.81 \times \sin 20°}{\cos 40°} = 109$ N

Perpendicular to the plane

$$R + T \sin 40° - 25g \cos 20° = 0$$

giving $R = 25 \times 9.81 \times \sin 20° - 109 \times \sin 40° = 160$ N

Exercise 4.1

Take g as 9.8 m s^{-2} where necessary.

A1 A gardener wants to lift a garden roller vertically. The mass of the roller is 50 kg. Find the normal contact force between the ground and the roller if the tension in the vertical handle is:

(a) 20 N (b) 200 N (c) 500 N.

A2 A lantern L of mass 2 kg is suspended from the roof of a theatre by two light inextensible wires LA and LB which are inclined at 30° and 60° to the vertical. Draw a vector triangle of forces acting on the lantern and calculate the tensions in the wires LA and LB.

A3 A particle is suspended by two light inextensible strings and hangs in equilibrium. One string is inclined at 40° to the horizontal and has a tension of 30 N. The second string is inclined at 70° to the horizontal. By considering the horizontal and vertical components of the forces acting on the particle, calculate:

(a) the tension in the second string

(b) the mass of the particle.

A4 A demolition ball B of mass 100 kg is held in equilibrium by two wires. Wire BA is horizontal and wire BC is inclined at an angle of 70° to the horizontal. Calculate the tensions in the wires BA and BC.

A5 A light bulb of mass 0.2 kg is suspended by two wires each inclined at an angle θ to the horizontal. The maximum tension allowed in each wire is 3 N.

(a) Calculate the tension in the wires when $\theta = 70°$.

(b) What is the minimum possible value of θ allowed (i.e. when the wires are about to break)?

A6 A crate of mass 200 kg rests on the smooth horizontal deck of a ship and is supported by two cables each inclined at 50° to the horizontal. Find the normal contact force between the crate and the deck of the ship when the tensions in the cables are:

(a) 500 N (b) 2000 N.

What is the minimum tension in the cables required to lift the crate off the deck?

A7 A microphone in a concert hall has a mass of 2 kg and is suspended by two wires inclined at 20° and 50° to the horizontal respectively. Calculate the tensions in the wires.

Exercise 4.1 *continued*

B1 A body of mass 8 kg is placed on a smooth plane inclined at 25° to the horizontal. It is kept in equilibrium by a horizontal force P. By taking components of the forces acting on the body parallel and perpendicular to the line of greatest slope calculate:

(a) the magnitude of the horizontal force P

(b) the magnitude of the normal contact force between the body and the plane.

B2 A particle of mass 12 kg is placed on a smooth plane inclined at 15° to the horizontal. Find the magnitude of the force required to keep the particle in equilibrium if it acts:

(a) horizontally

(b) parallel to the plane, up the line of greatest slope.

B3 Figure 4.11 shows a wire ABC which passes through a light smooth ring at B. A mass of 40 kg hangs from a wire BD, and equilibrium is maintained by a horizontal wire BE.

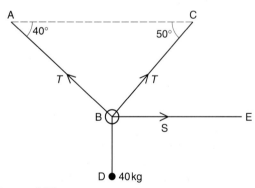

Figure 4.11

(a) What is the tension in the wire BD?

(b) By considering horizontal and vertical components of the forces acting at B, calculate the tensions S and T.

B4 Figure 4.12 shows three 'objets d'art' in a gallery suspended by three wires AB and BC and BD, two of which pass over smooth hooks at P and Q.

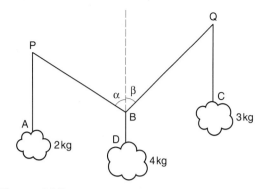

Figure 4.12

(a) If the system is in equilibrium what are the tensions in AB and BC?

(b) Draw a triangle of forces acting at point B and calculate the angles α and β.

B5 Figure 4.13(a) shows a new design for a cycle rack on the back of a car. Figure 4.13(b) shows a model of this in which the cycle is treated as a particle A of mass 15 kg supported by two rods AB and AC.

(a) Calculate the magnitude of the forces on the cycle from the rods AB and AC.

(b) Which rod is under tension and which is under compression?

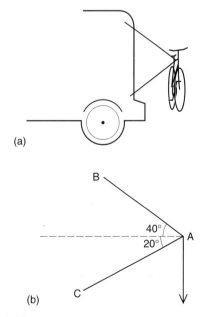

Figure 4.13

Exercise 4.1 *continued*

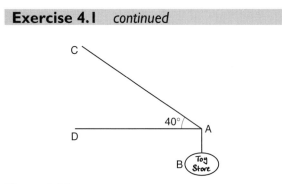

Figure 4.14

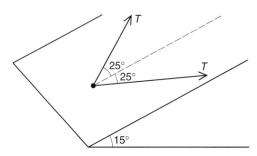

Figure 4.15

B6 Figure 4.14 shows a shop sign of mass 30 kg suspended by a wire AB. The wire AC is inclined at 40° to the horizontal. The rod AD is horizontal and the system is in equilibrium. By considering the horizontal and vertical components of the forces acting at A calculate:

(a) the tension in the wire

(b) the thrust from the rod.

B7 Figure 4.15 shows two men trying to drag a sledge up an icy slope. They each pull on ropes parallel to the plane but at 25° to the line of greatest slope. The mass of the loaded sledge is 80 kg. Calculate the tension in the ropes if the sledge is in equilibrium.

4.2 Friction

Key points

Friction is the force which prevents slipping between surfaces in contact. Where the frictional force is negligible (as in the case of a puck on ice) we say that the contact is smooth, otherwise we say that the contact is rough.

We may summarise two basic properties of frictional force as follows:

> (1) Frictional force always opposes the *relative* motion of surfaces in contact and acts along the common tangent to them.
>
> (2) Friction is a variable force and, when slipping does not take place, is just sufficient to prevent the relative motion of surfaces in contact. Slipping occurs when the frictional force reaches its maximum value.

Experiments lead to a further property of frictional force:

> (3) The maximum value of the frictional force between two surfaces depends on
>   (a) the magnitude of normal contact force between them
>   (b) the roughness of the surfaces in contact.

This property is summarised in the (experimental) law of friction.

$$F \leq \mu R$$

where μ is called the coefficient of friction between the surfaces and R is the normal contact force.

When slipping is about to occur we say that friction is limiting, in which case:

$$F = \mu R$$

Example 1

Figure 4.16(a) shows a boat on a slipway. The total mass of the boat is 500 kg. It is attached to a winch at the top of the slipway by a cable. Assuming that the boat is in equilibrium, calculate the normal and frictional components of the contact force on the boat when the tension in the cable is (a) 1000 N (b) 3000 N.

Take g as 9.8 m s^{-2} and give your answers to 2 significant figures.

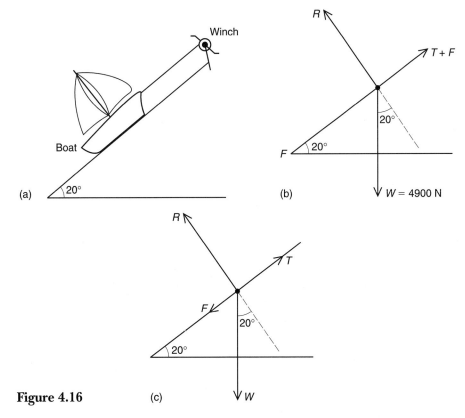

Figure 4.16

Solution

(a) The forces on the boat are shown in Figure 4.16(b) where we have assumed that F acts up the slope.

Consider the components parallel to the slope:

$$T + F - 4900 \sin 20° = 0$$

giving $F = 4900 \sin 20° - 1000 = 676$

i.e. $F = 680$ N

Taking components perpendicular to the slope:

$R - 4900 \cos 20° = 0$ giving R as 4600 N

(b) In this case it is likely that the boat will be about to slip up the slope, in which case F will act down the slope, as shown in Figure 4.16(c). Taking components parallel to the slope:

Note: the component of the weight force down the slope '$mg \sin \alpha$' is $4900 \sin 20° = 1676$ N which is greater than T in (a) but less than T in (b). If we had guessed wrong about the direction of F in either (a) or (b) then its magnitude would have turned out to be negative.

$$T - F - 4900 \sin 20° = 0$$

giving $F = T - 4900 \sin 20° = 1300$ N. Clearly $R = 4600$ N as before.

Example 2

(a) A girl pulls a suitcase of mass 30 kg along horizontal ground by a strap inclined at 30° to the horizontal as in Figure 4.17(a). The suitcase just moves when the tension in the strap is 100 N. Find the value of μ for contact between the case and the floor.

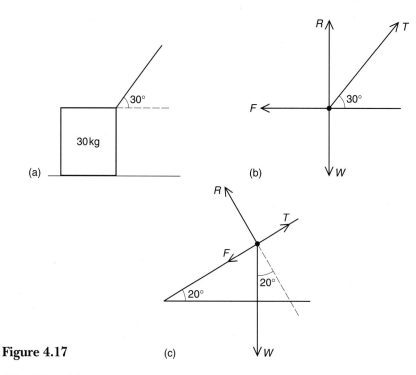

Figure 4.17

(b) The girl now encounters a ramp inclined at 20° to the horizontal. If she pulls parallel to the line of greatest slope, find the minimum tension in the strap required to move the case up the ramp.

Take g as 9.81 m s^{-2}, giving your answers to 3 significant figures.

Solution

(a) Treating the case as a particle we show all the forces acting on it in Figure 4.17(b). In equilibrium the forces balance.

Consider the horizontal components:

$$T \cos 30° - F = 0$$

giving

$$F = 100 \cos 30° = 86.6 \text{ N}$$

Consider vertical components

$$R + T \sin 30° - W = 0$$

giving

$$R = 30 \times 9.81 - 100 \sin 30° = 244 \text{ N}$$

Since the case just moves, friction is limiting:

$$F = \mu R \text{ giving } \mu = \frac{F}{R} = \frac{86.6}{244.3} = 0.354 \text{ N}$$

(b) The forces acting on the case are shown in Figure 4.17(c). In this case it is convenient to consider components parallel and perpendicular to the line of slope.

Notice the direction of the force labelled T.

Perpendicular to the slope $\quad R = W \cos 20° = 277 \text{ N}$

Parallel to the slope $\quad T - F - W \sin 20° = 0 \quad$ (1)

The minimum tension occurs when friction is limiting

$$F = \mu R = 0.354 \times 277 = 97.9 \text{ N}$$

In (1) we get $\quad T = 97.9 + 30 \times 9.81 \times \sin 20° = 199 \text{ N}$

Exercise 4.2

Take the value of g as 9.81 m s^{-2} where necessary.

A1 A book of mass 0.25 kg resting on a rough horizontal plane is on the point of moving when a horizontal force of magnitude 1.25 N is applied to it.

  (a) Find the coefficient of friction between the book and the plane.

  (b) Three similar books are now piled on top of the first. What is the minimum horizontal force required to move the pile of books?

A2 A box of mass 12 kg rests on a rough horizontal plane. The coefficient of friction between the box and the plane is 0.4. Find the magnitude of the least horizontal force which will make the box slide along the plane.

A3 A case of mass $8\,m$ is placed on a rough horizontal floor. It will just begin to slide when a horizontal force of $3\,mg$ is applied to it.

  (a) Find the coefficient of friction between the case and the floor.

  (b) The case is now placed on a ramp inclined at 30° to the horizontal. Find in terms of m and g the magnitude of the least force applied up the line of greatest slope which will keep the particle in equilibrium.

A4 A book is placed on a desk lid which is slowly tilted. The book begins to slide down when the lid is inclined at an angle of 35° to the horizontal. Find the coefficient of friction between the lid and the book.

continued

Exercise 4.2 continued

A5 A rough plane is inclined at an angle of 40° to the horizontal. A body of mass 10 kg is placed on the plane. The coefficient of friction between the body and the plane is 0.7. A force of magnitude *P* is applied to the body up the line of greatest slope. Find the value of *P* when the body is about to slide up the plane.

A6 A boat of mass 200 kg is on a slipway inclined at an angle of 20° to the horizontal, as shown in Figure 4.18.

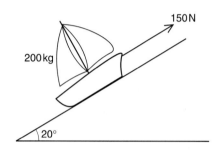

Figure 4.18

The boat is just held in equilibrium by a rope which has a tension of 150 N.

(a) Calculate the coefficient of friction between the boat and the ramp.

(b) The tension in the rope is slowly increased. What is the tension when the boat is on the point of sliding up the ramp?

A7 A parcel P of mass 20 kg is on a ramp inclined at 25° to the horizontal. The coefficient of friction between the parcel and the ramp is 0.3. The parcel is supported by a rope being pulled up the line of greatest slope, as shown in Figure 4.19.

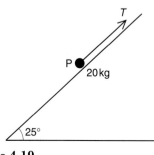

Figure 4.19

(a) Find the minimum value of the tension, *T* required to prevent the parcel from slipping down the plane

(b) Find the maximum value of *T* allowed before the parcel begins to slide up the plane.

A8 Figure 4.20 shows two particles connected by a light inextensible string passing over a smooth pulley P. The particle A rests on a

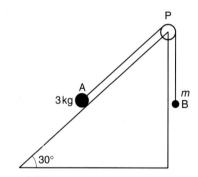

Figure 4.20

rough plane with coefficient of friction $\frac{1}{4}$. If the system is to remain in equilibrium with A at rest on the plane, find:

(a) the least value of *m*

(b) the greatest value of *m*.

B1 A particle of mass *M* is placed on a rough horizontal plane. The coefficient of friction between the particle and the plane is μ. A force *F* acting at an angle φ to the horizontal is just sufficient to make the particle slide along the plane (see Figure 4.21). Prove that

$$F = \frac{\mu Mg}{\cos \phi + \mu \sin \phi}$$

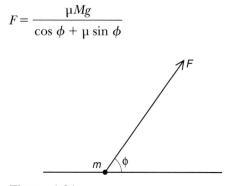

Figure 4.21

Exercise 4.2 *continued*

B2 The coefficient of friction between a box of mass 8 kg and the level floor, on which it is standing, is 0.5. A light rope attached to the box is pulled at 20° to the horizontal. If the box is on the point of sliding along the floor calculate:

(a) the tension in the rope

(b) the normal contact force between the box and the floor.

B3 A broom of mass 0.5 kg can be modelled as a particle B on the end of a light rod, as shown in Figure 4.22. The coefficient of friction between the broom and the floor is 0.6. Find the minimum force required to push the broom along the floor when θ is:

(a) 30° (b) 50° (c) 0°.

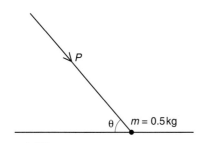

Figure 4.22

B4 A particle of mass 2 kg rests on a rough plane inclined at an angle θ to the horizontal where $\sin \theta = \frac{3}{5}$. It is just prevented from slipping down the plane by a horizontal force of 10 N.

(a) Calculate the coefficient of friction between the particle and the plane

(b) Find the magnitude of the least horizontal force required to move the particle up the plane.

B5 A particle of mass 5 kg rests on a rough plane inclined at an angle α to the

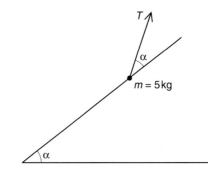

Figure 4.23

horizontal, as shown in Figure 4.23, where $\tan \alpha = \frac{5}{12}$. The coefficient of friction between the particle and the plane is $\frac{1}{4}$.

Find the tension, T in the string if the particle is about to slip:

(a) down the plane

(b) up the plane.

B6 A rough plane is inclined at 30° to the horizontal. A particle of mass 2 kg is held in equilibrium by a force of magnitude 40 N acting at an angle of 40° to the line of greatest slope, as shown in Figure 4.24. Given that the particle is on the point of sliding up the plane, calculate the coefficient of friction between the particle and the plane. If the 40 N force is removed determine whether or not the particle will slide down the plane.

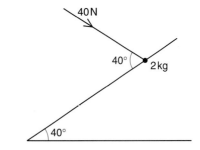

Figure 4.24

Revision questions

Take g as 9.8 m s^{-2} where necessary.

C1 A small package of mass 3 kg is suspended in equilibrium by two strings which are inclined at 20° and 40° to the horizontal respectively. Calculate the tension in the two strings.

C2 A particle of mass 6 kg is held in equilibrium by two strings. One string is horizontal and has a tension of T. The other string is inclined at an angle α to the horizontal and has a tension of 100 N. Calculate the tension T and the angle α.

C3 A small boat of mass 100 kg is on a ramp inclined at an angle of 15° to the horizontal. When a force of magnitude 300 N is applied down the ramp the boat is in limiting equilibrium. Calculate the coefficient of friction between the boat and the ramp.

C4 A particle of mass m is placed on a plane inclined at an angle α to the horizontal, where $\tan \alpha = \frac{3}{4}$. The coefficient of friction between the particle and the plane is $\frac{1}{2}$. A horizontal force P acts on the particle. Find P in terms of m and g if the particle is about to slip:

(a) down the plane

(b) up the plane.

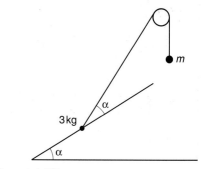

Figure 4.25

C5 A body of mass 3 kg rests on a rough plane inclined at an angle α to the horizontal where $\tan \alpha = \frac{3}{4}$. A light inextensible string is attached to the body and passes over a smooth pulley. The other end of the string is attached to a mass m which hangs vertically, as shown in Figure 4.25.

When $m = 1$ the particle is on the point of slipping down the plane.

(a) Calculate the coefficient of friction between the 3 kg mass and the plane.

(b) Find the value of m for which the 3 kg mass is on the point of slipping up the plane.

Chapter 5

NEWTON'S LAWS OF MOTION

5.1   Newton's laws of motion

Key points

> **N1: Any body will move with a constant speed in a straight line unless there is a resultant external force acting upon it.**

Thus a resultant force changes the velocity of a body.

If a body has an acceleration there is a resultant force acting upon it.

If a body has no acceleration there is no resultant force acting upon it.

> **N2: The acceleration of a body is proportional to the resultant external force and takes place in the direction of the force.**

In SI units, $F = ma$, where F is measured in Newtons (N), m is measured in kilograms (kg), and a is measured in metres per second per second (m s^{-2}).

Mass and weight

The mass of an object is characterised by:
- the amount of matter it contains
- the fact that it is constant
- its reluctance to accelerate.

Mass is a scalar quantity.

The weight of an object is the force of gravitational attraction on it towards a specific body, usually the Earth. It is sometimes referred to as its weight force.

The weight $W = mg$, where g is the acceleration due to gravity.

The direction of g is towards the centre of the Earth.

Weight is a vector quantity.

Hints on problem solving

(1)   Diagrams

    (a)   It is often helpful to draw an outline sketch of a problem, which can show masses, velocities, forces and accelerations. This should be purely descriptive and should contain all the information given in a particular question to avoid the need for constant referral back to the examination paper.

(b) A force diagram must be drawn showing all the forces acting on a body.

(c) Forces are labelled with single arrows.

Accelerations are shown with double arrows.

Whilst different notations may be used, always distinguish between forces and accelerations.

(d) All the quantities on a vector triangle or polygon must represent the same quantities, e.g. forces, or quantities which have the same dimensions. Thus, forces (N) and mass-accelerations (kg m s^{-2}) may be mixed.

(e) Units need not be specified as long as they are dimensionally consistent.

(2) Equations

(a) Always state the law or principle from which any equation is derived.

For example:

N2 horizontally gives . . .

Taking components vertically . . .

Since the system is in equilibrium . . .

(b) Do not include units in equations, but ensure that all quantities in an equation are consistent dimensionally.

(c) If the units in a given question are not SI, always convert them.
- To convert km h^{-1} to m s^{-1}, divide by 3.6.
- To convert m s^{-1} to km h^{-1}, multiply by 3.6.

(d) If g, the acceleration due to gravity, is not given a value, then write the weight of a given mass as a multiple of g, e.g. mg, $2g$, $10g$, in your initial equations and evaluate it in subsequent working.

(3) Inclined slopes

Many problems in mechanics involve motion on inclined slopes, so it is useful to learn the components of a weight force parallel to and perpendicular to a slope.

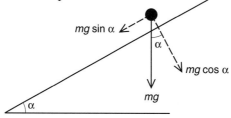

Figure 5.1

In Figure 5.1:
- the component of the weight force down the slope is $mg \sin \alpha$
- the component of the weight force perpendicular to the slope is $mg \cos \alpha$.

Often the inclination of a slope is given in the form $\alpha = \sin^{-1}(1/a)$, in which case the component of the weight force down the slope is simply mg/a.

Example 1

A boy pushes a trolley of mass 20 kg with a force P and gives it an acceleration of 0.5 m s^{-2} against a constant resistance R. A second boy assists him and their combined push, twice that of the first boy on his own, gives the trolley an acceleration of 2.5 m s^{-2}. What is the resistance to motion if it is assumed to be the same in both cases?

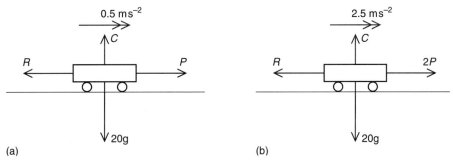

(a)   (b)

Figure 5.2

Solution

Let the resistance be R and the push of a boy be P.

From Figure 5.2(a), using N2 forward: $P - R = 20 \times 0.5 = 10$ (1)

From Figure 5.2(b), using N2 forward: $2P - R = 20 \times 2.5 = 50$ (2)

Subtracting (1) from (2) gives: $P = 40$

Substituting for P in (1) gives: $40 - R = 10$

Giving $R = 30$, and the resistance to the motion as 30 N.

Example 2

Two girls are pushing a trolley with forces 10 N and 12 N respectively at angles of $30°$ and $55°$ to the line from front to back, as shown in Figure 5.3. The mass of the trolley is 6 kg and there is a constant resistance to motion of 15 N. What will be its acceleration and in what direction will it move relative to its original direction?

Solution

Stage 1 – find the resultant force on the trolley from the girls.

Stage 2 – subtract the resistance to find the effective forward f orce.

Stage 3 – use N2 to find the acceleration.

The resultant force can be found by either using the cosine rule or by components (see Chapter 2).

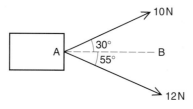

Figure 5.3

Taking components along and at right angles to the line AB in Figure 5.3, the resultant of the two pushes can be written:

$$\mathbf{R} = \begin{pmatrix} 10 \cos 30° \\ 10 \sin 30° \end{pmatrix} + \begin{pmatrix} 12 \cos 55° \\ -12 \sin 55° \end{pmatrix} = \begin{pmatrix} 15.54 \\ -4.83 \end{pmatrix}$$

The magnitude of $\mathbf{R}$ is 16.3 N and its direction is 17.3° to the line AB. The net forward force has magnitude $R - 15 = 6.99$ and the direction will be the same.

Using N2 in this direction, $a = \dfrac{F}{m} = \dfrac{1.3}{6} \approx 0.22$

Hence the acceleration has magnitude 0.22 m s^{-2} and its direction is at 17.3° to the line AB.

Exercise 5.1

Take g as 9.81 m s^{-2} where necessary.

A1 A skater of mass 45 kg is moving at 3 m s^{-1} across the ice. She slows down to rest in a distance of 15 m. What is the magnitude of the constant force causing her to stop?

A2 A man pulls a garden roller of mass 200 kg with a constant force across a lawn such that its speed increases from rest to 2 m s^{-1} in 5 s. Given a constant resistance to its motion of 100 N, find the magnitude of his pulling force.

A3 A squash ball of mass 25 g hits the front wall of a court at 40 m s^{-1} and rebounds 0.5 s later at 30 m s^{-1}. Find the acceleration of the ball during that interval and the force exerted upon it by the wall, if it is assumed to be constant.

A4 A golf ball of mass 45 g is hit by a club and leaves the tee with a speed of 60 m s^{-1} at an angle of 40° to the horizontal. If the club is in contact with the ball for 0.5 s, find the force on the ball if it is assumed to be constant.

A5 A particle of mass 2 kg is acted upon by two forces $\mathbf{P}$ and $\mathbf{Q}$. The force $\mathbf{P}$ is of magnitude 8 N and acts on a bearing of 060°, and the force $\mathbf{Q}$ has magnitude 7 N and acts due south. What is the acceleration of the particle?

A6 A particle of mass 3 kg is acted upon by two forces $\mathbf{P}$ and $\mathbf{Q}$, so that it has a constant acceleration of 5 m s^{-2} due east. If the magnitude of force $\mathbf{P}$ is 10 N which acts on a bearing of 020°, find the magnitude and direction of force $\mathbf{Q}$.

Exercise 5.1 *continued*

A7 A particle of mass 3 kg is at rest at an origin O. Taking unit base vectors $\mathbf{i}$ and $\mathbf{j}$ parallel to the x and y axes respectively, two forces acting upon it are given as $\mathbf{P} = (2\mathbf{i} + 3\mathbf{j})$ N and $\mathbf{Q} = (\mathbf{i} - 4\mathbf{j})$ N. Find the magnitude and direction of its acceleration.

A8 A man of mass 75 kg is wearing a parachute of mass 12 kg and is free-falling at a constant speed of 30 m s^{-1} when the parachute opens to provide a lift force of 500 N.

   (a) What is the initial acceleration of the man?

   (b) Calculate his speed after 3 s and how far he will have moved vertically in that time, assuming all the forces on him remain constant.

A9 A boy of mass 30 kg who is stranded on a cliff is being hoisted to safety by a vertical cable attached to him and a helicopter which is hovering above him. If the tension in the cable is 450 N, find his vertical acceleration, assuming air and other resistances can be neglected.

B1 A force $\mathbf{A}$ of magnitude 10 N acts at an angle of 80° to a force $\mathbf{B}$ on a particle of mass 6 kg. If the particle has an acceleration of 2 m s^{-1}, what is the magnitude of force $\mathbf{B}$ and the resultant direction of the particle?

   (Hint: this question requires knowledge of the method of solution of quadratic equations.)

B2 Two forces of magnitude 20 N and 16 N respectively are acting on a particle of mass 4 kg at an angle of 70° to each other.

   (a) Find the acceleration of the particle if it is on a smooth surface.

   (b) If the same forces act on the particle on a rough surface which produces a resistance to motion of 10 N, what is its acceleration?

   (Hint: find the resultant first and the resistance will act in a direction opposite to the resultant.)

B3 A boat of mass 500 kg is being pulled by two motor launches by means of ropes attached to its bows. The tensions in the ropes are T_1 and T_2 and these are inclined at angles of 25° and 35° to the line parallel to the length of the boat. The resistance to the motion of the boat is 100 N. Find the tension in each rope if

   (a) the boat is moving at steady speed

   (b) the boat has an acceleration of 0.2 m s^{-2}.

B4 Two boys are pushing a heavy trunk of mass 45 kg across a rough floor with horizontal forces of 25 N and 36 N at an angle of 65° between them. There is a resistance to motion of 15 N which is constant. What is the acceleration of the trunk and in which direction does it move relative to the push of 25 N?

B5 Two huskies are pulling a loaded sledge of mass 50 kg. One pulls with a force of 30 N and the other with a force of 34 N. The angle between them is 15° and there is a resistance to the motion of 23 N. What is the acceleration of the sledge and in what direction does it move relative to the 30 N pull?

B6 An aircraft of mass 80 tonnes is climbing at an angle of 15° to the horizontal. The thrust of the engines is 3×10^5 N and there is a drag force (parallel to its line of flight) of 5×10^4 N. Find the acceleration of the plane and the lift force (perpendicular to its line of flight) on it.

B7 A woman of mass 55 kg is wearing a parachute of mass 12 kg and is free-falling to reach a constant speed of 30 m s^{-1}. The parachute then opens to provide a further lift force of 450 N. What is her initial acceleration after the parachute opens? Calculate her speed after a further 2 s, and find how far she will have moved vertically in that time. Assume that the forces on her are constant over this period.

B8 A hot-air balloon together with its occupants and ballast have a total mass of 1500 kg. The balloon is flying at a steady speed and at a constant height when 75 kg of ballast is released. If air resistance is neglected, find the magnitude of the acceleration of the balloon.

5.2   Contact forces

Key points

Contact forces were introduced in Chapter 4.

> **N3: If two bodies A and B interact, then the force which A exerts on B is equal in magnitude and opposite in direction to the force exerted by B on A.**

Such forces are referred to as contact forces or reactions.

Example I

A girl of mass 30 kg is standing in a lift of mass 500 kg. Find the total tension in the lift cables and the thrust on her feet from the lift floor when:

(a)   the lift is ascending at a steady speed of 5 m s^{-1}

(b)   the lift is ascending with an upward acceleration of 2 m s^{-2}

(c)   the lift is ascending but slowing down with a deceleration of 2 m s^{-2}.

Take g as 9.81 m s^{-2}, and give your answers to 3 significant figures.

Solution

Assumptions:
- The many cables and attachments to the top of the lift will be simplified to a single cable in which the total tension, T, acts.
- The girl and the lift will be treated as two particles in contact. Let the contact force between them be R.
- In cases of particles in contact, there are several diagrams which can be drawn, as shown in Figure 5.4. However, the solution of a problem does not usually require all of them.

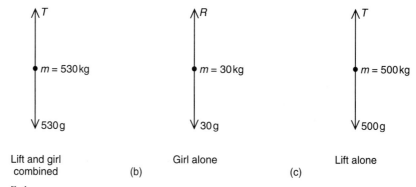

(a)   Lift and girl combined   (b)   Girl alone   (c)   Lift alone

Figure 5.4

(a)   Consider the girl and the lift as a single particle of mass 530 kg, as in Figure 5.4(a). Since the lift is moving at a steady speed there is no acceleration, so $T = 530g = 5199$, giving the tension in the lift cable as 5200 N.

The forces on the girl alone are shown in Figure 5.4(b) and are the thrust from the lift floor, R, and her own weight force, $30g\,$N.

At steady speed, $R = 30g = 294$, giving the thrust on her feet as 294 N, which is her weight force.

The above answers are independent of the constant upward speed of the lift.

(b) In Figure 5.4(a), $a = 2$ in the upward direction.

Using N2 vertically upwards $\qquad T - 530g = 530a$

giving $T = 530 \times 2 + 530 \times 9.81 = 6259$

The tension in the lift cables is 6260 N.

In Figure 5.4(b), using N2 vertically upwards: $R - 30g = 30a$

giving $R = 30 \times 9.81 + 30 \times 2 = 354$

So the thrust on her feet is 354 N, which is greater than her weight force of 294 N, so she feels the lift pushing her upwards.

(c) In Figure 5.4(a), $a = -2$ in the upward vertical direction.

Using N2 vertically upwards: $\qquad T - 530g = 530a$

giving $T = 530 \times -2 + 530 \times 9.81 = 4139$

The tension in the cables is reduced to 4140 N.

In Figure 5.4(b), using N2 vertically upwards: $R - 30g = 30a$

giving $R = 30 \times -2 + 30 \times 9.81 = 234$

The thrust on her feet is now 234 N, which is less than her weight force and so she has a slight sensation of becoming lighter.

Example 2

A car mass 950 kg is moving with an acceleration of 3 m s^{-2} up a hill inclined to the horizontal at an angle α, where $\sin \alpha = \frac{1}{10}$. There is a constant resistance to motion of 600 N. What is the tractive force of the engine and the contact force between the car and the road?

On reaching the top of the hill, as the road levels out, the driver keeps his foot on the accelerator pedal so that the tractive force remains the same. What is the initial acceleration of the car, assuming all other resistances remain the same?

Take g as 9.81 m s^{-2}, and give your answers to 3 significant figures.

Solution

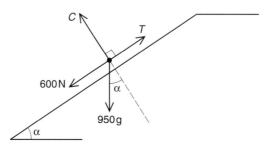

Figure 5.5

Let the acceleration of the car be a, the tractive force of the car be T and the normal contact force between the car and the slope be C.

Using N2 up the slope $T - 600 - 950g \sin \alpha = 950a$

giving $T = 600 + 950 \times 9.81 \times 0.1 + 950 \times 3 = 4382$

The tractive force of the car is 4380 N

Using N2 perpendicular to the slope $C - 950g \cos \alpha = 0$

giving $C = 950 \times 9.81 \times 0.9949 = 9273$

The normal contact force is 9270 N, which is less than the weight force of the car.

Note that, since there is no acceleration perpendicular to the slope, the forces in that direction are in equilibrium, so those into the slope and those away from the slope may be equated.

Thus, $C = mg \cos \alpha$, in general, so that as α increases, $\cos \alpha$ decreases.

At the top of the hill, as the road levels out, the forces on the car are as shown in Figure 5.6.

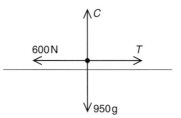

Figure 5.6

Suppose the acceleration on the level is a.

Using N2 parallel to the road $T - 600 = 950a$

giving $a = (4380 - 600)/950 = 3.98$

Notice that the increase in the acceleration is $(3.98 - 3) = 0.98$ and this is the value of $g \sin \alpha = g/10 = 0.98$), which is the component of the weight force down the slope divided by the mass.

Exercise 5.2

Take g as 9.81 m s^{-2} where necessary.

A1 A lift of mass 1 tonne can carry 10 passengers each of average mass 65 kg.

   (a) What is the tension in the lift cable if a full lift is slowing down and moving upwards with a retardation of 2 m s^{-2}?

   (b) What is the reaction of the floor on an individual passenger of mass 40 kg?

A2 A woman of mass 55 kg is alone in a lift of mass 1200 kg which is suspended by a vertical cable. The lift is descending with an acceleration of 2 m s^{-2} and she is carrying a parcel of mass 2 kg.

   Find:

   (a) the tension in the lift cable

   (b) the reaction between the woman and the lift floor

   (c) the reaction between her hand and the parcel.

   Suppose that, whilst the lift is descending, she drops the parcel. What is

   (d) the tension in the lift cable while the parcel is falling

   (e) the tension in the cable after the parcel hits the floor?

A3 A man of mass 75 kg is standing in a lift of mass 600 kg. Find the force exerted by the floor on the man and the total tension in the lift cables

   (a) when the lift is accelerating upwards at 1.5 m s^{-2}

   (b) when the lift is accelerating downwards at 1.5 m s^{-2}.

A4 A man of mass 85 kg is standing in a lift of mass 1 tonne. Find the total tension in the lift cables and the thrust of the floor on the man when:

   (a) the lift is ascending at steady speed

   (b) the lift is accelerating upwards at 1.5 m s^{-2}

   (c) the lift is moving upwards but slowing down with a retardation of 1.5 m s^{-2}.

A5 A hot-air balloon together with its passengers has a mass of 200 kg. It is descending with a steady speed of 4 m s^{-1}, when 10 kg of ballast is thrown out. Find:

   (a) the subsequent acceleration of the balloon

   (b) the distance it continues to fall before coming instantaneously to rest

   (c) the time before it starts to rise.

B1 A car of mass 1 tonne has an engine which exerts a constant tractive force of 950 N. The car moves up a hill which is inclined to the horizontal at an angle given by $\sin^{-1}(1/8)$ to the horizontal. The car initially approaches the hill with a speed of 25 m s^{-1}. If there is a constant resistance to motion of 350 N, how long is it before the car comes to rest and how far has it then travelled.

B2 A train of mass 350 tonnes is travelling at 160 km h^{-1} when it reaches a slope of $\sin^{-1}(1/180)$ to the horizontal. The tractive force of the engines is 35 000 N and there is a constant resistance to its motion of 25 000 N. What is its speed after it has travelled 4 km up the slope?

B3 A car of mass 800 kg is at the top of a hill when its brakes fail, so that it free-wheels down the hill for 100 m until its speed is 10 m s^{-1}. Assuming there is a constant resistance to motion of 400 N, find the angle of inclination of the hill to the nearest degree.

B4 A particle of mass 3 kg is pushed with a force of magnitude P up a slope which is inclined at an angle of 15° to the horizontal. The particle accelerates at 1.5 m s^{-2} and there is a constant resistance to motion of 5 N. Find P and the normal reaction to the slope if:

   (a) P is applied parallel to the slope

   (b) P is applied horizontally.

continued

Exercise 5.2 *continued*

B5 A girl is standing on a skateboard at the top of a slope which is inclined at 10° to the horizontal. The combined mass of the girl and the board is 42 kg and there is a frictional resistance to her motion of 50 N. She pushes herself off with a speed of 3 m s^{-1}.

(a) Find her initial acceleration down the slope.

(b) How long is it before her speed is 4.5 m s^{-1}?

(c) How far will she have then moved down the slope?

After she has travelled 15 m, she encounters a slope inclined upwards at an angle of 25° to the horizontal. Assuming the same resistance to her motion, how far will she move up the new slope?

Revision questions

Take g as 9.81 m s^{-2} where necessary.

C1 A particle of mass 5 kg is at rest on a smooth horizontal plane. It is acted upon by a force of 7 N due west and one of 9 N due north. Find its acceleration and its bearing to the nearest degree.

C2 An aircraft of mass 80 tonnes is climbing at an angle of 5° to the horizontal. The thrust of the engines is 2.5×10^5 N and there is a drag force (parallel to the line of flight) of 5.7×10^4 N. Find the acceleration of the plane and its lift force (perpendicular to the line of flight).

C3 A sledge with rider of total mass 85 kg slides down a slope inclined at 15° to the horizontal at a constant speed. Find the magnitude of the resistance to the motion. If the angle of the slope increases to 20° and the resistance remains the same, calculate the acceleration of the sledge.

C4 Jack of mass 30 kg and Jill of mass 20 kg are sitting on a toboggan of mass 10 kg at the top of a hill of slope $\sin^{-1}(1/5)$, when they push off with a speed of 2 m s^{-1}. There is a resistance of 50 N on the toboggan due to the ground and 15 N on each of the children due to the wind. What is their initial acceleration and speed after they have travelled 20 m down the slope? At this time, they both fall off the toboggan. What is its speed after a further 3 m?

C5 A woman of mass 50 kg is in the basket of a hot-air balloon whose total mass including ballast is 200 kg. The balloon is drifting upwards at a steady speed of 4 m s^{-1}.

(a) What is the lift force on the balloon?

(b) If 10 kg of ballast is thrown out of the balloon, (i) what is the initial acceleration of the balloon, and (ii) what is its speed 20 s later?

(c) If gas is released to reduce the lift force by 250 N, (i) what is the new acceleration, and (ii) what is the speed of the balloon after a further 20 s? The mass of the gas released may be ignored.

C6 A lift of mass 1000 kg is carrying a woman of mass 50 kg. It is descending with an acceleration of 1.5 m s^{-2}.

(a) Find the tension in the lift cable and the vertical force exerted by the lift floor on the woman.

(b) If she drops a parcel from a height of 1.5 m, how long will it take to hit the lift floor?

(c) If the maximum acceleration the lift can have is 1.8 m s^{-2} and the maximum tension in the lift cable is 18 000 N, find the maximum number of passengers it can safely take. Assume a maximum mass per passenger of 80 kg.

C7 A car of mass m starts initially at rest at the bottom of a hill inclined to the horizontal at an angle α where $\sin \alpha = \frac{1}{10}$. It has a tractive force of P which increases its speed to 3 m s^{-1} in 5 s. After that time, the tractive force is doubled to $2P$. Find:

(a) the time it then takes to reach a speed of 5 m s^{-1}

(b) the total distance travelled up the slope.

C8 A lorry is towing a glider of mass 210 kg at a steady speed by means of a tow rope. The rope is inclined at an angle of 25° to the horizontal and the glider is inclined at an angle of 50° to the tow rope. The resistance to the glider acts along its fuselage and the lift on it is perpendicular to the fuselage. If the tension in the tow rope is 1200 N, find:

(a) the total resistance on the glider

(b) the lift force on the glider.

Chapter 6

APPLICATIONS OF NEWTON'S LAWS OF MOTION

Key points

In Section 4.1 we saw that the tension in a string is constant throughout its length. When solving problems involving bodies connected by strings or ropes, it is often convenient to consider the two (or more) bodies both as a single particle and as separate particles.

Example 1

A car of mass 1.5 t is towing another car which has broken down by means of a tow-rope attached to their bumpers. The mass of the car being towed is 1 t and there is a constant resistance to each of 500 N t^{-1}. If the acceleration of the system is 0.7 m s^{-2}, find the tractive force of the car which is towing and the tension in the tow-rope.

Solution

Figure 6.1 shows a sketch of the two cars, together with force diagrams for (a) the two cars treated as a single particle and (b) the cars as two separate particles.

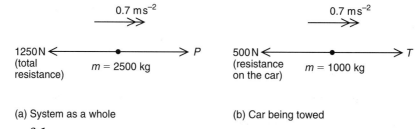

(a) System as a whole   (b) Car being towed

Figure 6.1

Let the tension in the tow-rope be T and the tractive force of the engine be P. Using N2 along the road on the system as a whole

$$P - 1.5 \times 500 - 1 \times 500 = 2550 \times 0.7$$

giving $$P = 3000$$

To find the tension, consider the forces on the second car, as shown in Figure 6.1(b).

Using N2 along the road

$$T - 1 \times 500 = 1000 \times 0.7$$

giving
$$T = 1250$$

The tractive force of the car is 3000 N and the tension in the rope is 1250 N.

Example 2

Suppose the first car in Example 1 attempts to pull the second car up a slope inclined to the horizontal at an angle α where $\sin \alpha = \frac{1}{10}$. Assuming the resistances remain the same but the tractive force is increased to 4000 N, find the acceleration up the slope of the two cars and the tension in the rope.

Take g as 9.81 m s^{-2}, and give your answers to 3 significant figures.

Solution

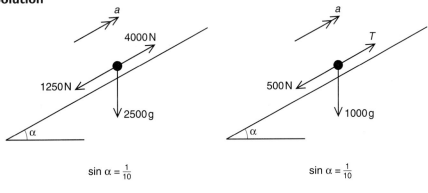

| (a) System as a whole | (b) Car being towed |

Figure 6.2

Let the tension in the rope be T and the acceleration of the system be a. Using N2 along the road on the system as a whole:

$$4000 - 1.5 \times 500 - 1 \times 500 - 2500 \times g \sin \alpha = 2500a$$

which gives $a = 0.119$

To find the tension in the rope, apply N2 to the car being towed:

$$T - 1000g \sin \alpha - 1 \times 500 = 1000a$$

giving $T = 1600$

So the acceleration is 0.119 m s^{-2} and the tension in the rope is 1600 N.

Note that, in this example, the contact forces are not needed to analyse the motion along the road. Later in the chapter their connection with friction and motion will be examined.

Exercise 6.1

Take g as 9.81 m s^{-2} where necessary.

A1 Three trucks each of mass 8 t are being pulled along a smooth railway track by a force of 12 000 N.
  - (a) What is the acceleration of the trucks?
  - (b) What is the tension in the coupling between the second and third trucks?

A2 Three trucks each of mass 5 kg are being pulled along a smooth horizontal floor by a force of 10 N.
  - (a) What is the acceleration of the trucks?
  - (b) What is the tension in the rope joining the second and last trucks?

A3 A car of mass 1200 kg is pulling a trailer of mass 100 kg along a horizontal road. If the car exerts a constant driving force of 2000 N, find:
  - (a) the acceleration of the trailer
  - (b) the tension in the tow-bar.

  Assume all resistances can be ignored.

A4 A car of mass 1 t is towing a caravan of mass 400 kg. There is a resistance of 500 N to the motion of each vehicle. If the car exerts a driving force of 3000 N, find:
  - (a) the acceleration of the caravan
  - (b) the tension in the tow hitch

A5 A car of mass 1200 kg is pulling a caravan of mass 900 kg along a level road. There is a resistance of 100 N t^{-1} on the car and 250 N t^{-1} on the caravan. Find the tractive force of the car and the thrust in the tow-bar when:
  - (a) the car is moving at a steady speed of 25 m s^{-1}
  - (b) the car is accelerating at 2.5 m s^{-2}.

A6 A car of mass 1200 kg is towing another car of mass 900 kg by means of a tow-rope attached to their bumpers. There is a resistance to motion of 100 N t^{-1} on each car.
  - (a) Find the driving force of the first car and the tension in the tow-rope if it is moving at steady speed.
  - (b) If the tow-rope breaks when the car is travelling at 20 m s^{-1}, what is the acceleration of the first car and how far will the second car travel before it comes to rest?

B1 A miniature train of mass 1.5 t pulls a carriage of mass 500 kg at a steady speed up a slope inclined at an angle of $\sin^{-1}(1/125)$ to the horizontal. The resistive force of the track on the train is 150 N and on the carriage is 75 N.
  - (a) Calculate the tractive force of the train.
  - (b) What is the tension in the coupling?

B2 A car of mass 1500 kg is pulling a caravan of mass 750 kg along a straight road. The tractive force of the engine is 4000 N and there is a total resistance of 600 N to the car and 400 N to the caravan. What is the acceleration of the system if:
  - (a) the road is level
  - (b) the road is inclined at 5° to the horizontal?

B3 A car of mass 1700 kg tows a caravan of mass 700 kg up a slope inclined at an angle of $\sin^{-1}(1/10)$ to the horizontal. There is a resistance of 300 N t^{-1} on the car and 400 N t^{-1} on the caravan. The engine produces a constant tractive force of 8000 N. Find:
  - (a) the acceleration of the car and the caravan
  - (b) the tension in the tow-bar.

B4 An engine of mass 300 t is pulling 20 trucks each of mass 5 t along a horizontal track. The resistance to motion is 2×10^4 N on the train and 500 N on each of the trucks.
  - (a) If the engine moves at a steady speed of 30 m s^{-1}, what is the tractive force of the engine?
  - (b) What is the tension in the coupling between the 10th and 11th trucks?
  - (c) If suddenly the last 10 trucks become disengaged, what is the initial acceleration of the train at that instant?
  - (d) How far will the last 10 trucks travel before coming to rest?

Exercise 6.1 *continued*

B5 Suppose the engine in question **B4** pulls the 10 trucks up a slope inclined to the horizontal at an angle α, where $\sin \alpha = 1/120$.

    (a) What is the tractive force needed to move up the slope with:

        (i) a steady speed,

        (ii) an acceleration of 0.5 m s^{-2}?

    (b) What is the tension in the coupling between the 9th and 10th trucks in parts (i) and (ii) above?

B6 A car of mass 900 kg is exerting a driving force of 2500 N and is pulling a light trailer of mass 250 kg up a slope inclined to the horizontal at an angle α where $\sin \alpha = 0.1$. There is a resistance to motion of 200 N t^{-1} on the car, but that on the trailer is negligible.

    (a) Find the acceleration of the car and trailer.

    (b) Find the tension in the tow-rope.

    (c) If the tow-rope breaks when the car is travelling at 15 m s^{-1}, what will be the new acceleration of the car and how far will the trailer travel up the hill before coming instantaneously to rest?

6.2 Pulleys

Key points

A very common set of examples on connected particles arises when objects are joined by strings or ropes which pass over pegs or around pulleys, which are most often assumed to be smooth, i.e. there are no frictional forces over the pegs or pulleys themselves.

Modelling assumptions (see also Chapter 4):

- Pulleys are assumed to be light and to have negligible mass.
- Strings are assumed to be light and inextensible.
- The tension in a string is the same throughout its length.
- Particles connected by a string have accelerations with the same magnitude.

Figure 6.3 shows several common configurations.

Note: In questions involving pulleys, the particles attached to them are often moving in different directions. For example, one may be moving upwards and the other downwards. To avoid confusion the motion of each particle is analysed separately.

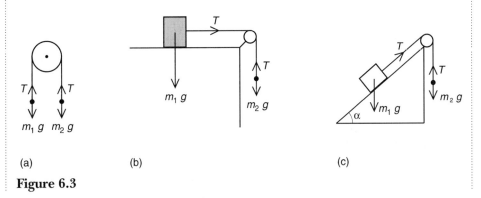

    (a)   (b)   (c)

Figure 6.3

Example I

A man of mass 70 kg working on a building site sees a barrel of mass 40 kg attached to a rope which passes over a pulley attached to the top of a high building of height 10 m, the other end of the rope being hitched to a post near the ground, as shown in Figure 6.4. He thinks the barrel is empty and so unhitches the rope. Unfortunately, however, the barrel is full of bricks of total mass 100 kg and, hanging onto the rope, he is lifted off the ground.

(a)   Find his acceleration and the tension in the rope as he leaves the ground.

(b)   Find the speed with which he reaches the top of the building.

When the barrel hits the ground its contents spill out, leaving a mass of 20 kg on the end of the rope, and the man hits the platform, coming instantaneously to rest.

(c)   What is the speed of the man when he subsequently hits the ground?

(d)   If he then releases the rope, what will be the speed of the 20 kg barrel as it descends and hits the man?

Take g as 9.81 m s^{-2} and give your answer to 3 significant figures.

Solution

Figure 6.4 shows the system as a whole, together with the man and the barrel as two separate systems.

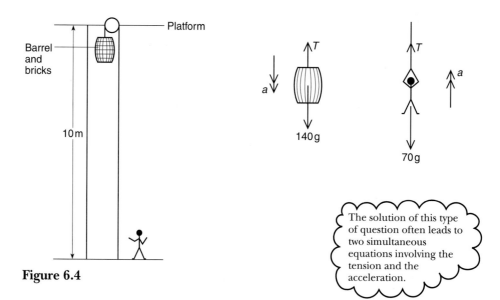

Figure 6.4

> The solution of this type of question often leads to two simultaneous equations involving the tension and the acceleration.

(a)   Let the tension in the rope be T and the initial acceleration be a.

Applying N2 vertically upwards on the man $T - 70g = 70a$ (1)

Applying N2 vertically downwards on the barrel and bricks
$$140g - T = 140a$$ (2)

Adding these equations $\qquad 70g = 210a$

giving $a = g/3$, so the initial acceleration is 3.27 m s^{-2}.

Substituting in (1) $\qquad T = 70 \times 3.27 + 70 \times 9.81 = 915.6$

The tension in the rope is 916 N

(b) As the man ascends from rest with a constant acceleration of 3.27 m s^{-2} and travels a distance of 10 m before reaching the top of the building, we can use the constant acceleration formula $v^2 = u^2 + 2as$.

So $v^2 = 0 + 2 \times 3.27 \times 10$, giving $v = 8.09$ m s^{-1}.

(c) Figure 6.5 shows the part of the motion with the man descending and the barrel of mass 20 kg rising.

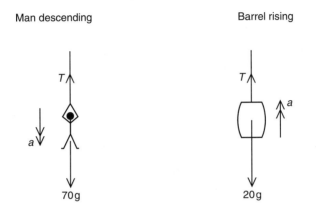

Figure 6.5

Let the tension in the rope be T and the initial acceleration be a.

Applying N2 vertically downwards on the man
$$70g - T = 70a \qquad (3)$$

Applying N2 vertically upwards on the empty barrel
$$T - 20g = 20a \qquad (4)$$

Adding these equations $\qquad 50g = 90a$

giving $a = 5g/9$, so the initial acceleration is 5.45 m s^{-2}.

Substituting in (4) $\qquad T = 20 \times 5.45 + 20 \times 9.81 = 305.2$

The tension in the rope is 305 N (3 sig. fig.)

The speed of the man on hitting the ground is found using $v^2 = u^2 + 2as$, with $u = 0$, $a = 5.45$ and $s = 10$.

$v^2 = 2 \times 5.45 \times 10$, giving $v = 10.4$ m s^{-1}.

(d) For this part of the motion, the barrel falls freely from rest under gravity. Thus, its speed on reaching the ground is $\sqrt{2 \times 9.81 \times 10} = 14$ m s^{-1}.

Exercise 6.2

Take g as 10 m s^{-2}, where necessary.

AI Two particles of masses 2 kg and 4 kg hang freely and are connected by a light inextensible string passing over a smooth pulley. Find the tension in the string and the acceleration of each mass.

A2 A particle of mass 5 kg is lying on a smooth horizontal table and is connected to a second particle of mass 7 kg which hangs vertically. The string connecting them passes over a smooth pulley fixed to the edge of the table, as shown in Figure 6.6.

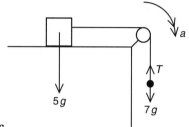

Figure 6.6

Find the acceleration of the 7 kg mass.

A3 A particle of mass 3 kg is lying on a smooth horizontal table. It is attached by light inextensible strings to two particles of masses 4 kg and 5 kg, which hang over the edges of the table, as shown in Figure 6.7.

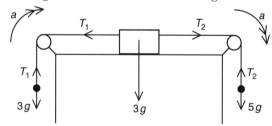

Figure 6.7

Find the acceleration of the 3 kg mass and the tension in each string.

A4 Two particles, A and B, of mass 0.3 kg and 0.45 kg respectively, are connected by a light inextensible string passing over a fixed smooth light pulley. The particles are released from rest with the string taut and the particles hanging vertically.

(a) Find the acceleration of particle B.

(b) Calculate the tension in the string.

A5 A particle of mass 0.5 kg is connected to a particle of mass 0.7 kg by a light inextensible string which passes over a smooth light fixed pulley. The particles hang freely and the system is released from rest with the string taut. Find the acceleration of the greater mass.

A6 Two particles of mass 3 kg and 4 kg and are connected by a light inextensible string which passes over a smooth pulley. The 3 kg mass is on a smooth horizontal plane and the 4 kg mass hangs freely. Find the acceleration with which the 4 kg mass descends.

BI Two particles of masses 2 kg and 3 kg which are lying on two sides of a smooth wedge with inclinations of 20° and 30° respectively are connected by a light inextensible string which passes over a pulley, as shown in Figure 6.8.

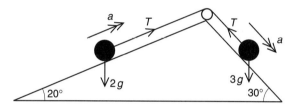

Figure 6.8

Find the tension in the string and the acceleration of the particles.

Assuming that the 30° slope was fixed, what would the angle of the other slope have to be to keep the system in equilibrium?

B2 The two particles in question **BI** are interchanged. What is the new tension in the string and the acceleration of the system?

B3 A particle of mass 5 kg is hanging vertically by a string which passes over a pulley attached to the top of a smooth right-angled wedge, as shown in Figure 6.9. The other end of the string is attached to a particle of mass 3 kg, which is lying on the sloping face of the wedge, inclined at 30° to the horizontal. Find the acceleration of the 5 kg mass and the tension in the string.

Exercise 6.2 *continued*

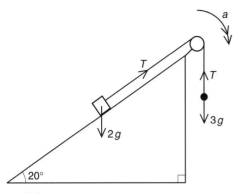

Figure 6.9

B4 Two masses of 4 kg and 3 kg are lying on a smooth wedge the faces of which are inclined at 40° and 30° respectively, as shown in Figure 6.10. Find the tension in the string and the acceleration of the 4 kg particle.

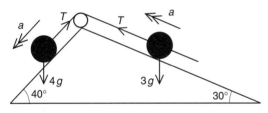

Figure 6.10

If the steeper slope were to be fixed, how would the angle of the other face have to be altered to keep the system in equilibrium?

B5 A particle of mass 3 kg is at rest on a smooth plane inclined at an angle of 50° to the horizontal. It is attached to one end of a light inelastic string which passes over a fixed smooth pulley at the top of the plane. The other end of the string carries a mass of 1.5 kg which hangs vertically. Find:

(a) the acceleration of the system

(b) the tension in the string.

B6 A particle of mass 3 kg is at rest on a smooth plane which is inclined at an angle of 45° to the horizontal. It is attached to a light inextensible string which passes over a smooth pulley which is fixed at the top of the plane. The other end of the string is attached to a particle of mass of 4 kg. Find:

(a) the tension in the string

(b) the acceleration of the system.

After the 3 kg particle has travelled 3 m up the plane the string is cut. Find how much further up the plane it travels before coming to instantaneous rest.

6.3 Friction and motion

Key points

In all examples in this chapter, when motion occurs, friction will be limiting and so $F = \mu R$ where F is the frictional force and R is the normal contact force.

Example 1

A trunk of mass 30 kg is pulled across a horizontal floor by a woman using a rope which is inclined at an angle of 50° to the horizontal and which is attached to the handle of the trunk. The force needed to move it is 20 N along the rope. If it moves at steady speed, what is the coefficient of friction?

Take g as 9.81 m s^{-2} and give your answer to 3 significant figures.

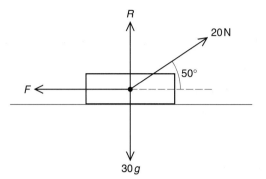

Figure 6.11

Solution

Let the friction force be F.

Since there is no acceleration, forces can be resolved in two directions, which in this case are along and perpendicular to the floor.

Resolving along the horizontal $\qquad P\cos\alpha = F$

giving $F = 20\cos 50° = 12.86$

Resolving vertically $\qquad\qquad R + P\sin\alpha = mg$

giving $R = 30 \times 9.81 - 20\sin 50° = 279$

Since friction is limiting, $F = \mu R$, so that $\mu = 12.86/279 = 0.046$

Example 2

A particle of mass 3 kg is lying on a horizontal table and is connected by a light inextensible string which passes over a smooth pulley. To the other end of the string is attached a particle of mass 4 kg which hangs vertically, as shown in Figure 6.12.

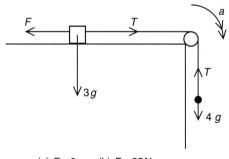

Figure 6.12 $\qquad$ (a) $F = 0$ $\qquad$ (b) $F = 25\,\text{N}$

Find the acceleration with which the 4 kg mass descends and the tension in the string when:

(a) the horizontal surface is smooth

(b) there is a frictional resistance on the surface of 25 N.

Take g as 9.81 m s^{-2} and give your answers to 3 significant figures.

Solution

Let the tension in the string be T and the acceleration over the peg be a

(a)   Smooth surface

Applying N2 vertically downwards on the 4 kg mass:
$$4g - T = 4a \tag{1}$$

Applying N2 horizontally on the 3 kg mass:
$$T = 3a \tag{2}$$

Adding equations (1) and (2) $4g = 7a$

giving $a = 4g/7$, giving the acceleration as 5.61 m s^{-2}

From equation (2), the tension in the string, $T = 3a$, giving the tension as 16.8 N

(b)   Rough surface

Applying N2 vertically downwards on the 4 kg mass $4g - T = 4a$ (3)

which is exactly the same equation as in part (a)

Applying N2 horizontally on the 3 kg mass $T - 25 = 3a$ (4)

Adding equations (3) and (4) $4g - 25 = 7a$

giving the acceleration as 2.03 m s^{-2}.

Example 3

A particle A of mass 10 kg rests on a rough plane which is inclined at an angle α to the horizontal where $\sin \alpha = \frac{4}{5}$. The particle is attached to one end of an inextensible string which passes over a smooth pulley at the top of the plane. A particle B of mass 2 kg is attached to the other end and

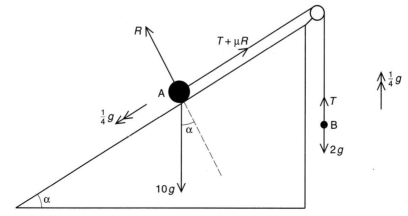

Figure 6.13

hangs freely, as shown in Figure 6.13. Particle A moves down the plane with acceleration $\frac{1}{4}g$. Calculate:

(a)   the tension in the string

(b)   the coefficient of friction between particle A and the inclined plane

(c)   the magnitude of the force that the string exerts on the pulley.

Take g as 9.81 m s^{-2}, giving your answers to 3 significant figures.

Solution

(a)   Applying N2 vertically on particle B $T - 2g = 2(\frac{1}{4}g)$ (1)

giving $T = 2.5g = 24.5$

The tension in the string is 24.5 N.

(b)   Applying N2 to particle A

> Since $\sin \alpha = \frac{4}{5}$
> $\cos \alpha = \frac{3}{5}$

perpendicular to the slope $R = 10g \cos \alpha = 6g$ (2)

parallel to the slope $10g \sin \alpha - T - \mu R = 10(\frac{1}{4}g)$ (3)

Substituting for R and T in (3) $8g - 2.5g - 6\mu g = 2.5g$

giving $\mu = \frac{1}{2}$

(c)   From the cosine rule, the total force on the pulley is given by:

$$\sqrt{[T^2 + T^2 + 2T^2 \cos (90 - \alpha)°]} = T\sqrt{(2 + 2 \sin \alpha)} = 55.9$$

The total force on the pulley from the string is 55.9 N

Exercise 6.3

Take g as 9.8 m s^{-2} where necessary.

A1   A particle of mass 4 kg has an acceleration of 1.5 m s^{-2} along a horizontal plane under the action of a constant force of 35 N. Calculate the coefficient of friction between the particle and the plane.

A2   If the coefficient of friction is the same find the force needed to pull the particle in question **A1** up a slope inclined at an angle of 10° to the horizontal with the same acceleration, .

A3   A particle of mass 0.8 kg rests on a horizontal plane. The coefficient of friction is 0.25. A force of 10 N is applied downwards onto the particle at an angle α to the horizontal. Find the magnitude of the frictional force and the acceleration of the particle if:

(a) $\alpha = 0°$ (b) $\alpha = 90°$ (c) $\alpha = 55°$.

A4   A particle is projected with a speed 10 m s^{-1} up a slope which is inclined to the horizontal at an angle of 20°. If the coefficient of friction is 0.4, how far up the slope will it travel before coming to rest?

A5   Two particles of mass 1 kg and 3 kg are held at rest on the faces of a wedge whose sides make equal angles of 45° to the horizontal. They are connected by a light inextensible string which passes over a smooth fixed pulley at the top of the wedge. The surfaces of the wedge are rough and the coefficient of friction between them and the particles is $\frac{1}{4}$. If the particles are released what is the acceleration of the system and the tension in the string?

A6   A particle of mass 2 kg is lying on a rough horizontal table and is connected by a light inextensible string which passes over a smooth pulley which is fixed to the edge of the table. The other end of the string is attached to a particle of mass 3.5 kg. If the coefficient of friction between the particle and the table is 0.1, find the acceleration of the system and the tension in the string.

Exercise 6.3 *continued*

BI A particle of mass m is projected with a speed of 15 m s^{-1} up a plane which is inclined at an angle of 15° to the horizontal. For the first 3 m the coefficient of friction is 0.3, after which it is 0.5. How far up the plane will it travel before coming to rest?

B2 Figure 6.14 shows a fixed wedge with a particle on either face connected by a light inextensible string which passes over a smooth peg P. The coefficient of friction on each face is μ.

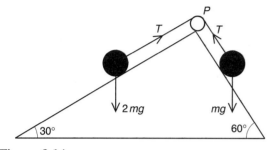

Figure 6.14

(a) Find the minimum value of μ for which the system can remain in equilibrium.

(b) Repeat part (a) when the two masses are interchanged.

B3 A trunk of mass 75 kg is held at rest on a ramp which is inclined at 25° to the horizontal by a rope. The tension in the rope which is parallel to the slope is 500 N. The trunk is on the point of moving up the slope (so friction is limiting), when the rope snaps. Find the speed with which the trunk hits the bottom of the ramp if it is 5 m long.

B4 A fixed wedge has a particle on each face joined by a light inextensible string which passes over a smooth pulley fixed at P. The masses are 2 kg and 4 kg and the faces inclined at angles of 20° and 40° respectively. If the coefficient of friction between each particle and each inclined face is 0.2, find:

(a) the acceleration of the system

(b) the tension in the string joining the particles.

B5 A particle of mass 0.5 kg is projected with speed 5 m s^{-1} up a slope which is inclined at an angle of 20° with the horizontal which has a coefficient of friction of 0.3. Find:

(a) the acceleration of the particle up the slope

(b) the distance the particle moves up the slope before coming to instantaneous rest

(c) the time taken for it to come to rest

(d) the acceleration of the particle down the slope

(e) the speed with which the particle returns to its original position

(f) the total time taken to return.

B6 A particle A of mass 5 kg is on a rough horizontal plane. It is attached to one end of an inelastic string which passes over a smooth pulley P, as shown in Figure 6.15.

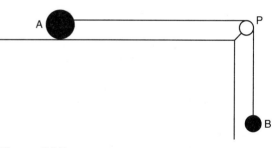

Figure 6.15

A particle B of mass 2 kg hangs freely from the other end of the string. When the system is released from rest with the string taut particle B has an acceleration downwards of $\frac{1}{10}g$. Calculate:

(a) the tension in the string

(b) the coefficient of friction between the particle A and the horizontal plane

(c) the magnitude of the resultant force exerted by the string on the pulley.

Revision questions

Take g as 9.8 m s^{-2} where necessary.

C1 Two particles of masses 100 g and 110 g are joined by means of a light inelastic string which passes over a smooth pulley. Initially they are held with the larger mass 60 cm above a horizontal table. Find:

(a) the speed of the larger mass when it hits the table

(b) how long it takes to hit the table

(c) the time which passes before the smaller mass comes instantaneously to rest.

C2 A particle of mass 5 kg is at rest on a horizontal table and is connected to a particle of mass 2 kg by a light inextensible rope which passes over a fixed smooth pulley which is attached to the edge of the table, so that the 2 kg mass hangs vertically.

(a) If the table is smooth, find the tension in the rope and the acceleration of the 2 kg mass.

(b) If the table is rough, and the 2 kg mass has an acceleration of 0.6 m s^{-2}, find the resistive force and the tension in the rope.

(c) If an additional mass of 3 kg is added to the 5 kg mass, what mass should be added to the 2 kg mass in order that the acceleration remains 0.6 m s^{-2}? Assume that the resistive force does not change.

C3 Two particles of mass 400 g and 600 g are attached to the ends of a light inextensible string which passes over a smooth pulley fixed to the edge of a rough horizontal table. The 400 g mass lies on the table and the 600 g mass hangs vertically over the pulley. There is a resistive force on the table of 4 N. The system is released from rest.

(a) Find the acceleration of the 400 g mass.

After 2 s and before the 400 g mass hits the pulley, the string breaks.

(b) Find the speed of the 400 g mass just before the string breaks and how far it travels before coming to rest after being released. Assume it does not reach the pulley.

C4 A breakdown truck of mass 1800 kg is pulling a car of mass 750 kg up a hill which is inclined at an angle α to the horizontal where $\sin \alpha = \frac{1}{8}$. There is a resistance to the motion of each vehicle which is proportional to its mass. The tractive force of the truck is 4000 N. If the system moves up the hill with an acceleration of 0.2 m s^{-2}, find, to 2 significant figures, the constant of proportionality and hence the resistance on each vehicle.

When the vehicles have reached a speed of 6 m s^{-1}, the tow rope breaks. Find:

(a) the initial acceleration of the truck

(b) the distance taken by the car before it comes instantaneously to rest.

C5 A engine of mass 50 t is pulling four wagons each of mass 25 t. The tractive force of the engine is 6×10^4 N. There is a resistance to motion of 500 N t^{-1} on the engine and 300 N t^{-1} on each truck. Assuming the track is level, find:

(a) the acceleration of the train

(b) the tensions in the first and the last couplings.

If when the train is moving at 20 m s^{-1}, it encounters an incline which is at an angle α to the horizontal, where $\sin \alpha = 1/120$, find:

(c) by how much the tractive force must be increased to maintain this speed

(d) how far up the slope it will travel before coming to rest if the tractive force is not increased.

C6 A particle of mass m moves up a line of greatest slope of a plane inclined to the horizontal at an angle α where $\tan \alpha = \frac{3}{4}$ under the action of a force $\frac{3}{2}mg$ acting parallel to the plane. The coefficient of friction between the particle and the plane is $\frac{1}{2}$. Find the normal contact force between the particle and the plane and the acceleration of the particle in terms of m and g.

C7 Figure 6.16 shows a fixed pulley A and a light pulley B which is free to move.

   (a) Find the acceleration of B and the tensions in the strings.

   (b) If one of the 2 kg masses is replaced by a 3 kg mass, what are the accelerations of each of the masses and the tensions in the strings?

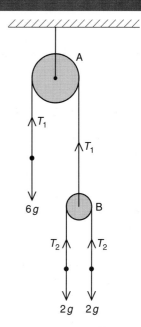

Figure 6.16

Chapter 7

ENERGY, WORK AND POWER

7.1 Work done by a force, kinetic energy and the work–energy equation

Key points

Suppose a constant force F N acts on a particle of mass m kg over a distance s metres.

From Newton's second law: $\qquad F = ma$

Since the acceleration is constant: $2as = v^2 - u^2$

Multiplying by $\frac{1}{2}m$ we get: $\qquad mas = \frac{1}{2}mv^2 - \frac{1}{2}mu^2$

and substituting $\qquad\qquad F = ma$

we get the **work–energy equation**

$$Fs = \tfrac{1}{2}mv^2 - \tfrac{1}{2}mu^2 \qquad\qquad (1)$$

Fs is defined to be the work done by the force F acting over the distance s.

The unit of work is the joule which is the work done by a force of 1 Newton acting over a distance of 1 metre: $1\text{ N m} = 1\text{ J}$

This is quite a small unit and we often use the kilojoule, where:

$$1\text{ kJ} = 1000\text{ J} = 1000\text{ N m}$$

The quantity $\frac{1}{2}mv^2$ is defined to be the kinetic energy (often shortened to KE) of a particle of mass m moving with a speed v. Kinetic energy has the same units as work. Both work and energy are scalar quantities.

Equation (1) states that 'the work done by the resultant external force on a body is equal to the change in kinetic energy of the body'.

These are two special cases.

(a) Resistance to motion

When a particle slips on a rough surface or experiences wind resistance, for example, there is a force acting in the opposite direction to the motion. In these cases the work done by the resistance is negative. In Figure 7.1 the work done by the resistance R between points A and B is $-Rs$.

(b) Force not in the direction of motion

Suppose a sledge is pulled along horizontal ground by a rope inclined at an angle θ to the horizontal, as shown in Figure 7.2.

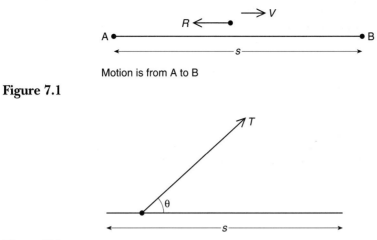

Figure 7.1

Figure 7.2

If the sledge moves a distance s, the work done by the tension is

$$(T \cos \theta) \times s$$

where $T \cos \theta$ is the component of T in the direction of motion.

The other component, $T \sin \theta$ does no work since the sledge does not move in the direction of $T \sin \theta$.

- Work and kinetic energy are scalar quantities.
- A force only does work when it moves an object.
- Work done by a force may be positive or negative.
- Only the component of a force in the direction of motion does any work.
- If more than one force acts on a particle, the change in kinetic energy is equal to the work done by the resultant force.

Example 1

A car of mass 1 tonne increases its speed from 10 m s^{-1} to 20 m s^{-1} over a distance of 50 m. There is a constant resistance to the motion of 500 N. Find:

(a) the increase in kinetic energy of the car

(b) the magnitude of the driving force of the car.

Solution

Remember: 1 tonne = 1000 kg

(a) KE at the end of 50 m = $\frac{1}{2} \times 1000 \times 20^2$ = 200 000

KE at start = $\frac{1}{2} \times 1000 \times 10^2$ = 50 000

The increase in KE = 150 000 J = 150 kJ

(b) If the driving force is P, the resultant forward force is $P - 500$

Work done over 50 m is $(P - 500) \times 50$

From the work–energy equation: $(P - 500) \times 50 = 150\,000$

giving $P = 3500$.

Therefore the magnitude of the driving force is 3500 N.

Note. We could have found the work done by P and the resistance separately.

Work done by P is $50P$

Notice the negative sign.

Work done by resistance is $-500 \times 50 = -25\,000$

which gives total work done as $50P - 25\,000$,

From the work–energy equation, $50P - 25\,000 = 150\,000$

leading to $P = 3500$ as before.

Example 2

A girl pulls a sledge of mass 15 kg across horizontal ground by a rope inclined at an angle of 20° to the horizontal. The sledge starts from rest and there is a constant tension in the rope of 8 N. After 60 m the sledge is travelling at a speed of 4 m s^{-1}. Find the magnitude of the resistance to the motion to 3 significant figures.

Solution

Let the resistance be R, see Figure 7.3.

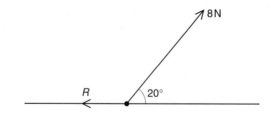

Figure 7.3

KE gained by the sledge $= \frac{1}{2} \times 15 \times 4^2 = 120$

Total work done $= (8 \cos 20° - R) \times 60$

where $8 \cos 20°$ is the horizontal component of the 8 N force.

From the work–energy equation

$(8 \cos 20° - R) \times 60 = 120$ giving $R = 5.52$

The magnitude of the resistance is 5.52 N.

Exercise 7.1

Take g as 9.8 m s^{-2} where necessary.

A1 Find the kinetic energy in joules of:

   (a) a bird of mass 0.4 kg flying at 12 m s^{-1}

   (b) a woman of mass 50 kg running at 8 m s^{-1}

   (c) a ball of mass 0.2 kg moving at 25 m s^{-1}.

A2 Find the kinetic energy of:

   (a) a car of mass 1.5 t moving at 90 km h^{-1}

   (b) a boat of mass 40 t moving at 3 m s^{-1}

   (c) a proton of mass 1.67×10^{-27} kg moving with a speed of 10^7 m s^{-1}

   (d) a ball of mass 200 g moving at 15 cm s^{-1}.

A3 A particle of mass 3 kg increases its speed from 2 m s^{-1} to 7 m s^{-1} over a distance of 40 m. Find the magnitude of the force acting on the particle.

A4 A train of mass 25 tonnes travelling at 72 km h^{-1} applies its brakes and stops over a distance of 300 m. Calculate the braking force on the train, assumed constant.

A5 A car of mass 800 kg has its speed reduced from 20 m s^{-1} to 12 m s^{-1} by a constant retarding force of 2000 N. Use the work–energy equation to find the distance travelled.

A6 A body accelerates from 5 m s^{-1} to 8 m s^{-1} over a distance of 50 m, under the action of a force of 6 N. Calculate the mass of the body.

B1 A cyclist and her bicycle have a combined mass of 90 kg. She rides along a horizontal road against a constant resistance of 40 N. If her speed increases from 4 m s^{-1} to 12 m s^{-1} over a distance of 80 m, find:

   (a) the change in KE over the 80 m

   (b) the magnitude of the driving force.

B2 A man pushes a heavy crate along a horizontal floor. The crate has a mass of 80 kg and the man pushes downward with a force of 250 N at an angle of 25° to the horizontal. There is a frictional resistance to the motion of 150 N. Find the speed of the crate after it has been pushed a distance of 20 m.

B3 A woman pushes a mower of mass 35 kg along horizontal ground with a force of 80 N at an angle of 40° to the horizontal against a resistance of 40 N. Find the speed of the mower after it has travelled a distance of 10 m.

B4 A box of mass 2 kg is at rest on rough horizontal ground. It is given a push as a result of which it begins to move with a speed of 7 m s^{-1}. The coefficient of friction between the box and the floor is $\frac{1}{4}$. Calculate:

   (a) the frictional force acting on the box

   (b) the initial KE of the box

   (c) the distance travelled by the box before coming to rest.

7.2 Work done by gravity: gravitational potential energy

Key points

If a particle of mass m falls vertically from rest through a height h, the work done by the weight force, mg, is mgh. This is often referred to as the work done by gravity.

The work–energy equation gives $mgh = \frac{1}{2}mv^2 - 0$

The work done by gravity is equal to the kinetic energy gained. By virtue of its height the particle has potential to gain kinetic energy and this is referred to as the gravitational potential energy (GPE).

It is important to realise that the work done by gravity is only dependent on the height gained or lost and not on the shape of the path.

For example, suppose that a particle slides down a smooth slope, as shown in Figure 7.4.

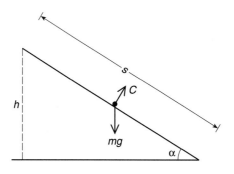

Figure 7.4

The component of mg down the slope is $mg \sin \alpha$.

The normal contact force C is perpendicular to the path and does no work.

The work done by gravity is $\quad mg \sin \alpha \times s = mg \times (s \sin \alpha) = mgh$

For a particle of mass m the work done by gravity when it falls through a height h is the same value (mgh) in each of the situations in Figure 7.5.

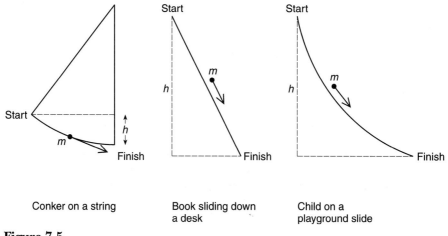

Conker on a string Book sliding down Child on a
       a desk   playground slide

Figure 7.5

Throughout the motion there may be other forces present such as air resistance or friction, as Example 2 shows.

Example 1

A demolition ball of mass 100 kg is held at 70° to the downward vertical on the end of a wire of length 6 m. It is released from rest. Find the speed of the ball at the bottom of the swing. Take g as 9.81 m s^{-2} giving your answers to 3 significant figures.

Solution

See Figure 7.6.

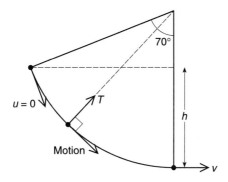

Figure 7.6

The height fallen by the ball is given by

$$h = 6 - 6\cos 70°$$

Work done by gravity $= 100 \times 9.81 \times (6 - 6\cos 70°)$

The work–energy equation gives

$$\tfrac{1}{2} \times 100 \times v^2 = 100 \times 9.81 \times (6 - 6\cos 70°)$$

giving $v = 8.80$

> Notice that the other force acting, the tension in the wire, T, is always perpendicular to the motion. Therefore T does no work.

The speed of the ball at the bottom of the swing is 8.80 m s^{-1}.

Example 2

A car of mass 1.5 tonnes is driven up a slope of inclination α to the horizontal where $\sin \alpha = \tfrac{1}{15}$. There is a constant resistance to motion of 500 N. At the foot of the slope the speed of the car is 30 m s^{-1} and after travelling 600 m up the slope the speed is reduced to 20 m s^{-1}. Find, to 3 significant figures, the constant driving force on the car. Take g as 9.81 m s^{-2}.

Solution

See Figure 7.7.

Notice that the normal contact force C is perpendicular to the path and does no work.

Let P be the driving force

Work done by P is $600P$

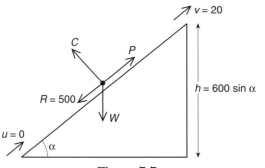

Figure 7.7

Work done by resistance $= -600 \times 500 = -300\ 000$

Work done by gravity $= -1500 \times 9.81 \times 600 \times \frac{1}{15} = -588\ 600$

> Both negative since resistance and weight oppose the motion.

KE gained $= \frac{1}{2} \times 1500 \times 20^2 - \frac{1}{2} \times 1500 \times 30^2 = -375\ 000$

From the work–energy equation

$$600P - 300\ 000 - 588\ 600 = -375\ 000$$

giving $P = 856$

The driving force is 856 N.

Note: There is no absolute value for GPE, it depends on the choice of a zero level which is arbitrary. However, in any given situation we must specify the zero level clearly.

Exercise 7.2

Take g as 9.81 m s^{-2} where necessary.

A1 A man of mass 80 kg climbs a ladder of length 12 m inclined at an angle of 60° to the horizontal. What is his gain in GPE?

If he fell off the ladder with what speed would he hit the ground? Assume the man can be treated as a particle and there are no resistances.

A2 A girl of mass 40 kg swings on the end of a rope of length 3 m. She starts at rest when the rope makes an angle of 80° with the downward vertical. Neglecting any resistance to motion, calculate her speed at the bottom of the swing.

A3 A ball of mass 0.2 kg is thrown vertically in the air with a speed of 20 m s^{-1} and reaches

a maximum height of 15 m. Calculate the resistance to the motion. Assuming that the resistance is the same on the way down, calculate the speed of the ball when it returns to the ground.

A4 A particle of mass 3 kg is pulled 7 m up a slope inclined at 20° to the horizontal. There is no resistance to the motion, and the speed at the bottom is 2 m s^{-1}. Calculate the magnitude of the pulling force if:

(a) the particle is pulled at a constant speed

(b) the speed increases to 4 m s^{-1} at the top of the slope.

A5 A child of mass 20 kg is on a swing. The ropes are 3.5 m long. She is pulled back until the rope makes an angle of 40° with the downward vertical and is then pushed

Exercise 7.2 *continued*

with a speed of 2 m s^{-1} perpendicular to the rope. What is her speed at the lowest point of the swing and how far does she rise on the other side of the swing (ignore any resistances)?

B1 A boy of mass 45 kg is at the top of a helter-skelter which is 8 m high and 20 m long. Calculate his speed at the bottom:

(a) if there is no resistance to the motion

(b) if there is a constant resistance of 20 N.

B2 A car of mass 800 kg arrives at the foot of a hill inclined at an angle of α to the horizontal where sin $\alpha = 0.2$. Its speed at the bottom is 25 m s^{-1} and after travelling a distance of 200 m its speed is reduced to 20 m s^{-1}. Assuming that there is a constant resistance to motion of 300 N, calculate the driving force of the car.

B3 A block is projected up a rough plane inclined at an angle α to the horizontal where sin $\alpha = \frac{1}{2}$. The block starts at the bottom with a speed of 4 m s^{-1}. The coefficient of friction between the block and the plane is 0.3.

(a) Calculate how far up the plane the block will travel before coming to rest.

(b) What is the speed of the block when it returns to the bottom of the plane?

B4 A train of mass 200 t is moving down a slope inclined at an angle α to the horizontal where sin $\alpha = \frac{1}{100}$. Its initial speed is 72 km h^{-1}, and it comes to rest 200 m after braking. Calculate the total resistance to motion (due to the braking force and other resistances), assumed constant.

7.3 Power

Key points

Suppose an athlete of mass 45 kg runs up a hill of height 30 m at a constant speed and reaches the top in 40 s. Taking g as 10 m s^{-2}:

the work done by the athlete against gravity = $45 \times 10 \times 30$ J = 13 500 J, so

the work done per second against gravity = $\dfrac{13\,500}{40}$ J s^{-1} = 337.5 J s^{-1}

Work done per second or the rate of doing work is defined as **power**.

The unit of power is the watt, where 1 J s^{-1} = 1 W.

This is quite a small quantity and it is more common to measure power in kilowatts

1 kilowatt (kW) = 1000 W

In the above example the power of the athlete is 0.3375 kW.

If a constant force F acts over a distance s, the work done = Fs

This leads to the useful formula for the power P, $P = F\dfrac{ds}{dt} = Fv$

Often the resistance to the motion is not constant but depends on the speed, as Example 2 illustrates.

Example 1

A car of mass 1.5 t has a maximum power of 30 kW. There is a constant resistance to the motion of 600 N. Calculate to 2 significant figures the maximum possible (steady) speed of the car:

(a)   on level ground

(b)   up a hill inclined at an angle α to the horizontal where $\sin \alpha = \frac{1}{10}$.

(c)   If the hill in part (b) levels off and the resistance remains constant what would be the initial acceleration of the car?

Take g as 9.8 m s^{-2}.

Solution

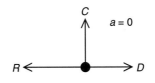

Figure 7.8

(a)   See Figure 7.8. Let the driving force be D. When the speed is maximum, the acceleration is zero and N2 gives:

$$D - R = 0$$

giving $D = 600$

Power $P = Dv = 30\,000$

$$\Rightarrow v = \frac{30\,000}{600} = 50$$

The maximum speed of the car is 50 m s^{-1}.

(b)   See Figure 7.9. At maximum speed, the acceleration is zero, and applying N2 on the car up the slope:

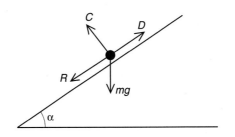

Figure 7.9

$$D - R - mg \sin \alpha = 0$$

giving $D = 600 + 1500 \times 9.8 \times \frac{1}{10} = 2070$

Power, $P = Dv = 30\,000$

giving $v = \dfrac{30\ 000}{2070} = 14.5$

The maximum speed up the slope is 15 m s^{-1}.

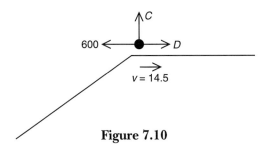

Figure 7.10

(c) See Figure 7.10. N2 horizontally on the car gives: $D - 600 = 1500a$

Multiplying by v: $Dv - 600v = 1500av$

Since $v = 14.5$ and $Dv = 30\ 000$

$$30\ 000 - 600 \times 14.5 = 1500 \times 14.5 \times a$$

giving $a = 0.98$

The initial acceleration on the level is 0.98 m s^{-2}.

Notice that the acceleration is not constant – it decreases as the speed increases. Suppose for instance that the car has reached a speed of 40 m s^{-1} (we know that the maximum steady speed is 50 m s^{-1}),

$$D - 600 = 1500a \text{ (as before)}$$

and $Dv - 600v = 1500av$

When $v = 40$, $30\ 000 - 600 \times 40 = 1500 \times a \times 40$

giving $a = 0.1$

The car has an acceleration of 0.1 m s^{-1}.

Example 2

A car of mass 1 t is driven along level ground and experiences a total resistance given by $(300 + Av^2)$ N where v is the speed of the car and A is a constant. If a driving power of 20 kW is required to maintain a steady speed of 40 m s^{-1}, what power is required to maintain a steady speed of 60 m s^{-1}?

Solution

Suppose D is the driving force at a steady speed of 40 m s^{-1},

N2 horizontally gives $D - (300 + A \times 40^2) = 0$

giving $D = 300 + 1600A$

The power, $P = 40D = 20\ 000$

$D = 500$ and $300 + 1600A = 500$, giving $A = \dfrac{200}{1600} = \frac{1}{8}$

At a steady speed of 60 m s^{-1}: $D = 300 + \frac{1}{8} \times 60^2 = 750$

Power, $P = Dv = 750 \times 60 = 45\,000$

The power required is 45 kW.

Exercise 7.3

Take g as 9.8 m s^{-2} where necessary.

A1 A car is travelling at a steady speed of 30 m s^{-1} on a horizontal road against a constant resistance of 2000 N. Calculate the power output of the engine in kW.

A2 A girl cycles at a steady speed of 15 m s^{-1} up an incline of angle α where $\sin \alpha = \frac{1}{5}$. If the mass of the cycle and rider is 50 kg and there is a constant resistance to motion of 200 N find her power output.

A3 The power of a motorbike on a horizontal road is 30 kW. Calculate the resistance to motion at a steady speed of 144 km h^{-1}.

A4 A car has a maximum speed of 108 km h^{-1} up an incline of $\sin^{-1} \left(\frac{1}{20} \right)$. The power output is 36 kW and the mass of the car is 1 t. Find the magnitude of the constant resistance to motion.

A5 A car of mass 1.5 t has maximum power output of 60 kW. The resistance to motion is 2000 N. Find the maximum steady speed of the car:

(a) on level ground

(b) up a slope inclined to the horizontal at angle α where $\sin \alpha = 0.1$

(c) down a slope inclined to the horizontal at angle β where $\sin \beta = 0.05$.

A6 An engine is travelling at a steady speed of 10 m s^{-1} on a level track against a constant resistance of 50 000 N.

(a) Calculate the power of the engine, in kW.

(b) The engine is coupled to carriages which provide a further resistance of 30 000 N. Find the new maximum steady speed on level ground.

(c) The total mass of the engines and carriages is 400 t. If the resistance remains the same calculate the maximum steady speed up an incline of slope $\sin^{-1} \left(\frac{1}{50} \right)$.

B1 A car of mass 800 kg is moving along a straight level road against a constant resistance of 600 N. At a particular instant the speed of the car is 20 m s^{-1} and the acceleration is 0.5 m s^{-2}. Find the power of the engine in kW.

B2 A car of mass 1.5 t moves at a steady speed of 15 m s^{-1} up a slope of inclination α where $\sin \alpha = \frac{1}{20}$. Given that there is a constant resistance to motion of 500 N, calculate the power output of the car.

The slope suddenly levels off. If the resistance remains the same, calculate the initial acceleration of the car.

B3 A car of mass 1.2 t moves along a horizontal road against a constant resistance of 2500 N.

(a) Find the power in kW required to maintain a steady speed of 20 m s^{-1}.

(b) Find the increase in power required to produce a sudden acceleration of 1.5 m s^{-1}.

(c) The car now comes to a hill of incline α where $\sin \alpha = \frac{1}{4}$. Find the maximum steady speed when the power output is 60 kW.

B4 A train has mass 50 t and the resistance to motion is a constant 8000 N.

(a) Find the power in kW required to maintain a steady speed of 15 m s^{-1} on horizontal ground.

(b) If the power is suddenly increased by 40 kW, find the initial acceleration of the train.

Exercise 7.3 *continued*

(c) The train now climbs a hill of slope α. When the power output is 180 kW the speed is a steady 8 m s^{-1}. Find sin α.

B5 A car of mass 1 t moves with an acceleration of 0.2 m s^{-2} along a horizontal road against a constant resistance of 1000 N. Find in kW the power output of the engine when the speed is 30 m s^{-1}.

The car now travels down a hill of slope sin^{-1} ($\frac{1}{20}$). Find the steady speed of the car when the power output is 15 kW.

B6 The resistance to the motion of a car is $(150 + Av^2)$ N where A is a constant and v is the speed of the car. The mass of the car is 1 t and when the power of the engine is 20 kW the maximum speed of the car is 20 m s^{-1}. Find the value of A.

The car climbs a slope of angle α where sin $\alpha = \frac{1}{20}$. If the engine has the same power find the acceleration when the speed is 10 m s^{-1}.

Revision questions

Take g as 9.8 m s^{-2} where necessary.

C1 A cyclist and his bicycle have a total mass of 100 kg. There is a constant resistance to motion of 50 N. Find the total work done in joules in increasing speed from 5 m s^{-1} to 10 m s^{-1} while travelling a distance of 50 m:

(a) along level ground

(b) up a slope inclined to the horizontal at an angle α where sin $\alpha = 0.1$.

C2 Figure 7.11 shows a path which consists of a slope 50 m long inclined at 30° to the horizontal and a horizontal section.

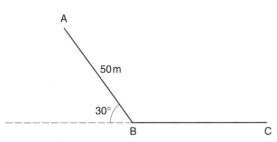

Figure 7.11

A boy on a skateboard starts at rest from A and reaches B with a speed of 15 m s^{-1}. The mass of the boy and the skateboard is 60 kg. Calculate:

(a) the work done by gravity on the boy in going from A to B

(b) the KE of the boy at B

(c) the magnitude of the constant resistance to motion

(d) the distance travelled along BC before coming to rest.

C3 A particle of mass 5 kg is projected from a point A up the line of greatest slope of a rough plane with an initial speed of 4 m s^{-1}. The coefficient of friction between the particle and the plane is $\frac{3}{5}$ and the angle of the slope is 40°. Calculate:

(a) how far up the slope the particle travels before coming to rest

(b) the speed of the particle as it passes A on its way down.

C4 A bus has mass 10 tonnes and moves at a speed of 10 m s^{-1} up a straight hill inclined at an angle α to the horizontal where sin $\alpha = 0.2$. There is a constant resistance to the motion of 20 000 N. Find the power of the engine.

C5 The resistance to motion of a car of mass 1.5 t is 750 N. The engine of the car has a power output of 30 kW. Find in km h^{-1} the maximum steady speed:

(a) on level ground

(b) on a slope of angle α where sin $\alpha = \frac{1}{12}$.

C6 A car has mass 1.5 t and is moving with a speed of 10 m s^{-1} at an acceleration of 0.2 m s^{-2} up a hill inclined at angle α to the horizontal where sin $\alpha = 0.3$. There is a constant resistance to the motion of 300 N. Find the power of the engine. *continued*

C7 A car has a maximum speed of 144 km h^{-1} on a level road with the engine working at 20 kW. Calculate the total resistance to motion at this speed.

Given that the mass of the car is 1 t and resistance is proportional to the square of the speed, calculate the power of the engine when the car climbs a hill of angle α where sin $\alpha = \frac{1}{20}$ at a steady speed of 54 km h^{-1}.

C8 A car starts from rest and travels on a horizontal road subject to a constant resisting force of 800 N. The mass of the car is 1300 kg and the maximum power of the engine is 45 kW. Calculate the maximum speed of the car when the engine is working at a constant rate of 32 kW. Assuming that the resistance remains constant at 800 N, find the maximum speed of the car up a hill inclined at 10° to the horizontal.

Chapter 8

MOMENTUM AND IMPULSE (1)

8.1 Impulse–momentum equation

Key points

The impulse-momentum equation is

$$\mathbf{I} = m\mathbf{v} - m\mathbf{u}$$

- where $\mathbf{I}$ is the impulse, measured in N s, and for a constant force $\mathbf{F}$ acting for a time, t, is given by $\mathbf{I} = \mathbf{F}t$
- $m\mathbf{v}$ is the momentum of a mass, m moving with velocity, $\mathbf{v}$.

Examples 1 and 2 illustrate motion in one dimension and Example 3 illustrates motion in two dimensions.

Example 1

A bullet of mass 25 g is fired with a speed of 900 m s^{-1} into a wall which it passes through to emerge 0.05 seconds later with a speed of 400 m s^{-1}.

Find the change in momentum of the bullet and hence the impulse on it.

What is the average force on it?

(Note: If a force is not constant, we define the average force as the total impulse divided by the total time.)

Solution

See Figure 8.1.

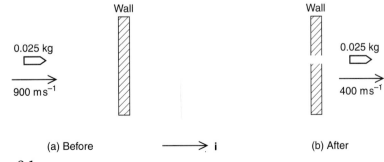

(a) Before $\longrightarrow$ **i**   (b) After

Figure 8.1

The initial direction of the bullet, **i**, is taken as positive call this **i**.

The initial momentum of the bullet is $m\mathbf{u} = 0.025 \times 900\,\mathbf{i} = 22.5\,\mathbf{i}$

The final momentum of the bullet is $m\mathbf{v} = 0.25 \times 400\,\mathbf{i} = 10.0\,\mathbf{i}$

Using the impulse–momentum equation: $\mathbf{I} = m\mathbf{v} - m\mathbf{u}$

The impulse is $10 - 22.5\,\mathbf{i} = -12.5\,\mathbf{i}$, which is in the opposite direction to its original motion.

The average force, $\mathbf{F}$, is given by $\mathbf{F}t = \mathbf{I}$, so that $\mathbf{F} = -12.5/0.5\,\mathbf{i} = -250\,\mathbf{i}$

The average force on the bullet is 250 N.

Example 2

A squash ball of mass 25 g hits the wall of a court at a speed of 40 m s^{-1} and rebounds at 32 m s^{-1}. Find the impulse on the ball.

Solution

See Figure 8.2.

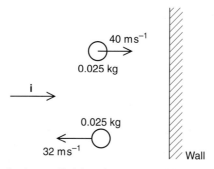

Figure 8.2

The direction towards the wall, $\mathbf{i}$ is taken as positive.

Using the impulse–momentum equation: $\mathbf{I} = m\mathbf{v} - m\mathbf{u}$

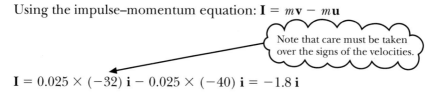

Note that care must be taken over the signs of the velocities.

$\mathbf{I} = 0.025 \times (-32)\,\mathbf{i} - 0.025 \times (-40)\,\mathbf{i} = -1.8\,\mathbf{i}$

The impulse on the ball is 1.8 N s, directed away from the wall.

Example 3

A squash ball of mass 25 g strikes a smooth wall of a court at an angle of 50° to the wall with a speed of 30 m s^{-1} and rebounds at an angle of 25° to the wall. The wall is smooth. Find:

(a)   the final speed of the ball

(b)   the impulse on the wall.

Solution

Method 1: using vector components

Unit vectors $\mathbf{i}$ and $\mathbf{j}$ are chosen as in Figure 8.3.

Figure 8.3

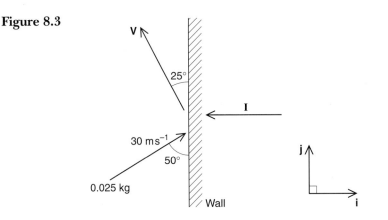

The initial velocity, $\mathbf{u} = \begin{pmatrix} 30 \sin 50° \\ 30 \cos 50° \end{pmatrix}$,

and the final velocity, $\mathbf{v} = v \begin{pmatrix} -\sin 25° \\ \cos 25° \end{pmatrix}$

Since the contact is smooth, the impulse, **I**, is at right angles to the wall, so that

$$\mathbf{I} = \begin{pmatrix} -I \\ 0 \end{pmatrix}$$

Using the impulse–momentum equation $\mathbf{I} = m\mathbf{v} - m\mathbf{u}$

$$\begin{pmatrix} -I \\ 0 \end{pmatrix} = 0.025 \times v \begin{pmatrix} -\sin 25° \\ \cos 25° \end{pmatrix} - 0.025 \times \begin{pmatrix} 30 \sin 50° \\ 30 \cos 50° \end{pmatrix}$$

Equating components,

$$-I = -0.025 \, (v \sin 25° + 30 \sin 50°) \tag{1}$$

$$0 = 0.025 \, (v \cos 25° - 30 \cos 50°) \tag{2}$$

From equation (2), $v \cos 25° = 30 \cos 50°$

giving $v = \dfrac{30 \cos 50°}{\cos 25°} = 21.28$

Substituting for v in equation (2)

$I = 0.025 \, (21.28 \sin 25° + 30 \sin 50°) = 0.799$

The final speed of the ball is 21 m s^{-1} and the magnitude of the impulse is 0.80 N s.

Method 2: using a vector diagram and trigonometry

The impulse–momentum equation can be rearranged as $m\mathbf{u} + \mathbf{I} = m\mathbf{v}$

A sketch of the vector triangle is shown in Figure 8.4.

Using the sine rule, $\dfrac{I}{\sin 75°} = \dfrac{30 \times 0.025}{\sin 65°}$ giving $I = 0.799$ as before.

Similarly, $\dfrac{0.025v}{\sin 40°} = \dfrac{30 \times 0.025}{\sin 65°}$ giving $v = \dfrac{30 \sin 40°}{\sin 65°} = 21.28$ as before.

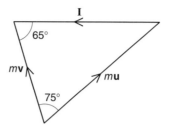

Figure 8.4

Notice that the component of the momentum parallel to the wall is unchanged:

before impact, $0.025 \times 30 \times \cos 50° = 0.48$

after impact, $0.025 \times 21.28 \times \cos 25° = 0.48$

This is a very useful general result:

> **the component of momentum of a particle is unchanged in the direction perpendicular to the inpulse.**

Exercise 8.1

Take g as 9.8 m s^{-2} where necessary.

A1 Calculate the magnitude of the momentum, in N s, of:

(a) a car of mass 850 kg travelling at 20 m s^{-1}

(b) a cricket ball of mass 150 g travelling at 15 m s^{-1}

(c) a golf ball of mass 45 g leaving the club head at 60 m s^{-1}.

A2 Calculate the impulse required to stop a car of mass 850 kg travelling at 20 m s^{-1}.

A3 A squash ball of mass 25 g hits a wall at right angles at 35 m s^{-1} and rebounds at 25 m s^{-1}. Find the change in its momentum and hence the impulse of the ball on the wall.

A4 A ball of mass 0.2 kg strikes the cushion of a billiard table at right angles with a speed of 2.5 m s^{-1} and rebounds with a speed of 1.5 m s^{-1}. What is the impulse on the ball?

A5 A snooker ball of mass 0.15 kg is travelling at 2 m s^{-1} towards the cushion of a horizontal snooker table when it hits the cushion at right angles. If the impulse of the cushion on the ball is 0.5 N s directed away from the cushion, with what speed does the ball rebound?

A6 A cricket ball of mass 150 g is travelling in a straight line at 30 m s^{-1} when it is hit by a bat and returns with a speed of 22 m s^{-1} in the same straight line. What is the impulse of the ball on the cricket bat?

A7 A tennis ball of mass 100 g travelling at 150 km h^{-1} strikes the racket of a tennis player at right angles to the strings. It is struck back at a speed of 100 km h^{-1} along its original path. What is the impulse on the ball?

A8 A car of mass 1.5 t is travelling at 25 m s^{-1}. Its brakes are applied for 5 s and supply a constant braking force of 1800 N. Find the impulse on the car and its speed after 5 s.

A9 A cricket ball of mass 150 g is hit vertically in the air with a speed of 18 m s^{-1}.

(a) What is the initial momentum of the ball?

(b) What is its momentum at its maximum height?

(c) What impulse destroyed the momentum of the ball and for how long did it act?

A10 A cricket ball of mass 150 g is travelling horizontally at 20 m s^{-1} when it is caught by a fielder. What is the average force on the fielder's hands if the ball is stopped in:

(a) 0.1 s (b) 0.5 s?

Exercise 8.1 *continued*

B1 A tennis player hits a ball of mass 100 g with his racket to give it a velocity of 15 m s^{-1}. Whilst travelling horizontally it strikes a smooth vertical wall at an angle of 50° to the wall and rebounds at an angle of 30° to the wall. What is the impulse of the wall on the ball?

B2 On a horizontal snooker table a ball of mass 0.4 kg hits the side cushion at 30° with a speed of 2 m s^{-1} and rebounds at an angle of 25° with a speed of 1.5 m s^{-1}. What is the magnitude of the impulse on the ball?

Is contact between the ball and the cushion smooth?

B3 An ice puck of mass 200 g is travelling horizontally at 15 m s^{-1} when it strikes the boards of a rink at an angle of 25°. The puck rebounds at an angle of 35° with a speed of 12 m s^{-1}. Find the magnitude and direction of the impulse on the puck from the boards.

B4 A football of mass 200 g is kicked horizontally with a speed of 5 m s^{-1} at a vertical wall, which it hits at an angle of 55°. It rebounds at an angle of 75° with a speed of 3 m s^{-1}. What is the magnitude and direction of the impulse on the ball from the wall?

B5 A ball of mass 0.3 kg is moving horizontally with a speed of 10 m s^{-1} when it is hit by a bat to give it an impulse of 10 N s at an angle of 150° to its line of flight. What is the angle through which the ball is deflected and what is its speed after being hit?

B6 A particle of mass 0.5 kg falling vertically at a speed of 3 m s^{-1} hits a smooth plane which is inclined at an angle of 20° to the horizontal. The impulse is perpendicular to the plane and after impact the particle moves down the slope.

(a) What is its subsequent speed down the slope?

(b) What is the change in momentum parallel to the slope?

B7 A ball of mass 2 kg is moving horizontally with a speed of 6 m s^{-1} when it is kicked at right angles to its path with an impulse of 15 N s. What is its speed and direction after the blow?

B8 A squash ball of mass 25 g hits a side wall of a court at 25 m s^{-1} at an angle of 30° to the wall. If the impulse of the wall on the ball is 0.35 N s at right angles to the wall, find the speed and direction of the ball after impact.

B9 A ball of mass 800 g strikes a wall with a speed of 13 m s^{-1} at an angle of 37° and rebounds at an angle of 53° with a speed of 5 m s^{-1}. Calculate the magnitude and direction of the impulse on the ball.

B10 A stock-car of mass 600 kg travelling on a slippery track loses control and hits a barrier at a speed of 20 m s^{-1} at an angle of 30° to the barrier. It rebounds at an angle of 20° to the barrier with a speed of 12 m s^{-1}. Calculate the magnitude and direction of the impulse of the barrier on the car.

8.2 Collisions

Key points

When a system of bodies collide, the principle of conservation of momentum states:

> **If there are no external impulses on a system, the total momentum of the system remains constant.**

This is usually paraphrased as:

total momentum before impact = total momentum after impact.

Example 1

A toy truck of 0.2 kg moving at a speed of 0.1 m s^{-1} collides with an engine of mass 0.4 kg moving at 0.05 m s^{-1} in the same direction in a straight line on a model railway track.

After the collision they move off as one body. Find:

(a)   the combined speed, v

(b)   the change in the total kinetic energy.

> We sometimes say the bodies coalesce.

Solution

See Figure 8.5.

| 0.1 ms^{-1} | 0.05 ms^{-1} | | v |

$m = 0.2$ $m = 0.4$ $m = 0.6$

(a) Before   (b) After

Figure 8.5

(a)   The initial direction is taken as positive:

the total momentum before impact is

$0.2 \times 0.1 + 0.4 \times 0.05 = 0.04$

Total momentum after impact is $0.6v$

Using the principle of conservation of momentum $0.6v = 0.04$

giving the combined velocity as 0.067 m s^{-1}.

(b)   The initial KE is $\frac{1}{2} \times 0.2 \times 0.1^2 + \frac{1}{2} \times 0.4 \times 0.05^2 = 0.0015$

The final KE is $\frac{1}{2} \times 0.6 \times 0.067^2 = 0.0013$

giving a loss of total KE of 0.0002 J.

Example 2

Two satellites of masses 1 t and 0.5 t are moving towards each other along paths at right angles to each other with speeds of 10 m s^{-1} and 15 m s^{-1} respectively. After the impact the smaller one has its speed increased to 20 m s^{-1} and is deflected through 60°. Find:

(a)   the speed and direction of the larger one

(b)   the change in KE of each satellite as a result of the impact.

Solution

Unit vectors **i** and **j** are taken in the directions shown in Figure 8.6.

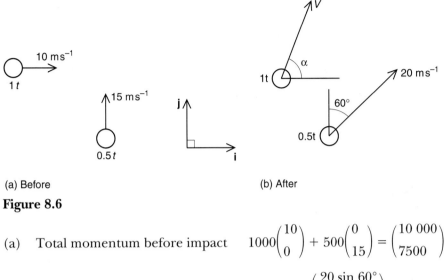

(a) Before   (b) After

Figure 8.6

(a)   Total momentum before impact $1000\begin{pmatrix} 10 \\ 0 \end{pmatrix} + 500\begin{pmatrix} 0 \\ 15 \end{pmatrix} = \begin{pmatrix} 10\,000 \\ 7500 \end{pmatrix}$

Total momentum after impact $1000\mathbf{v} + 500\begin{pmatrix} 20 \sin 60° \\ 20 \cos 60° \end{pmatrix}$

Using the principle of conservation of momentum
$$1000\mathbf{v} + 500\begin{pmatrix} 20 \sin 60° \\ 20 \cos 60° \end{pmatrix} = \begin{pmatrix} 10\,000 \\ 7500 \end{pmatrix}$$

giving $\mathbf{v} = \begin{pmatrix} 1.34 \\ 2.5 \end{pmatrix}$ m s^{-1}

The speed, $v = \sqrt{(1.34^2 + 2.5^2)} = 2.84$ m s^{-1} and direction $\alpha = \tan^{-1}(2.5/1.34) = 61.8°$

The larger satellite has its speed reduced to 2.84 m s^{-1} and is deflected through 61.8°.

(b)   For the larger satellite:

KE before impact $= \frac{1}{2} \times 1000 \times 10^2 = 50$ kJ ← $1\,kJ = 10^3\,J$

KE after impact $= \frac{1}{2} \times 1000 \times 2.84^2 = 4.04$ kJ

The loss in KE is 45.97 kJ

For the smaller satellite:

KE before impact $= \frac{1}{2} \times 500 \times 15^2 = 56.25$ kJ

KE after impact $= \frac{1}{2} \times 500 \times 20^2 = 100$ kJ

The gain in KE is 43.75 kJ ← Notice that there is an overall loss in KE of $45.97 - 43.75 = 2.22$ kJ due to the collision.

Exercise 8.2

A1 A particle A of mass 3 kg is moving with velocity of 3 m s^{-1} in the same straight line as a particle B of mass 2 kg moving at 0.5 m s^{-1}. After the collision they coalesce (move off as one body). Find the velocity with which the combined body moves when:

(a) they are initially moving in the same direction

(b) they are initially moving towards each other.

A2 Repeat question **A1** for the following:

(i) A has mass 5 kg and velocity 2 m s^{-1}, B has mass 3 kg and velocity 1 m s^{-1}

(ii) A has mass 6 kg and velocity 4 m s^{-1}, B has mass 10 kg and velocity 2 m s^{-1}

(iii) A has mass 4 kg and velocity 2 m s^{-1}, B has mass 5 kg and velocity 2.5 m s^{-1}.

A3 A child's truck of mass 3 kg moving at 2 m s^{-1} collides with another of mass 2.5 kg moving in the opposite direction at 1.8 m s^{-1}. After the collision the smaller truck rebounds with a speed of 0.5 m s^{-1}. Find the speed of the larger truck.

A4 In a game of bowls a wood of mass 0.9 kg hits a stationary jack (white ball) of mass 0.3 kg and its speed is reduced from 2.5 m s^{-1} to 1.5 m s^{-1}. The whole motion takes place in a straight line. What is the final speed of the wood?

A5 A space module of mass 500 kg is moving at 6 m s^{-1} when it collides with and hooks-up to a command module of mass 1500 kg moving in the same direction at 2 m s^{-1}.

(a) What is their combined speed after impact?

(b) Find the loss of energy of the space module as a result of the collision.

(c) Find the total change of energy of the combined system.

A6 In a game of snooker a cue ball, A, of mass 0.2 kg is moving with a speed of 2.5 m s^{-1} when it strikes a stationary green ball, B, of equal mass. Immediately after the collision

the cue ball continues in the same straight line with speed 1 m s^{-1}. Calculate:

(a) the impulse on the cue ball

(b) the speed of the green ball after the impact

(c) the change in energy of the cue ball.

A7 A car of mass 1.5 t is moving at 20 km h^{-1} when it shunts into the rear of a stationary car of mass 750 kg. The bumpers of the cars become entangled so they move off as one body.

(a) What is their combined speed in km h^{-1} after the impact?

(b) What is the total energy loss as a result of the collision?

A8 A bullet of mass 5 g is moving horizontally with speed 300 m s^{-1} when it strikes and becomes embedded in a stationary block of mass 15 kg which is free to slide without resistance along a horizontal table. The bullet moves through the block for 0.01 s. Find:

(a) the combined speed of the block and the bullet after the impact

(b) the resistance of the block, assumed constant

(c) the change in energy of the bullet.

B1 A particle of mass 3 kg is moving horizontally in a straight line with a speed of 5 m s^{-1} when it is hit by another particle of mass 2 kg moving with a speed of 3 m s^{-1} at an angle of 30° to the line of motion of the 3 kg mass. After the collision the first particle is deflected through 25° and has a speed of 6 m s^{-1}.

(a) Find the final speed and angle of deflection of the 2 kg mass.

(b) What is the change in the total kinetic energy of the system?

B2 Two billiard balls each of mass 0.1 kg collide. The first is moving with a speed of 2 m s^{-1} and the second with a speed of 4 m s^{-1} at an angle of 135° to the direction of the first. After the collision the first is deflected through an angle of 70° and the second is then moving at right angles to it.

(a) Find their final speeds.

(b) Find the loss of energy of the system as a whole.

B3 Two satellites of masses 1500 kg and 1200 kg are moving with speeds of 3 m s^{-1} and 5 m s^{-1} respectively when they collide. After the collision they move off as one body. Find their combined speed when:

(a) they are initially moving in the same straight line

(b) they are moving at right angles to each other

(c) they are approaching each other at an angle of 120°.

In each case calculate the total energy loss as a result of the collision.

B4 A ball of mass 200 g collides with another of mass 50 g. Their initial speeds are 3 m s^{-1} and 1 m s^{-1} respectively. They approach each other at an angle of 120° and after the collision the smaller ball is deflected through 90° with its speed

increased to 1.5 m s^{-1}. Find the speed of the larger ball after the collision and the angle through which it is deflected. What is its change in energy?

B5 A boy kicks a ball of mass 300 g at a constant speed of 3 m s^{-1} across a school playground. Another boy tries to knock it off course by kicking another ball of mass 250 kg at the first with a speed of 6 m s^{-1} to collide at an angle of 110°. After the collision the second ball has its speed reduced to 4 m s^{-1} and is deflected through 20°. Find the speed of the 300 g ball immediately after the collision and the angle through which it is deflected.

B6 Two smooth balls A and B of the same size are free to move on a smooth horizontal table. The mass of A is three times that of B, which is at rest. A moves with a speed of 3 m s^{-1} at an angle of 27° to their line of centres. After the collision A is deflected through 30°. Find the speeds of A and B immediately after impact. (Hint: the impulse on each ball is along the line of centres – what is the change in the component of momentum of A perpendicular to the line of centres?)

8.3 Explosions and jerks

Key points

In the case of collisions it is normally the case that mechanical energy will be lost. However, in the case of **explosions** mechanical energy may be released due to the input of chemical energy.

When a tow-rope attached to two cars becomes taut it will exert an impulsive tension on the two cars. This tension is referred to as a **jerk** and will cause a change in the momentum of the cars. For simplicity, we will assume the rope does not extend beyond its natural length.

Example I

A rocket of mass m is moving with a speed of 5 m s^{-1} in a straight line when it explodes into two parts. The larger part deflects through an angle of 40° with a speed of 2 m s^{-1}. The mass of the smaller part is half that of the larger. Find its speed and direction after the explosion.

Solution

Unit vectors are taken in the directions shown in Figure 8.7.

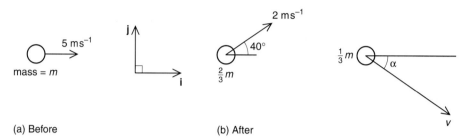

(a) Before   (b) After

Figure 8.7

Using the principle of conservation of momentum:

$$m\begin{pmatrix} 5 \\ 0 \end{pmatrix} = \frac{2m}{3}\begin{pmatrix} 2\cos 40° \\ 2\sin 40° \end{pmatrix} + \frac{m}{3}\mathbf{v}$$

Rearranging, $\mathbf{v}\begin{pmatrix} 15 \\ 0 \end{pmatrix} - \begin{pmatrix} 4\cos 40° \\ 4\sin 40° \end{pmatrix} = \begin{pmatrix} 11.93 \\ -2.57 \end{pmatrix}$

Giving $v = \sqrt{(11.93^2 + 2.57^2)} = 12.20$ and
$\alpha = \tan^{-1}(-2.57/11.93) = -12.15$.

The smaller part moves with speed of 12.2 m s^{-1} at an angle of 12.2° below its original path.

Example 2

In a cowboy film, a prisoner is lassoed by means of a rope around his waist, the other end of which is attached to the saddle of the sheriff's horse. The mass of the prisoner is 80 kg and the combined mass of the sheriff and his horse is 480 kg. The horse moves off with a speed of 5 m s^{-1}. What is the initial speed of the prisoner and the impulsive tension in the rope?

Solution

See Figure 8.8.

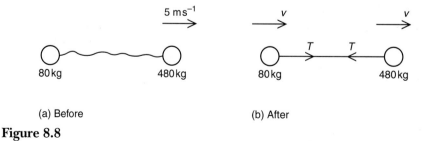

(a) Before   (b) After

Figure 8.8

It is assumed that the rope does not stretch when it becomes taut, so the impulsive tension is used solely to change the momentum. It is an internal impulse, so the total momentum of the system is conserved.

Using the principle of conservation of momentum:
$$80 \times 0 + 480 \times 5 = (80 + 480)v$$

giving $v = 4.29$

The impulsive tension is given by the change in momentum of the prisoner (or of the sheriff and horse).

$$I = 80 \times 4.29 - 80 \times 0 = 343.2$$

The combined speed is 4.29 m s^{-1} and the impulsive tension in the rope is 343 N s (to 3 significant figures).

Exercise 8.3

Questions **A1** to **A4** refer to two particles P and Q resting on a smooth horizontal table and connected by a slack inextensible string (see Figure 8.9).

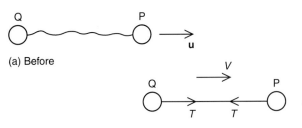

(a) Before

Figure 8.9 (b) After

A1 P is of mass 1 kg and Q is of mass 2 kg. P is projected with a speed of 6 m s^{-1}. Find:
  (a) the common speed of P and Q when the string becomes taut
  (b) the impulsive tension in the string
  (c) the loss of total KE due to the jerk.

A2 Repeat question **A1** with the masses of P and Q interchanged.

A3 Repeat question **A1** when the mass of P is m and the mass of Q is $4m$. P is projected with speed $5u$.

A4 Repeat question **A3** with the masses of P and Q interchanged.

A5 A man of mass 75 kg and his son of mass 35 kg are stuck on a very slippery sheet of ice. The man decides to push his son to the side to get help. If the boy moves off at 0.5 m s^{-1}, what is the initial speed of the man?

What is the total change in energy of the boy and the man as a result of the push?

A6 A girl of mass 40 kg is sitting in the middle of a frozen pond and has six stones in a bag, each of mass 0.5 kg. She throws one of them horizontally at 20 m s^{-1}. What is her speed of recoil assuming there is no friction between her and the ice? How far will she move in 10 s?

Assuming she throws stones every 10 s, how long will she take to reach the edge of the pond which is 10 m away?

A7 A machine gun is mounted on an armoured car and fires 10 rounds of ammunition every second. Each round has a mass of 100 g and a speed of 500 m s^{-1} when fired. Calculate the total impulse on the car during each 5 s burst of fire.

B1 A shell of mass $3m$ is moving horizontally with speed u when it splits into two parts of masses $2m$ and m, both of which still move along the same horizontal line. The small part moves with speed $5u$.
  (a) What is the speed of the larger part?
  (b) Find the total energy of both masses before and after the explosion.

B2 In an unsuccessful rocket launch, the carrier rocket which is moving vertically upwards with a speed of 2500 m s^{-1} explodes into two parts. The heavier part continues upwards with a speed of 2000 m s^{-1}. The ratio of the masses of the larger to the smaller parts is 3:1.
  (a) Find the speed of the smaller part immediately after the explosion.
  (b) What is the change in energy of the system in terms of the mass of the smaller part. *continued*

B3 Two railway trucks are moving together along a horizontal track with a combined speed of 8 m s^{-1}. The first truck has a mass of 4000 kg and the second a mass of 750 kg. They become uncoupled by an internal electronic explosion and the heavier truck then moves with a speed of 10 m s^{-1}.

(a) Find the speed of the smaller truck.

(b) What is the change in energy of the smaller truck?

(c) What is the total change of energy as a result of the uncoupling?

B4 A breakdown truck of mass 2 t is towing a car of mass 750 kg, which is initially at rest. The tow-rope becomes taut when the truck is moving at 6 m s^{-1}. Find:

(a) the initial speed of the car

(b) the impulsive tension in the rope

(c) the change in energy of the breakdown truck.

B5 In a competition to test the pulling power of two tractors, tractor A of mass 1.2 t is joined to tractor B of mass 1.5 t by a long piece of inextensible rope, which is initially slack. The tractors start to move and when they reach speeds of 12 m s^{-1} and 10 m s^{-1} respectively the rope becomes taut. The rope breaks and the speed of the heavier tractor is reduced to 8 m s^{-1}. Find the new speed of tractor A and the impulsive tension in the rope just before it breaks.

B6 After a jump, a skier of mass 40 kg lands vertically with a speed of 8 m s^{-1} onto a smooth slope which is inclined at an angle of 15° to the horizontal. After the impact, her speed down the slope is 5 m s^{-1}. Find the magnitude and direction of the impulse on her as a result of the collision and her change in KE.

Revision questions

C1 An unloaded railway wagon A of mass 500 kg and a loaded wagon B of mass 2000 kg are free to move on a straight horizontal track. A is travelling at 10 m s^{-1} when it runs into B which is stationary. After the impact B moves off with a speed of 2 m s^{-1}. Calculate:

(a) the speed of A immediately after the impact

(b) the total loss in KE due to the impact.

C2 A truck A of mass 15 tonnes moves along a straight railway line with a speed of 12 m s^{-1}. It catches up and collides with a truck B of mass 10 tonnes moving in the same direction with a speed of 6 m s^{-1}. The impulse on each truck during the collision is 60 000 N s. Find:

(a) the speed of each truck after the collision

(b) the loss in total kinetic energy due to the collision.

C3 A table tennis ball of mass 3 g strikes a smooth horizontal table. Just before impact the speed of the ball is 10 m s^{-1} and it is moving at an angle of 40° to the vertical. Just after impact it is moving at 50° to the vertical. Find:

(a) the speed of the ball after impact

(b) the magnitude of the impulse on the ball

(c) the loss of kinetic energy of the ball.

C4 A truck of mass 1200 kg moves along a straight horizontal track at 4 m s^{-1} when it hits buffers and rebounds at 3 m s^{-1}. The truck and buffers are in contact for 0.2 s. Calculate:

(a) the impulse on the truck

(b) the average force exerted on the truck by the buffers.

Revision questions *continued*

C5 A body A of mass 3 kg moving with velocity $\begin{pmatrix} 4 \\ 0 \end{pmatrix}$ m s^{-1} collides with a body B of mass 5 kg. After the impact they move off as one body with a velocity of $\begin{pmatrix} -1 \\ 5 \end{pmatrix}$ m s^{-1}.

Calculate:

(a) the velocity of B before the collision

(b) the impulse on A

(c) the total loss in KE due to the impact.

C6 A rocket explodes into three parts. Two parts separate at right angles to each other, a 1 kg piece at 12 m s^{-1} and a 2 kg piece at 8 m s^{-1}. The third part flies off at 40 m s^{-1}

(a) Find the mass of the third part and the direction in which it flies off.

(b) Must all three pieces fly off in the same plane?

(c) What is the total energy change as a result of the collision?

C7 A pair of ice dancers are moving horizontally at 4 m s^{-1}. The man throws his partner forward, in the air, at 40° to the horizontal with a speed of 6 m s^{-1}. The mass of the man is 75 kg and that of his partner is 48 kg.

(a) What is the speed of the man after this operation?

(b) What is the vertical impulse of the man on the ice?

C8 Figure 8.10 shows an apple of mass 50 g hanging vertically on the end of a string. It is struck from above by a small ball of mass 25 g moving with a speed of 4 m s^{-1} at an angle of 30° downward to the horizontal. After the collision the ball rebounds at an angle of 30° below the horizontal with a speed of 1 m s^{-1}. Find the speed of the apple immediately after impact, assuming the string is inextensible.

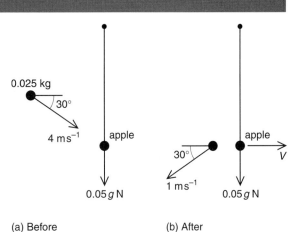

(a) Before   (b) After

Figure 8.10

Find also the impulsive tension in the string and the loss in kinetic energy due to the impact.

C9 A trapeze artist of mass 40 kg jumps from one trapeze to another. At the instant she reaches the second trapeze her speed is 5 m s^{-1} vertically downwards. The second trapeze is initially at rest with its supports at an angle of 45° to the vertical. If she moves on the arc of a circle of radius 4 m immediately after grabbing the trapeze, find:

(a) the impulse on her

(b) the initial speed of the second trapeze after she catches it.

How would the answers to the above alter if the supports of the second trapeze were to be shortened?

C10 A boy jumps from a tree to grab a rope hanging vertically from one of its branches. The mass of the boy is 30 kg and he catches and holds onto the bottom of the rope with a speed of 5 m s^{-1} and at an angle of 60° to the downward vertical. The rope is 10 m long and after the collision moves in a vertical circle.

What is the initial angular velocity of the boy and the rope and the impulsive tension in the rope?

Chapter 9

VARIABLE ACCELERATION (ONE DIMENSION)

9.1 Time-dependent acceleration

Key points

If acceleration is a function of t, we write $a = \dfrac{dv}{dt}$ and integrate to obtain v as a function of t, and since $v = \dfrac{dx}{dt}$ a second integration will give x as a function of t.

Example 1

A particle accelerates from rest at the origin in a straight line so that its acceleration at time t seconds is given by $a = (20 - 4t)$ m s^{-2}. Calculate the speed and the distance travelled after 3 seconds.

Solution

We have $\qquad \dfrac{dv}{dt} = 20 - 4t$

Integrating $\qquad v = 20t - 2t^2 + c \longleftarrow$ (*Don't forget the constant, c.*)

$v = 0$ at $t = 0$ gives $c = 0$ and thus $v = 20t - 2t^2$ $\qquad$ (1)

Hence when $t = 3$, $v = 42$ m s^{-1}

From (1), $\qquad \dfrac{dx}{dt} = 20t - 2t^2$

Integrating again $\quad x = 10t^2 - \dfrac{2}{3}t^3 + k \longleftarrow$ (*Don't forget the constant, k.*)

$x = 0$ when $t = 0$ gives $k = 0$, and when $t = 3$, $x = 72$

The distance travelled in 3 s is 72 m.

Example 2

A particle moving in a straight line starts at rest from the origin. Its acceleration at time t s is given by $a = e^{-(1/2)t}$. Find expressions for the speed v and displacement x after time t and hence sketch the (t,v) and (t,x) graphs for the motion.

Solution

We have $\dfrac{dv}{dt} = e^{-(1/2)t}$

Integrating $v = -2\,e^{-(1/2)t} + c$

$v = 0$ when $t = 0$ gives $0 = -2 + c$

Hence $c = 2$ and $v = 2 - 2\,e^{-(1/2)t}$ (1)

Notice that, as $t \to \infty$, $v \to 2$

The (t,v) graph is shown in Figure 9.1.

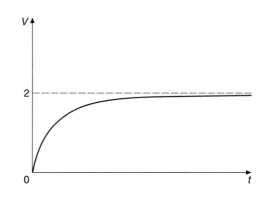

Figure 9.1

From (1) $\dfrac{dx}{dt} = 2 - 2\,e^{-(1/2)t}$

Integrating $x = 2t + 4\,e^{-(1/2)t} + k$

$x = 0$ when $t = 0$ gives $k = -4$

Hence $x = 2t - 4 + 4\,e^{-(1/2)t}$

As $t \to \infty$, $x \to 2t - 4$, and the (t,x) graph is shown in Figure 9.2.

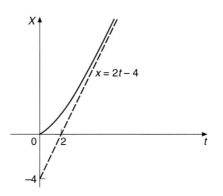

Figure 9.2

Exercise 9.1

In each of questions **A1** to **A5**, a particle starts at the origin with velocity u in the positive x direction. The acceleration at time t is a, the speed is v and the distance travelled is x.

A1 $a = 3t^2$, $u = 1$, $t = 4$. Calculate v and x.

A2 $a = 2t + 1$, $u = 0$, $t = 3$. Calculate v and x.

A3 $a = \dfrac{8}{(t + 2)^3}$, $u = 3$, $t = 2$. Calculate v and x.

A4 $a = 3\sqrt{t}$, $u = 8$, $t = 4$. Calculate v and x.

A5 $a = \dfrac{1}{(4 + t)^{1/2}}$, $u = 4$, $t = 5$. Calculate v and x.

A6 A particle moves along a straight line from a point O with acceleration $(2 + 3t)$ m s^{-2}. After 1 s it has travelled 10 m and after 2 s it has travelled 24 m. What is its speed and distance from O after 3 s?

B1 A particle starts at the point $x = 2$ m with a speed of 1 m s^{-1} in the positive x direction. Its acceleration at time t is given by $a = \cos t$.

Find expressions for v and x after time t.

B2 A particle starts from O with a speed of 2 m s^{-1} in the positive x direction.

The acceleration after time t is given by
$$a = -\sin \frac{1}{2}t$$
Find expressions for v and x after time t.

B3 A particle moves along the x-axis so that its acceleration at time t is given by
$$a = \frac{-1}{(t + 1)^2}$$. When $t = 0$, $v = 1$ and
$x = 0$.

Find expressions for v and x after time t.

B4 A particle moves along the x-axis so that its acceleration at time t is given by
$a = 3(1 - e^{-t})$. When $t = 0$, $v = 3$ and $x = 0$.

Find expressions for v and x after time t.

B5 A particle moves from rest along a straight line from a fixed point O so that its acceleration at time t is given by
$$a = 3 \sin t + \frac{1}{(t + 1)^2}$$. Find its distance
from O after 5 seconds.

B6 A man walks so that his speed after t hours is $\dfrac{20}{5 + t}$ km h^{-1}. How far has he walked by the time his speed has reduced to 2 km h^{-1}. How long does he take to walk 10 km?

9.2 Distance-dependent acceleration

Key points

From the chain rule: $\dfrac{dv}{dt} = \dfrac{dv}{dx} \times \dfrac{dx}{dt} = v\dfrac{dv}{dx} = \dfrac{d}{dx}(\tfrac{1}{2}v^2)$

If a is a function of x, we write $a = v\dfrac{dv}{dx}$ and integrate to obtain v as a function of x.

Newton's law of gravitation

An important example of distance-dependent acceleration arises from Newton's law of gravitation which states:

> For two bodies of masses m_1 and m_2 a distance x apart there is a force of attraction between them given by $F = \dfrac{Gm_1m_2}{x^2}$.
>
> G is called the universal constant of gravitation and its value is approximately 6.7×10^{-11} kg^{-1} m^3 s^{-2}.

For objects such as satellites which may be regarded as moving under the single force of attraction of a large body such as a planet this gives rise to the inverse square law for the acceleration of the satellite: $a = \dfrac{k}{x^2}$, where k depends on factors such as the mass of the planet, and the acceleration is directed towards the centre of the planet.

Example I

A particle of mass 2 kg is moving along the x-axis under the action of a force in the positive x direction of magnitude $-4x^3$ newtons. If the particle starts at the origin with an initial speed of 8 m s^{-1}, calculate:

(a)   the speed when $x = 2$

(b)   where the particle first comes to rest

(c)   the speed of the particle on its return to the origin.

Solution

From N2 $F = ma = mv\dfrac{dv}{dx}$

Hence $2v\dfrac{dv}{dx} = -4x^3$

and integrating $v^2 = -x^4 + c$

$v = 8$ when $x = 0$ gives $c = 64$ and $v^2 = 64 - x^4$

(a)   When $x = 2$, $v^2 = 48$ giving $v = 4\sqrt{3}$ m s^{-1}

(b)   When $v = 0$, $x^4 = 64$ giving $x = 2\sqrt{2}$ m

(c)   When $x = 0$, $v^2 = 64$ giving $v = -8$ m s^{-1} (on return the particle will be moving in the negative x direction).

Example 2

When a rocket of mass m is above the surface of the Moon, the force on it towards the centre of the Moon is given by

$$F = \frac{m \times 6.4 \times 10^{12}}{x^2}$$

where x is the distance of the rocket from the centre of the Moon. The Moon may be modelled as a sphere of radius 2×10^6 m, and the rocket is fired vertically from the surface.

(a) If the initial speed of the rocket is 1 km s^{-1}, how high will it reach before falling back?

(b) What initial speed will be required for the rocket to continue moving away from the Moon indefinitely?

Solution

We start with N2 in the form: $\qquad mv\dfrac{dv}{dx} = \dfrac{-m \times 6.4 \times 10^{12}}{x^2}$

Integrating $\qquad\qquad\qquad \displaystyle\int v \, dv = \int - \frac{6.4 \times 10^{12}}{x^2} \, dx$

(a) In this case the limits are 10^3 (m s^{-1}) to 0 (when the rocket stops rising) for v and 2×10^6 to X (the maximum distance from the centre) for x.

Therefore $\qquad \left[\dfrac{v^2}{2}\right]_{10^3}^{0} = \left[\dfrac{6.4 \times 10^{12}}{x}\right]_{2\times10^6}^{X}$

and $\qquad -\dfrac{10^6}{2} = \dfrac{6.4 \times 10^6}{X} - 3.2 \times 10^6$

giving $X = 2.37 \times 10^6$

The height reached above the surface of the Moon is 0.37×10^6 m, i.e. 370 km.

(b) In this case the limits are 2×10^6 to infinity for x and u (the initial speed) to 0 for v.

Therefore $\qquad \left[\dfrac{v^2}{2}\right]_{u}^{0} = \left[\dfrac{6.4 \times 10^{12}}{x}\right]_{2\times10^6}^{\infty}$

giving $\qquad -\dfrac{u^2}{2} = -\dfrac{6.4 \times 10^{12}}{2 \times 10^6}$

This is called the escape velocity from the Moon. In common practice it is called a velocity rather than a speed because its direction is implied.

from which u is 2.5×10^3 m s^{-1} or 2.5 km s^{-1}.

Exercise 9.2

In each of questions **A1** to **A5**, a particle starts from O with an initial speed u in the positive x direction subject to an acceleration a.

A1 $a = 3x$, $u = 10$. Calculate the speed when $x = 2$.

A2 $a = -3x$, $u = 10$. Calculate the speed when $x = 5$.

A3 $a = 3 - x$, $u = 4$. Calculate the speed when $x = 5$.

A4 $a = \sqrt{x}$, $u = 3$. Calculate the speed when $x = 16$.

A5 $a = 2 - \sqrt{x}$, $u = 4$. Calculate the speed when $x = 4$.

A6 A particle starts from O with a speed u in the positive x direction. The acceleration of the particle is kx towards O. Show that the particle comes to rest after it has travelled a distance $\dfrac{u}{\sqrt{k}}$.

A7 A particle has an acceleration $(3x^2 - 12x)$ m s^{-2} towards O, where x is the distance of the particle from O. If it starts from O with a speed of 16 m s^{-1} show that it travels 8 m before coming to rest.

A8 A particle starts from O in the positive x direction with a speed of 6 m s^{-1}. The acceleration of the particle is $(x - \frac{5}{2})$ m s^{-2} directed towards O. How far does the particle travel before coming to rest?

B1 A particle moves along the x-axis starting at the point $x = 2$ with a speed of 3 m s^{-1} away from O. The acceleration is $\dfrac{15}{x^2}$ towards O.

(a) Find the speed when $x = 3$.

(b) Find where the particle first comes instantaneously to rest.

B2 A charged particle of mass m is repelled from a fixed point O by a force of magnitude $\dfrac{16m}{x^2}$, where x is the distance

from O in metres. The particle is directed towards O from a point 1 m away with a speed of 4 m s^{-1}.

(a) Find the least distance of the particle from O.

(b) Show that the particle will ultimately move away from O with a speed of $4\sqrt{3}$ m s^{-1}.

B3 A particle moves along the x-axis towards O. When it passes a point $2b$ from O its speed is $\dfrac{1}{\sqrt{b}}$. The acceleration of the particle is $\dfrac{1}{2x^2} + \dfrac{1}{4b^2}$ in the positive x direction. Show that the particle comes to rest at a point distance b from O.

B4 A particle of mass m moves along the x-axis under the action of a force F which acts towards O. F has magnitude $\dfrac{4m}{x^3}$. Initially the particle is at the point $x = 1$ moving away from O with a speed of 2 m s^{-1}. Show that $v = \dfrac{2}{x}$ and that when $t = 2$, $x = 3$.

B5 A man starts walking at 4 km h^{-1} and his acceleration is $-\dfrac{1600}{(x + 10)^3}$ km h^{-2} where x is the number of kilometres he has walked. Find:

(a) the time taken to walk 20 km

(b) the distance he travels in 4 hours.

B6 A particle starts from rest at $x = 1$ and moves towards O with an acceleration $\left(x + \dfrac{1}{x^3} \right)$ where x is the distance from O. Show that it will reach O in time $\dfrac{\pi}{4}$.

Find the time taken to reach a point where $x = \dfrac{1}{\sqrt{2}}$.

9.3 Velocity-dependent acceleration

Key points

So far in our discussion of motion we have ignored air resistance, R, in order to keep the mathematical model as simple as possible. Air resistance is a complicated force, but we may begin to take account of it in two ways:

(i)   for small bodies at relatively low speeds we take $R \propto v$

(ii)   for large bodies at high speeds we take $R \propto v^2$.

Under these conditions it can occur that when a body reaches a critical velocity the resultant force on it is zero, in which case the acceleration will be instantaneously zero. At this point we say that the body has reached its **terminal velocity**.

Example 1

A particle of unit mass moves along the x-axis under a constant force of 2 N in the positive x direction and a resisting force of $0.1v$, where v is the speed of the particle. The particle is initially at rest at O.

(a)   Show that the particle tends to a limiting speed of 20 m s^{-1}.

(b)   Find the time taken to reach a speed of 10 m s^{-1}.

(c)   Find the distance travelled when the speed has reached 10 m s^{-1}.

Give your answers to 3 significant figures.

Solution

(a) $F = m\dfrac{dv}{dt} = 2 - 0.1\,v$

The maximum speed is reached when $\dfrac{dv}{dt} = 0$, i.e. $2 - 0.1v = 0$,

giving v as 20 m s^{-1}

(b)   Let time taken be T s. Since $m = 1$, $\dfrac{dv}{dt} = 2 - 0.1\,v$

Separating the variables and integrating:
$$\int_0^{10} \frac{dv}{2 - 0.1v} = \int_0^T dt$$

giving $[-10\ln|2 - 0.1v|]_0^{10} = T$

and $T = 10\ln 2 = 6.93$

The time taken is 6.93 s.

(c)   Let distance travelled be X. Since $a = v\dfrac{dv}{dx}$ $v\dfrac{dv}{dx} = 2 - 0.1v$

Separating the variables and integrating $\displaystyle\int_0^{10} \frac{v\,dv}{2 - 0.1v} = \int_0^X dx$

gives $[-10v - 200\ln |2 - 0.1v|]_0^{10} = X$

and $X = 200\ln 2 - 100 = 38.6$

The distance travelled is 38.6 m.

Hint: dividing gives

$$\frac{v}{2 - 0.1v} = -10 + \frac{20}{2 - 0.1v}$$

Example 2

In free-fall a parachutist has an acceleration given by $a = 10 - kv^2$ where k is a positive constant. If her terminal velocity is 50 m s^{-1}, find:

(a)   the value of k

(b)   the distance fallen before she reaches a speed of 25 m s^{-1}

(c)   the time taken to reach a speed of 25 m s^{-1}.

Solution

(a)   The terminal velocity is reached when $a = 0$.

$$a = 10 - k(50)^2 = 0, \text{ giving } k = 0.004$$

(b)   Let distance fallen be X. Using $a = v\dfrac{dv}{dx}$, $v\dfrac{dv}{dx} = 10 - 0.004v^2$

Separating the variables and integrating $\displaystyle\int_0^{25} \frac{v\,dv}{10 - 0.004v^2} = \int_0^X dx$

gives $\left[-\dfrac{1}{0.008} \ln \left|10 - 0.004v^2\right|\right]_0^{25} = X$

Evaluating this gives $X = 36$. The distance fallen is 36 m.

(c)   Let time taken be T. Using $a = \dfrac{dv}{dt}$, $\dfrac{dv}{dt} = 10 - 0.004v^2$

Separating the variables and integrating $\displaystyle\int_0^{25} \frac{dv}{10 - 0.004v^2} = \int_0^T dt$

gives $\left[\left(\dfrac{1}{0.004}\right)\dfrac{1}{100} \ln \left|\dfrac{50 + v}{50 - v}\right|\right]_0^{25} = T$

from which $T = 2.75$

The time taken is 2.75 s.

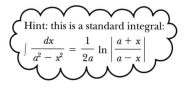

Hint: this is a standard integral:

$$\int \frac{dx}{a^2 - x^2} = \frac{1}{2a} \ln \left|\frac{a + x}{a - x}\right|$$

Exercise 9.3

Take g as 10 m s^{-2} where necessary.

A1 A particle moves along the x-axis with an acceleration $a = (2 + v) \text{ m s}^{-2}$. It starts at rest from O. Show that when $v = 10 \text{ m s}^{-1}$, $T = \ln 6$ and $x = 10 - 2\ln 6$.

A2 A parachutist in free-fall has an acceleration given by $a = 10 - 0.2v$. Find:

(a) her terminal velocity

(b) the time taken to reach a speed of 20 m s^{-1}

(c) the distance she will have fallen in that time.

A3 A parachutist is subject to a resisting force $0.1mv^2$ after he has opened his parachute, which he does when his speed has reached 15 m s^{-1}. Show that his terminal velocity is 10 m s^{-1} and that his speed t seconds after opening the parachute is given by

$$v = 10\left(\frac{5 + e^{-2t}}{5 - e^{-2t}}\right)$$

A4 A parachutist has an acceleration a given by

$$a = 10\left(1 - \frac{v^2}{u^2}\right) \text{ after falling from rest out}$$

of an aeroplane. Show that

$$t = \frac{u}{20} \ln \frac{u + v}{u - v}$$

Express v in terms of t. What value does v approach as t becomes large?

B1 When falling freely through the air a cricket ball has a terminal velocity of 30 m s^{-1}. Assuming that the resistance is proportional to the square of the speed, find the maximum height reached when it

is thrown up with a speed of 20 m s^{-1}. With what speed will the ball return to the ground?

B2 The resistance of a ship's motion is proportional to v^3. Prove that from the time the engines are shut off the speed, v, and the distance travelled, x, are connected by an equation of the form $\dfrac{dv}{dt} = -cv^2$.

Deduce that if the speed was u when the engines were shut off, $\dfrac{1}{v} - \dfrac{1}{u} = cx$.

B3 A car of mass 0.5 t is moving along a straight horizontal road. The power of the engine is 40 kW and there is a constant resistance to motion of magnitude 1000 N. If the speed of the car at time t is given by v, show that:

$$\frac{dv}{dt} = \frac{2(40 - v)}{v}$$

What is the maximum speed of the car?

Find the time taken for the speed to increase from 10 m s^{-1} to 15 m s^{-1}.

(Hint: if the driving force is D, $Dv = 40 \times 10^3$.)

B4 A particle moves on the x-axis and at time t its acceleration is $-(2v + 1)$ where v is the speed of the particle. When $t = 0$, $x = 0$ and $v = \frac{1}{2}$.

(a) Find an expression for v in terms of t.

(b) Show that as t increases v tends to a limiting value.

(c) Find an expression for x in terms of v.

Revision questions

C1 A particle moves in a straight line. When $t = 0$ the particle is at rest at the origin. The acceleration of the particle at time t is $e^{-2t}(t \geq 0)$.

(a) Show that after time t the speed v is given by $v = \dfrac{1}{2}(1 - e^{-2t})$.

(b) Find an expression for the displacement x after time t.

C2 A particle of mass m moves along the x-axis under a force of magnitude $\dfrac{mk}{2x + a}$, directed towards the origin O. The particle is released from rest at a point P where OP $= 4a$. Show that when the particle is a distance x from O its speed v is given by

$$v^2 = k \ln \left(\frac{9a}{2x + a} \right).$$

C3 A particle P of mass 0.1 kg moves along the x-axis under the action of a force of magnitude $\dfrac{8}{x^3}$ N directed away from the origin O where OP $= x$. The particle is projected towards O with a speed of 5 m s^{-1} from the point where $x = 4$.

(a) Prove that the closest distance of the particle from O is $\sqrt{\dfrac{8}{3}}$.

(b) Describe briefly the motion of the particle.

C4 At a distance x km from the centre of the Earth the gravitational acceleration is given by $\dfrac{k}{x^2}$, where, $k = 4 \times 10^5$. If a spacecraft 10^4 km from the centre of the Earth is moving with a speed of 10 km s^{-1}, how far from the centre will it be moving with a speed of:

(a) 5 km s^{-1}, (b) 12 km s^{-1}?

C5 After a boat of mass m has shut off its engines it is subject to a resistance of mkv^2 where k is a constant and v is the speed of the boat. Show that the kinetic energy of the boat will have dropped to one half of its initial value when it has gone a distance $\left(\dfrac{1}{2k} \right) \ln 2$.

C6 A small pleasure boat is driven by an outboard motor of power 1 kW. The force opposing the motion is $(75 + 25v)$ N where v is the speed of the boat. The mass of the boat and its occupants is 400 kg.

(a) Find the maximum speed of the boat.

(b) Find the acceleration when the speed is 3 m s^{-1}.

(c) If the boat starts from rest, find the time taken before the speed reaches 3 m s^{-1}.

C7 A 1 t rocket is fired vertically in the air from the surface of the Earth. The gravitational attraction of the Earth on it is $\dfrac{4 \times 10^{17}}{x^2}$ N, where x is its distance in metres from the centre of the Earth. The Earth may be regarded as a sphere of radius 6.4×10^6 m. Calculate:

(a) the speed required for the rocket to reach a height of 6.4×10^6 m above the surface of the Earth

(b) the escape velocity of the rocket.

C8 A particle starts with a speed u from the origin and moves along the positive x-axis.

The acceleration towards O is $k \left(\dfrac{v}{u} \right)^{3/2}$, where k is a positive constant.

Find an expression for x in terms of v, u and k and show that the particle never passes the point where $x = \dfrac{2u^2}{k}$.

C9 After it starts braking, the acceleration of a train is $-(A + Bv^2)$ where v is the speed and A and B are constants. Show that if its initial speed was u it would come to rest in a distance $\dfrac{1}{2B} \ln \left(1 + \dfrac{Bu^2}{A} \right)$.

Chapter 10

MOTION IN A CIRCLE

10.1 Velocity and acceleration

Key points

For a particle moving in a circle centre O and radius r, the distance travelled, s and the velocity v are given by:

$$s = r\theta$$

$$v = \frac{ds}{dt} = r\frac{d\theta}{dt}$$

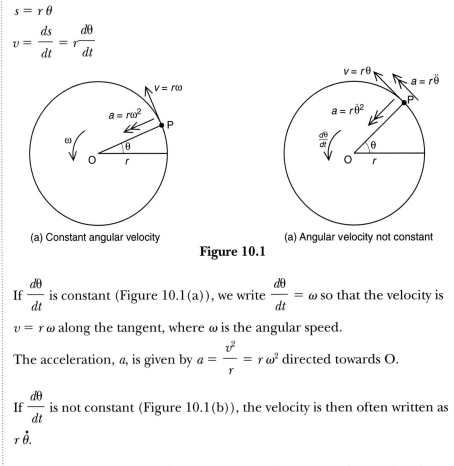

(a) Constant angular velocity   (a) Angular velocity not constant

Figure 10.1

If $\dfrac{d\theta}{dt}$ is constant (Figure 10.1(a)), we write $\dfrac{d\theta}{dt} = \omega$ so that the velocity is

$v = r\omega$ along the tangent, where ω is the angular speed.

The acceleration, a, is given by $a = \dfrac{v^2}{r} = r\omega^2$ directed towards O.

If $\dfrac{d\theta}{dt}$ is not constant (Figure 10.1(b)), the velocity is then often written as

$r\dot\theta$.

Although the velocity is still directed along the tangent, the acceleration has two components:

> $r\,\ddot\theta$ **along the tangent**
>
> $r\,\dot\theta^2 = \dfrac{v^2}{r}$ **along the radius towards the centre.**

The following examples illustrate uniform motion in a horizontal circle.

Example I

The Earth orbits the Sun approximately once every 365 days. Assuming the orbit is circular and has a radius of 149×10^6 km, find the orbital speed and the magnitude of the acceleration of the Earth.

Solution

The angular speed of the Earth is one revolution per 365 days.

This is converted to rad s^{-1} as follows:

1 revolution $= 2\pi$ radians

365 days $= 365 \times 24 \times 60 \times 60 = 3.1536 \times 10^7$
1 revolution per 365 days $= 2\pi/3.1536 \times 10^7 = 1.99 \times 10^{-7}$
i.e. $\omega = 1.99 \times 10^{-7}$ rad s^{-1}.

The orbital speed, $v = r\omega = 1.49 \times 10^{11} \times 1.99 \times 10^{-7} = 2.96 \times 10^4$,
i.e. the speed of the Earth in its orbit is approximately 30 km s^{-1}.

The acceleration of the Earth is given by
$a = r\omega^2 = 1.49 \times 10^{11} \times (1.99 \times 10^{-7})^2$

Giving the acceleration of the Earth towards the Sun as 5.91×10^{-3} m s^{-2}.

Example 2

At a certain stage in its flight a frisbee of radius 16 cm is moving horizontally and spinning about its axis, which is vertical, at 6 revolutions per second. If the centre of the frisbee is moving at 15 m s^{-1}, find the maximum and minimum speeds through the air of points on the rim.

Solution

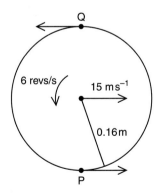

Figure 10.2

The angular speed of the frisbee is $\omega = 6 \times 2\pi$ rad s^{-1}.

If the frisbee were stationary in space, the point P at the top of the rim would have a forward speed of $v = r\omega = 0.16 \times 12\pi = 6.03$, as in Figure 10.2, whereas instantaneously Q would have a speed of 6.03 m s^{-1} backwards.

These two points represent the maximum and minimum values of the forward speeds – all other points have velocities of the same magnitudes, but have components both forwards and sideways.

If the centre of the frisbee were moving forward with speed 15 m s^{-1}, then all points on it would move forward with the same speed, so this speed would be added to that of the points P and Q.

Thus, P would move forward instantaneously with speed 15 + 6.03, i.e. 21.03 m s^{-1} and Q would move forward with speed 15 − 6.03, i.e. 8.97 m s^{-1}.

Exercise 10.1

Take g as 9.8 m s^{-2} where necessary.

A1 A car of mass 1200 kg moves around a circular roundabout of radius 500 m at 15 m s^{-1}. What is its acceleration towards the centre of the roundabout?

A2 The Moon orbits the Earth approximately once every 28 days. Assuming the orbit is circular with radius 3.8×10^5 km, find the orbital speed, v in m s^{-1}, and the magnitude of the acceleration of the Moon towards the centre of the Earth.

A3 A bicycle wheel has radius 25 cm. If it rolls without slipping, find its angular velocity when it is moving forwards at 10 m s^{-1}.

A4 A diver performs two and a half somersaults starting at rest from a point 11 m above the water. Ignoring all resistances, how long does she take to enter the water and what is her average angular velocity?

A5 A space shuttle orbits the Earth six times each day. What is its average angular velocity?

A6 A row of 20 ice skaters are in a single straight line with their arms linked so that 10 are facing forwards and 10 are facing backwards. Each skater is 0.5 m wide. The whole line rotates and performs 1 revolution every 8 seconds. What is the speed, v, of the outermost skater and what is the magnitude of her acceleration?

B1 A particle moves on a path given by the position vector:

$\mathbf{r} = (-2 + 4 \sin 3t)\mathbf{i} + (3 + 4 \cos 3t)\mathbf{j}$.
Find:

(a) the equation of its path

(b) expressions for its velocity and acceleration at time t

(c) the magnitudes of its velocity and acceleration when $t = 2$ and $t = 3$.

B2 A particle moves on a circle of radius 3 m with an angular speed given by:

$\dfrac{d\theta}{dt} = 5t^2$ rad s^{-1}. Find:

(a) its velocity and acceleration at time t

(b) the magnitude and direction of its acceleration when $t = 3$ s.

B3 Figure 10.3 shows the fan belt of a car. If

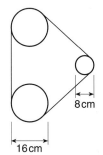

Figure 10.3

the belt is moving without slipping on the pulleys at a speed of 2 m s^{-1}, calculate the angular velocities of the pulleys.

Exercise 10.1 *continued*

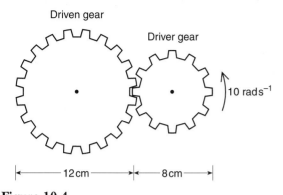

Driven gear

Driver gear

10 rad s^{-1}

|←————— 12 cm —————→|←—— 8 cm ——→|

Figure 10.4

B4 Figure 10.4 shows two gear wheels. If the driver gear is rotating at 10 rad s^{-1}, calculate the angular velocity of the driven gear, assuming there is no slipping.

B5 Figure 10.5 shows a pulley system. If there is no slipping and the free end of the rope is pulled down with a speed of 1.5 m s^{-1}, calculate:

(a) how fast the free pulley rises

(b) the angular velocity of the pulleys.

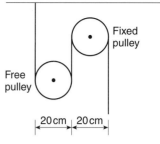

Fixed pulley

Free pulley

|← 20 cm →|← 20 cm →|

Figure 10.5

B6 The point of contact of a bicycle wheel with the ground is instantaneously at rest. Why?

(a) If the bicycle is moving at 5 m s^{-1}, what is the angular speed with which the hub rotates about the contact point if the radius of the wheel is 30 cm?

(b) What is the speed with which a point at the top of the wheel moves forward?

10.2 Motion in a horizontal circle

Key points

The force required to give a particle its acceleration towards the centre of a circular path is given by N2, so that $F = m\,r\omega^2 = m\,v^2/r$.

This force may be supplied in many ways, including:

> by friction between the wheels and the road when a car moves around a roundabout,

> by the tension in the string if an object is suspended from it and then swing round in a circle,

> by the gravitational attraction when one planet orbits another.

Example 1

A cyclist is moving in a horizontal circle of radius 150 m on a track which is banked at 10° to the horizontal. The mass of the cyclist and his cycle is 100 kg. What is the speed at which he must travel if there is no tendency for him to side-slip on a smooth track? Take g as 9.81 m s^{-2}.

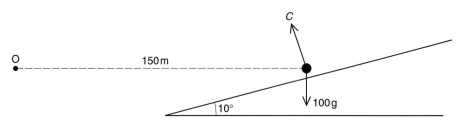

Figure 10.6

Solution

Figure 10.6 shows the forces on the man and the cycle combined. Note that he will have to lean inwards to avoid overbalancing, but we model the man and bicycle as a particle to stop this complication

Let C be the normal contact force between the cycle and the ground, and a be the inward acceleration.

Applying N2 to the man,

vertically $C \cos 10° - 100\,g = 100 \times 0$ *He has no vertical acceleration.*

which gives $C = 996$

horizontally $C \sin 10° = 100a$

Since $a = v^2/r = v^2/150$, $v^2 = 150 \times 996 \sin 10°/100 = 259$

giving the speed of the cyclist as 16.1 m s^{-1}.

Alternatively, the problem could be solved using a triangle of forces, as shown in Figure 10.7.

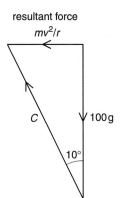

resultant force
mv^2/r

Figure 10.7

The magnitude of the resultant force, $ma = 100\,g \tan 10° = 173.0$

Since $m = 100$, and $a = v^2/150$, $v^2 = 173.0 \times 150/100 = 259.5$

giving $v = 16.1$ m s^{-1}, as before.

Example 2

A particle of mass m is attached to one end of a light inelastic string of length l, the other end of which is fixed at O, as shown in Figure 10.8. The particle is set rotating in a horizontal circle whose centre C is on the

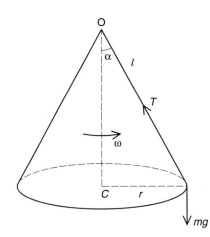

Figure 10.8

vertical line through O. The string makes an angle α with the line OC. Find:

(a)   the angular velocity of the particle

(b)   the time for a complete revolution (the periodic time).

Solution

Let the tension in the string be S and the angular velocity be ω.

Applying N2 to towards C:

$$S \sin \alpha = mr\omega^2 = m(l \sin \alpha)\omega^2 \text{ giving } S = lm\omega^2 \qquad (1)$$

Applying N2 vertically:

$$S \cos \alpha - mg = 0 \text{ giving } S = \frac{mg}{\cos\alpha} \qquad (2)$$

Eliminating S from equations (1) and (2),

$$lm\omega^2 = \frac{mg}{\cos \alpha} \text{ , giving the angular velocity as } \omega = \sqrt{\frac{g}{l \cos \alpha}}$$

The time for one revolution is given by: $T = \dfrac{2\pi}{\omega} = 2\pi\sqrt{\dfrac{l \cos \alpha}{g}}$

This system is known as a **conical pendulum** because the string traces out the surface of a cone as it rotates.

Exercise 10.2

Take g as 9.8 m s^{-2} where necessary.

A1   A car of mass 800 kg is travelling at a steady speed of 25 m s^{-1} on a banked surface of a circular track of radius 350 m. It reaches a part of the track which is suddenly very slippery and can be assumed to be smooth. At what angle to the horizontal is the track banked, if there is no tendency for the car to side-slip?

A2   A cyclist and her bicycle have a total mass of 65 kg. What is her speed on a smooth track of radius 120 m, which is banked at an angle of 15°, if there is no tendency to side-slip?

continued

Exercise 10.2 *continued*

A3 An aircraft of mass 10^5 kg is flying at a constant speed in a circle of radius 4 km. The plane is banked at 20° to the horizontal. If there is no tendency for the plane to side-slip and ignoring resistances, what is the speed of the plane?

A4 A particle of mass 0.3 kg is attached to a fixed point O by means of a light inextensible string of length 0.4 m and describes a horizontal circle of radius 0.2 m with a uniform speed of 5 m s^{-1}, in a horizontal plane vertically below O. What is the angular speed with which the particle moves?

A5 A particle of mass 30 g is attached to a string of length 25 cm, the other end of which is attached to a fixed point P. The particle is rotating at 7 rad s^{-1} in a horizontal circle to form a conical pendulum. Find:

    (a) the tension in the string

    (b) the angle the string makes with the downward vertical.

A6 A smooth hemispherical bowl of radius 12 cm is fixed with its open end facing upwards. A particle is projected so that it moves in a horizontal circle inside the bowl with an angular speed of 10 rad s^{-1}. Find the distance below the top of the bowl of the centre of the circle in which the particle moves.

B1 A particle of mass 100 g is attached to one end of a string of length 16 cm which hangs vertically at rest. The string passes through a smooth fixed ring 12 cm above the mass, as shown in Figure 10.9.

The other end of the string is attached to a particle of mass 50 g which rotates in a horizontal circle about the vertical part of the string.

Find the distance below the ring of the centre of this circle and the angular velocity of the 50 g mass.

B2 A particle of mass 200 g is attached to a fixed point O on a smooth horizontal table by a string of length 50 cm. The particle

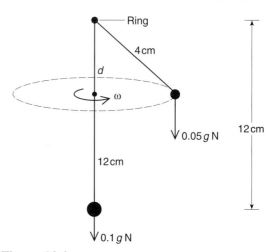

Figure 10.9

moves in a circle about O with a constant angular velocity of 5 rad s^{-1}. Find the tension in the string.

If the point O of the string is raised to a point 30 cm above the table directly above its previous position, leaving the particle to rotate in a horizontal circle, find the maximum angular speed the particle can have without losing contact with the table.

B3 A vinyl 'long playing' disc rotates about a vertical axis with constant angular speed 33 rpm. A particle of mass 0.05 kg is situated on the disc at a point 0.15 m from its centre O, and the coefficient of friction between the particle and the disc is μ. As the disc spins the particle moves with it and no sliding takes place. Find:

    (a) the speed of the particle

    (b) the horizontal and vertical components of the force exerted on the particle by the disc.

Show that, correct to 2 significant figures, $\mu \geq 0.18$.

Assuming $\mu = 0.4$, find the greatest value of ω (in rpm) for which the particle can move on the disc, remaining at a distance of 0.15 m from O and with no sliding taking place.

Exercise 10.2 *continued*

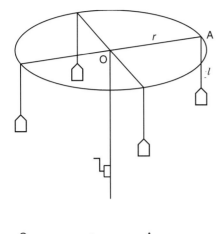

(a)

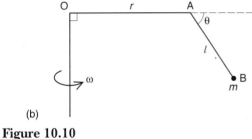

(b)

Figure 10.10

B4 Figure 10.10(a) shows a hand-driven roundabout used at a school fete. In Figure 10.10(b) the chains are modelled as light inextensible strings and the child and seat are modelled as a particle, and other factors such as air resistance are neglected. If the angular velocity of the roundabout is ω and the inclination of the chain AB is a constant θ, derive an expression connecting ω, θ, r and l.

B5 A particle of mass m is attached by a light inextensible string of length l to the vertex of a cone of semi-vertical angle α. The cone is fixed with its circular base on a horizontal table, and the particle moves as a conical pendulum on the smooth surface of the cone with angular velocity ω.

   (a) Find, in terms of m, g, α, l and ω, the tension T in the string and the normal contact force R between the cone and the particle.

   (b) Show that the particle will stay in contact with the cone provided

$$\omega^2 < \frac{g}{l \cos \alpha}.$$

10.3 Motion in a vertical circle

Key points

A case of non-uniform motion in a circle occurs when a ball is attached by a taut light string of length r to a fixed point and is released or projected from rest in a vertical plane, as shown in Figure 10.11.

Suppose the particle is given an initial horizontal velocity when hanging vertically. When it has turned through an angle θ, the two forces acting on the ball are $\mathbf{W}$, its weight force and $\mathbf{T}$, the tension in the string.

Since the tension in the string is always at right angles to the direction of motion – along the tangent – it does no work, so the only work done will be by the weight force.

We can derive two equations as follows:

(a) Applying N2 on the particle towards the centre of the circle:

$T - W \cos \theta = mr \, \dot{\theta}^2$ ◀——

Remember: $\dot{\theta}$ is an alternative notation for $\dfrac{d\theta}{dt}$.

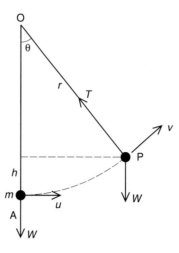

Figure 10.11

We will use this in the form $\qquad T - W\cos\theta = m\dfrac{v^2}{r}$ (1)

(b) Using the energy equation $PE_P + KE_P = PE_A + KE_A$

where A is taken as the zero level of PE: $mgh + \frac{1}{2}mv^2 = \frac{1}{2}mu^2$ (2)

where $h = r(1 - \cos\theta)$

Equations (1) and (2) are used to analyse the motion in particular examples.

Since in a general position as shown the angular velocity, $\dot{\theta}$, is greater than zero, the string being taut, there will be a component of the acceleration towards the centre, as well as along the tangent. However, at the point of release, $\dot{\theta} = 0$, so there will be no acceleration inwards. At the lowest point there is no force horizontally, so the acceleration will be solely inwards.

Example 1

A girl of mass 40 kg swings on the end of a rope of length 4 m which is attached to a branch of a tree, as shown in Figure 10.12. Initially the rope is taut and when the girl is 2 m below the point of suspension her speed is 3 m s^{-1}.

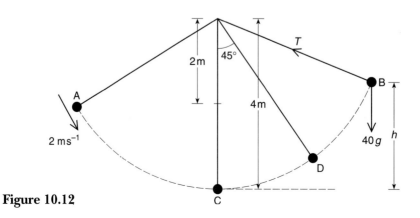

Figure 10.12

Find to 3 significant figures:

(a) the maximum height to which she will rise

(b) the tension in the rope when it is in the vertical position

(c) the tension in the rope when it is inclined at 45° to the downward vertical and the girl is rising.

Take g as 9.81 m s^{-2}.

Solution

Throughout the motion energy is conserved, since there are no collisions and we assume no energy loss due to friction, etc.

The lowest point of the swing will be taken as the zero level of GPE.

(a) Using the principle of conservation of energy:
$$GPE_A + KE_A = GPE_B + KE_B$$

where A is the starting point and B the highest point, which is h metres above the ground.

This gives:
$$40 \times 9.81 \times 2 + \tfrac{1}{2} \times 40 \times 9 = 40 \times 9.81 \times h + 0$$

Thus, $392.4h = 964.8$, so the girl will rise 2.46 m above the ground.

(b) To find the tension at the lowest point, C, conservation of energy is first used to calculate the speed.
$$GPE_A + KE_A = GPE_C + KE_C$$

giving $964.8 = 0 + \tfrac{1}{2} \times 40 \times v^2$

and $v^2 = 48.24$

The tension, T, at the bottom of the swing is found by using N2 towards the centre of the circle,
$$T - mg = m\frac{v^2}{r}$$

giving $T = 40 \times 9.81 + 40 \times 48.24/4$

When the rope is vertical, the tension is 875 N.

(c) At the point, D, when the rope is inclined at 45° to the vertical, the distance risen by the girl is $d = 4 - 4 \cos 45° = 1.172$.

To find her speed at D we use conservation of energy:
$$GPE_D + KE_D = GPE_A + KE_A$$

giving $40 \times 9.81 \times 1.17 + \tfrac{1}{2} \times 40 \times v^2 = 964.8$

$\Rightarrow v^2 = 25.28$

To find the tension, T, we use N2 towards the centre
$$T - mg \cos 45° = m\frac{v^2}{r}$$

giving $T = 40 \times 9.81 \times 0.707 + 40 \times 25.28/4 = 530$

The tension in the rope at this point is 530 N.

Example 2

Figure 10.13 shows part of a ski slope which is in the shape of a quarter of a circle of radius 40 m. A skier of mass 45 kg meets the top of this section with a horizontal speed of 15 m s^{-1}. Assuming there is no friction, find expressions in terms of g and the angle turned through, α, for the speed

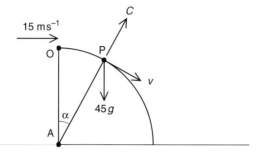

Figure 10.13

and the normal contact force between the skier and the slope at the position P, as shown. Find her speed when she leaves the slope. Take g as 9.81 m s^{-2} and give your answers to 3 significant figures.

Solution

Suppose the speed at P is v and the normal contact force is C.

Applying N2 along the line PA, $mg \cos \alpha - C = m\dfrac{v^2}{r}$

giving $C = 45\,g \cos \alpha - \dfrac{45v^2}{40}$ (1)

Using the energy equation: $PE_P + KE_P = PE_O + KE_O$

$$-45\,g \times 40(1 - \cos \alpha) + \tfrac{1}{2} \times 45 \times v^2 = 0 + \tfrac{1}{2} \times 45 \times 15^2 \qquad (2)$$

> Note the negative sign for the PE at P, since O is above P.

where O is taken as the zero level of PE.

Thus, $v^2 = 225 + 2g \times 40(1 - \cos \alpha)$ (3)

Substituting for this in equation (1):

$$C = 45\,g \cos \alpha - \frac{45}{40}[225 + 2g \times 40(1 - \cos \alpha)], \text{ which simplifies to}$$

$$C = 45\left(3g \cos \alpha - \frac{225}{40} - 2g\right)$$

She leaves the slope when $C = 0$, which gives $\cos \alpha = \left[\dfrac{225}{120g} + \dfrac{2}{3}\right]$

Hence $\alpha = 30.9°$, at which point equation (3) gives her speed as 18.3 m s^{-1}.

Exercise 10.3

Take g as 9.81 m s^{-2} where necessary.

A1 A child of mass 15 kg is seated on a swing, the ropes of which are 2 m long. He is pulled back through an angle of 25° by his sister and then pushed with a speed of 3 m s^{-1}. Find:

(a) his speed at the lowest point

(b) how high he will rise on the other side of the swing.

A2 A conker is attached to one end of a string of length 0.3 m, which is held vertically. It is hit so that its initial horizontal speed is 1.5 m s^{-1}. Through what angle will it turn before coming to instantaneous rest? What is the initial speed needed for it to turn through 90° before coming to rest?

A3 A boy of mass 35 kg is standing on the branch of a tree 3 m above the ground. He is holding a rope of length 4 m, which is attached to a branch of a nearby tree at a height of 2 m above him and the rope is taut. He jumps off with a speed of 1.5 m s^{-1}. Find:

(a) his speed at the lowest point of the swing

(b) how high he will rise on the other side of the vertical.

A4 A bead of mass 10 g is threaded onto a smooth circular wire of radius 0.4 m and it is initially at the lowest point of the wire. Find the height to which it rises and the reaction on the bead if it is given an initial speed of:

(a) 2 m s^{-1} (b) 3 m s^{-1}.

A5 A particle of mass 0.2 kg is suspended from a fixed point O by a light inextensible string of length 0.8 m. It is given a horizontal speed of 5 m s^{-1}.

(a) Find the tension in the string when it has turned through an angle of 50°.

(b) Find the height to which it rises before it becomes slack.

A6 A small bead of mass 0.1 kg is threaded on a smooth circular wire of radius 0.5 m and centre O. The wire is fixed in a vertical position and the bead is displaced from the highest point of the wire with a speed of 0.5 m s^{-1}.

(a) Find the speed of the bead when it has turned through an angle of 50°.

(b) Find the magnitude and direction of the force on the bead at this point.

B1 A particle of mass 10 g is released from rest at a point on the inside of the rim of a smooth hemispherical bowl of radius 12 cm which is fixed with its open face uppermost. Find the magnitude of the contact force between the particle and the bowl when it has turned through an angle of 75° with the horizontal.

B2 A skier hits a lump in the shape of an arc of a circle of radius 3 m. What is the maximum speed, u, of the skier at the top if she does not take off at that point?

If her speed at the top is $\dfrac{u}{2}$, will she take off at some point on the far side of the hump?

B3 A particle of mass 0.1 kg slides down the outside of a fixed smooth hemisphere of radius 0.2 m. Initially at the top it has a horizontal speed of 0.5 m s^{-1}. Find:

(a) an expression for the speed of the particle when it has turned through an angle α with the upward vertical through the centre of the hemisphere

(b) an expression for the reaction between the particle and the hemisphere at that point.

(c) Hence find the angle it turns through before it loses contact with the hemisphere.

B4 A small bead of mass 50 g is threaded onto a smooth circular wire of radius 50 cm which is fixed in a vertical plane. Find the speed with which it must be projected from the lowest point of the circle if it is to come to instantaneous rest after it has turned through 110°. What is the reaction of the wire at that point? *continued*

B5 A particle of mass 200 g is on the end of a light inextensible string of length 80 cm. It is held with the string taut at an angle of 45° to the downward vertical. If it is given an initial speed of 4 m s^{-1} so that it begins to move downwards in a vertical circle, find:

(a) its speed when the string is in the vertical position

(b) the tension in the string at that point

(c) the height to which it rises before the string becomes slack.

B6 A small ball of mass 0.1 kg is attached to a string of length 40 cm, the other end of which is attached to a fixed point, A. The ball is held at the same horizontal level as the point A and is 20 cm away from it. The ball is then released and falls freely until the string becomes taut after which it moves in a vertical circle. Find:

(a) the speed of the ball immediately before the string becomes taut

(b) the speed of the ball immediately after the string becomes taut

(c) the height to which it subsequently rises.

10.4 Conditions for complete vertical circles

Example 1

A particle of mass m is moving on the end of a light inextensible string of length l in a circular arc so that, at time t, its position is at an angle α radians with the downward vertical. At its lowest point its speed is u.

Analyse its subsequent motion.

Solution

In Figure 10.14, suppose the particle starts at the point A and rises to P when it has turned through angle α.

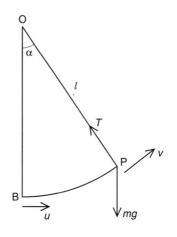

Figure 10.14

Using the principle of conservation of energy $GPE_P + KE_P = GPE_A + KE_A$

giving $0 + \frac{1}{2}mu^2 = mgh + \frac{1}{2}mv^2$

where $h = l(1 - \cos \alpha)$

Cancelling m and rearranging gives $v^2 = u^2 - 2gl(1 - \cos \alpha)$ (1)

Applying N2 to the particle at P along the radius towards O:

$$T - mg \cos \alpha = m\frac{v^2}{l}$$

giving $T = m\frac{v^2}{l} + mg \cos \alpha$ (2)

Substituting for v^2 from equation (1):

$$T = \frac{mu^2}{l} + mg(3 \cos \alpha - 2)$$ (3)

These equations can be considered for different values of u, the initial speed.

(i)   For $u^2 \leq 2gl$.

     From equation (1), $v = 0$ when $u^2 - 2gl(1 - \cos \alpha) = 0$

     Rearranging this gives $\cos \alpha = 1 - u^2/2gl$

     If $u^2 \leq 2gl$, then $\cos \alpha \geq 0$ and so $v = 0$ for $\alpha \leq \pi/2$.

     From equation (2), $T \geq 0$ if $\alpha \leq \pi/2$.

     Thus the particle will reach its maximum height before it becomes horizontal at $\pi/2$ and will swing to and fro in its subsequent motion.

(ii)   For $u^2 \geq 2gl$, we consider the initial speed which is needed for it to perform complete circles.

     From equation (3), we note that T will be a minimum when $\cos \alpha$ is a minimum, i.e. when $\cos \alpha = -1$, which is at the top of the circle.

     If T is greater than zero at this point then, from equation (3),

     $\frac{mu^2}{l} + mg(-5) > 0$

     giving $u^2 > 5gl$

     Thus it reaches the top and the string remains taut provided $u^2 > 5gl$.

     If $u^2 = 5gl$, the speed at the top given by equation (1) will be $v^2 = 5gl - 2gl(2) = gl$ which is greater than zero.

     Thus, provided $u^2 \geq 5gl$, the particle will perform complete vertical circles.

(iii) We now investigate what happens when u^2 takes values between those in (i) and (ii), i.e. $2gl < u^2 < 5gl$.

     From equation (1), the speed v becomes zero when $\cos \alpha = 1 - \dfrac{u^2}{2gl}$

From equation (3), the tension T becomes zero when

$$\frac{mu^2}{l} + mg(3\cos\alpha - 2) = 0$$

Rearranging this gives $\cos\alpha = \dfrac{2}{3}\left(1 - \dfrac{u^2}{2gl}\right)$

Thus, T becomes zero before v does. At this point the particle will continue to rise but on a free trajectory under gravity until the string becomes taut again.

Example 2

A particle of mass 500 g is hanging vertically at one end, P, of a light inextensible string of length 0.8 m, the other end of which is attached to a fixed point O. The particle is given an initial horizontal speed of 5 m s^{-1}.

(a)   How far above P will the particle be when the string becomes slack?

(b)   What will be the greatest height above P to which the particle will rise?

Take g as 9.81 m s^{-2} and give your answers to 3 significant figures.

Solution

(a)   Figure 10.15(a) shows the particle at a general position, Q, when the string has turned through an angle α with the downward vertical and the particle has a speed v.

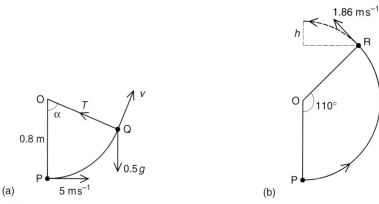

Figure 10.15

Conservation of energy gives: $PE_P + KE_P = PE_Q + KE_Q$

$$0 + \tfrac{1}{2}(0.5)5^2 = 0.5g(0.8 - 0.8\cos\alpha) + \tfrac{1}{2}(0.5)v^2$$

giving $v^2 = 9 + 16\cos\alpha$ (1)

Applying N2 along QO, with T as the tension in the string:

$$T - mg\cos\alpha = \frac{mv^2}{l}$$ (2)

When the string becomes slack, $T = 0$ so that: $v^2 = -gl \cos \alpha$
$= -10 \cos \alpha$

Substituting for v^2 from equation (1) we get $\cos \alpha = -9/26$, so that
$\alpha = 110°$

The string becomes slack when it has turned through $110°$.

(b) At the point R in Figure 10.15(b), where the string becomes slack,
     the particle has a speed given by equation (1), i.e. $v^2 = 90/26$, so
     $v = 1.86 \text{ m s}^{-1}$.

     Its direction is along the tangent, and therefore makes an angle of
     $70°$ with the horizontal.

     The particle will now behave like a projectile executing motion
     under gravity until the string becomes taut again. The maximum
     height is given by using the equation

     $v^2 = u^2 - 2gh$, where $u = 1.86 \sin 70° = 1.747$.

     Thus $h = 1.747/20 = 0.0874$.

     At this point the total height above P is $0.8 (1 - \cos 110°) + 0.0874$
     $= 1.16$ m.

Exercise 10.4

Take g as 10 m s^{-2} where necessary.

In the following exercises complicated formulas
should not be quoted. Begin each question with
the basic equations of motion.

A1 A particle of mass 0.1 kg is attached to a
       light inextensible string of length 3 m and
       hangs vertically. How high will it rise in its
       subsequent motion if it is given an initial
       speed of:

       (a) 3 m s^{-1}, (b) 10 m s^{-1}, (c) 16 m s^{-1}?

A2 A small bead of mass m is attached to a
       smooth circular wire of radius a which is
       fixed in the vertical plane. Initially the bead
       is at the lowest point of the wire and it is
       given an initial horizontal speed of u. Find
       the range of values for u for the bead to:

       (a) turn through a total angle of less than
            $90°$ with the downward vertical

       (b) turn through between $90°$ and $180°$

       (c) perform complete circles.

A3 A particle of mass 200 g is hanging
       vertically at one end, P, of a light

inextensible string of length 70 cm, the
other end of which is attached to a fixed
point, O. It is given an initial horizontal
impulse of 1 N s. Find the height to which
it initially rises above P before the string
becomes slack.

A4 A particle of mass 50 g hangs by a light
       inextensible string of length 50 cm from a
       point O. Find the least horizontal speed
       with which it must be projected in order to
       describe complete vertical circles about
       O. Find the tension in the string at its
       highest point.

A5 A particle of mass m is held horizontally
       and is attached to a light inextensible
       string of length 40 cm, the other end of
       which is attached to a fixed point O. If the
       string is initially taut, with what speed
       should the particle be projected
       downwards so that it subsequently performs
       complete vertical circles about O?

continued

Exercise 10.4 *continued*

A6 A particle of mass 300 g is attached to one end of a light inextensible string of length 40 cm and is held horizontally with the string taut. The other end of the string is attached to a fixed point O. The particle is released and when it reaches the vertical position the string strikes a small peg at P, where OP = 20 cm. The particle then moves in a vertical circle centre P. How high will it rise before the string becomes slack?

B1 An eskimo is sitting at the top of a smooth hemispherical igloo of radius 3 m when he starts to slide off.

   (a) Through what angle will he have turned when he loses contact with the igloo?

   (b) What will be his speed at this point?

   (c) How far from the base of the igloo will he hit the ground, assuming he is treated as a particle and falls freely under gravity?

B2 A particle P of mass 0.1 kg is free to move on the surface of a smooth fixed cylinder of radius 0.5 m in a vertical plane, which is perpendicular to the axis of the cylinder. It is initially at the top of the cylinder and is slightly displaced with a velocity of 0.2 m s^{-1}. Find:

   (a) an expression for the speed v when it has moved through an angle α with the upward vertical

   (b) the magnitude of the force on the particle in this position

   (c) the angle through which it has turned when it leaves the surface of the cylinder

   (d) the speed and direction of the particle when it leaves the cylinder

   (e) its distance from the lowest point on the cylinder when it hits the ground.

B3 A particle of mass 150 g lies inside a fixed hollow sphere of internal radius 0.3 m and centre O. When it is at rest at the lowest point, A, of the cylinder it is given an initial speed of 3 m s^{-1}. Find:

   (a) the point B at which it loses contact with the surface of the sphere

   (b) its speed and direction at B

   (c) the greatest height above A reached by the particle.

B4 A particle of mass 0.4 kg is suspended at P by a light inextensible string of length 1.5 m attached to a fixed point O. It is given a horizontal speed of 7.5 m s^{-1}, so that it begins to rotate in a vertical circle about O. Find:

   (a) the angle the string makes with the vertical when the string becomes slack

   (b) the speed of the particle at that point

   (c) the maximum height above P reached by the particle.

B5 One end of a light inextensible string of length 20 cm is attached to a particle of mass 100 g. The other end is fixed to a point O which is at a height 50 cm above the ground. Initially the string is taut and horizontal. The particle is projected downwards with a vertical speed of 2 m s^{-1}. Find an expression for the speed, v of the particle and hence the tension in the string when the string has turned through an angle α.

   (a) If the string can take a tension of at least 5 N before it breaks, show that the string will not break.

   (b) If the string can take a tension of at most 3 N, find the value of α and v when the string breaks.

Revision questions

Take g as 10 m s^{-2} where necessary.

C1   Figure 10.16 shows a racing track for a model car. The car is released from a point C on the straight slope at a height $2d$ above the ground.

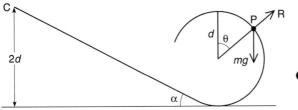

Figure 10.16

(a)   If the slope is inclined at an angle α to the horizontal, find an expression for the speed of the car at the lowest point, A.

(b)   Find an expression for the speed of the car at P on the circular part of the track of radius d, where the angle OP makes with the vertical through the highest point, B, is θ.

(c)   Find an expression for the normal contact force at P.

(d)   Find the value of θ for which the car leaves the track.

C2   A light inextensible string of length 30 cm is attached to a point on the circumference of a horizontal disc of radius 20 cm. To the other end of the string is attached a particle of mass 500 g. The disc rotates about its centre, O, with angular velocity ω, so that the string makes a fixed angle α with the downward vertical, as shown in Figure 10.17.

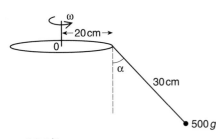

Figure 10.17

Find the angular velocity ω so that α takes the value 30°.

C3   A string of length 50 cm is attached to two points A and B, where B is 40 cm vertically below A. A smooth ring, C, of mass 500 g is free to slide on the string, and it is projected so that it rotates in a horizontal circle about the line AB. Given that AC = 30 cm, find the tension in the string and the angular velocity of the ring.

C4   One end of a light inelastic string is attached to a fixed point O. Particles of mass m and $2m$ respectively are attached to the string at A and B. The string OAB lies in a vertical plane and rotates about the vertical through O with constant angular speed $\sqrt{(g/a)}$. The particles at A and B move in horizontal circles of radius a and $2a$ respectively.

Find the inclinations to the horizontal of OA and AB.

C5   A bullet of mass 15 g is moving horizontally with a speed of 400 m s^{-1} when it hits and becomes embedded in a block of wood of mass 800 g which is hanging vertically on the end of a light inelastic string of length 1 m which is suspended from a point O. Show that in the subsequent motion the bullet and block combined will perform a vertical circle about O.

C6   Figure 10.18 shows two light inextensible strings AB and AC of lengths $13a$ and $5a$ respectively each attached to a particle A of

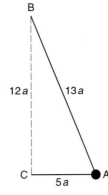

Figure 10.18   *continued*   **135**

mass m. The ends B and C are fixed with B vertically above C and BC = $12a$. With both strings taut the particle moves in a horizontal circle with constant angular speed ω.

(a) Find, in terms of m and g, the tension in the string AB.

(b) Find, in terms of m, g, a and ω, the tension in AC.

(c) Hence find the minimum value of ω in terms of g and a.

C7 In a fairground ride children sit in seats attached by wires of length 6 m to the edges of a rotating disc of radius 5 m, as shown in Figure 10.19. Safety rules state that during the ride tan α must be less than

$\frac{3}{4}$. Making clear any assumptions you use, find the maximum safe angular speed of the disc.

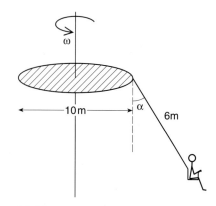

Figure 10.19

Chapter 11

ELASTIC STRINGS AND SPRINGS

11.1 Hooke's law

Key points

> **Hooke's law for an elastic string states that**
>
> $$T = \frac{\lambda}{l}x$$
>
> **where T is the tension in the string, x is the extension, l is the natural length and λ is the modulus of elasticity.**

Notice that if $x = l$ then $T = \lambda$. Thus λ is the tension required to double the length of the string.

For a string, Hooke's law only applies for $x > 0$. When $x < 0$, $T = 0$ and we say that the string is slack.

For a spring, when $x < 0$, $T < 0$ and we say that the spring is under compression (it exerts a thrust rather than a tension).

The work done in stretching a string by an amount x is given by

$$W = \frac{\lambda x^2}{2l}$$

In this case the string has energy stored in it with potential to do work. This is referred to as the elastic potential energy (EPE) of the string. Thus

$$EPE = \frac{\lambda x^2}{2l}$$

Example 1

An elastic string AB of natural length 1.5 m is hanging from a fixed point A. A mass of 5 kg is suspended from the end B and produces an extension of 3 mm. Calculate:

(a)   the modulus of elasticity of the string

(b)   the EPE of the string.

Take g as 9.8 m s^{-2}.

Solution

(a)   We first draw a diagram showing the relevant lengths and the forces acting on the particle, as in Figure 11.1.

In equilibrium, N2 gives $T - 5g = 0$

$\Rightarrow T = 49$

From Hooke's law

Take care over the units.

$$\frac{\lambda(3 \times 10^{-3})}{1.5} = 49$$

giving $\lambda = 2.45 \times 10^4$

The modulus of elasticity is 25 000 N (2 sig. figs.).

(b) $EPE = \dfrac{\lambda x^2}{2l}$, where $x = 3 \times 10^{-3}$

Hence, $EPE = \dfrac{2.45 \times 10^4 \times 9 \times 10^{-6}}{2 \times 1.5} = 7.35 \times 10^{-2}$

The elastic potential energy is 0.074 J (2 sig. figs.).

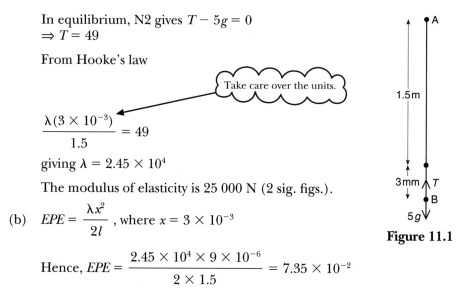

Figure 11.1

Example 2

A light elastic string has natural length 2 m and modulus of elasticity 200 N. The ends of the string are attached to two fixed points P and Q which are on the same horizontal level 3 m apart. An object is attached to the midpoint of the string and hangs in equilibrium at a point 0.5 m below PQ. Calculate to 2 significant figures:

(a)   the mass of the object

(b)   the EPE stored in the string in this position.

Take g as 9.8 m s^{-2}.

Solution

(a)   Figure 11.2 shows the forces
on the object.

Applying N2 vertically $2T \cos \theta = mg$ (1)

Hooke's law gives $T = \dfrac{\lambda x}{l} = 100x$ (2)

where x is the extension.

From Pythagoras' theorem: $y = \sqrt{(1.5^2 + 0.5^2)}$

and $x = 2y - 2 = 1.16$

From (2) $T = 116$ and from (1) $m = \dfrac{2 \times 116 \times \cos \theta}{9.8} = 7.49$

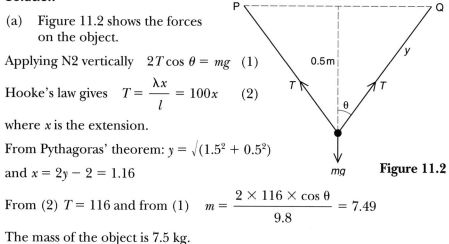

Figure 11.2

The mass of the object is 7.5 kg.

(b) $\text{EPE} = \dfrac{\lambda x^2}{2l} = \dfrac{200 \times 1.16^2}{4} = 67.3$

The elastic potential energy is 67 J.

Exercise 11.1

Take g as 9.8 m s^{-2} where necessary.

A1   A string of natural length 2.5 m extends by 4 mm under a tension of 250 N. Calculate the modulus of elasticity of the string.

A2   A string trebles its length under a tension of 20 N. Calculate the modulus of elasticity of the string.

A3   A string of modulus 200 N hangs in equilibrium with an object attached to the lower end. The natural length of the string is 80 cm and the extension is 1.5 cm. Calculate the mass of the object.

A4   An elastic string has natural length 1.8 m and modulus of elasticity 250 N. Calculate the EPE when the extension is:

(a) 0.2 m   (b) 0.4 m.

Hence, calculate the work done in extending the string from 2 m to 2.2 m.

A5   In a test a motorbike spring of natural length 60 cm is compressed by 10 cm by a force of 800 N. Calculate:

(a)   the modulus of elasticity of the spring

(b)   the EPE in the spring.

A6   A light spring has a thrust of 80 N when compressed by 5 cm. Calculate:

(a) $\dfrac{\lambda}{l}$ for the spring

(b)   the EPE in the spring

(c)   the work done in compressing the spring by a further 5 cm.

A7   A string of natural length 2 m will stretch 2.5 cm under a tension of 4 N. Find the work done in stretching the string from:

(a) 2 m to 2.1 m   (b) 2 m to 2.3 m
(c) 2.1 m to 2.3 m.

B1   An elastic string of natural length 8 cm is attached to two points A and B 10 cm apart. The modulus of elasticity of the string is 40 N. What is the tension in the string?

With A and B in a horizontal line an object is attached to the midpoint and lowered gently until it rests in equilibrium at a depth 3 cm below AB. Find the mass of the object and the EPE stored in the string.

B2   An elastic string of natural length 40 cm is pulled at the midpoint and held by a force of 10 N in the position shown in Figure 11.3. Find:

(a)   the tension in the string

(b)   the energy stored in the string.

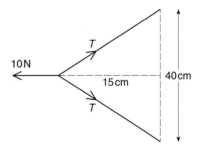

Figure 11.3

B3   A string of natural length 40 cm is stretched between two points A and B in a horizontal line, as shown in Figure 11.4. A mass of 2 kg is attached to the midpoint

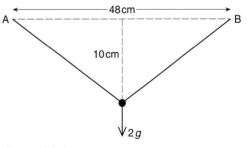

Figure 11.4

continued

Exercise 11.1 *continued*

and hangs in equilibrium. Find the modulus of elasticity of the string.

B4 A light elastic string has natural length 5 m and modulus of elasticity 200 N. The ends of the string are attached to fixed points P and Q which are on the same horizontal level 6.3 m apart. Calculate the tension in the string.

An object is attached to the midpoint of the string and hangs in equilibrium 0.8 m below PQ. Calculate:

(a) the EPE in the string in this position

(b) the mass of the object.

B5 One end of a light elastic string of natural length a and modulus $2mg$ is attached to a fixed point O on a smooth plane inclined at 30° to the horizontal. The other end is attached to a particle of mass m.

Find, in terms of a, the length of the string when the particle rests in equilibrium on the plane. What is the EPE stored in the string in this position?

11.2 The energy equation

Key points

In Chapter 7 we saw that for a body moving under the action of a force

work done by the force = change in kinetic energy of the body

For a body of mass m falling freely through a distance h under gravity, its speed increases from u to v where $\frac{1}{2}mv^2 - \frac{1}{2}mu^2 = mgh$

Figure 11.5

When a string is extended, as shown in Figure 11.5, the work done by the string is negative:

$$\frac{1}{2}mv^2 - \frac{1}{2}mu^2 = -\frac{\lambda x^2}{2l}$$

If a body attached to a string falls vertically from A to B, as shown in Figure 11.6, both gravity and the string do work on the particle and the work–energy equation gives:

change in KE = total work done

$$\frac{1}{2}mv^2 - \frac{1}{2}mu^2 = mg(l + x) - \frac{\lambda x^2}{2l}$$

Rearranging we get:

$$\frac{1}{2}mu^2 = \frac{1}{2}mv^2 - mg(l + x) + \frac{\lambda x^2}{2l} \qquad (1)$$

Taking the zero level of GPE at A

the EPE at A is zero (the string is slack) and

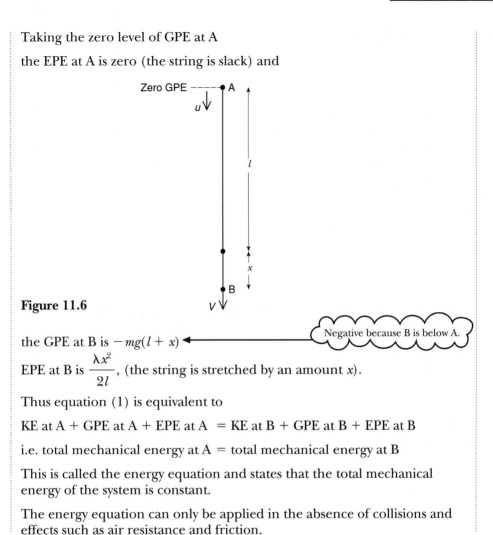

Figure 11.6

the GPE at B is $-mg(l + x)$ ◄──── Negative because B is below A.

EPE at B is $\dfrac{\lambda x^2}{2l}$, (the string is stretched by an amount x).

Thus equation (1) is equivalent to

KE at A + GPE at A + EPE at A = KE at B + GPE at B + EPE at B

i.e. total mechanical energy at A = total mechanical energy at B

This is called the energy equation and states that the total mechanical energy of the system is constant.

The energy equation can only be applied in the absence of collisions and effects such as air resistance and friction.

Example 1

A particle of mass 20 g is attached to one end of a light elastic string of natural length 15 cm. The other end is attached to a fixed point O on a smooth horizontal table. The string is stretched to a length of 20 cm when the particle is released. The particle passes through O with a speed of 10 m s^{-1}. Find the modulus of elasticity of the string.

Solution

See Figure 11.7.

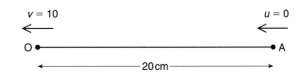

Figure 11.7

At A $\quad KE = 0$ $\qquad\qquad EPE = \dfrac{\lambda(0.05)^2}{2 \times 0.15}$

At O $\quad KE = \frac{1}{2}mv^2 = 1$ $\qquad EPE = 0$ (string is slack)

From the energy equation $\qquad \dfrac{\lambda(0.05)^2}{2 \times 0.15} = 1$

This gives the modulus of elasticity as 120 N.

Example 2

A girl of mass 40 kg is climbing a rock face. She is attached to one end of a rope of natural length 20 m and modulus of elasticity 4800 N. The other end of the rope is attached to a point O, 10 m below her. If she falls from the rock face calculate to 2 significant figures:

(a) her speed as she passes O

(b) how far she falls before she comes to rest for the first time

(c) how far below O she finally comes to rest.

What assumptions are made in (a) and (b) that are not made in (c)?

Take g as 9.8 m s^{-2}.

Solution

(a) Throughout the part of the motion from A to O in Figure 11.8 the rope is slack.

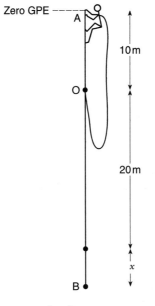

Zero GPE ---- A

10 m

O

20 m

x

Figure 11.8 $\qquad\qquad$ B

The energy equation is $\frac{1}{2}mv^2 = mgh$

giving $v^2 = 20g$

The climber's speed at O is 14 m s^{-1}.

(b) Suppose that the rope is stretched by an amount x when she comes to rest. The energy equation gives:

GPE at B + EPE at B + KE at B = 0

$$-40g(30 + x) + \frac{\lambda x^2}{2l} + 0 = 0$$

Thus $\qquad \dfrac{4800x^2}{80} - 40g(30 + x) = 0$

giving $\qquad 3x^2 - 19.6x - 588 = 0$

$\Rightarrow x = 17.6$, and she falls 48 m before coming instantaneously to rest.

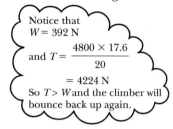

Notice that
$W = 392$ N
and $T = \dfrac{4800 \times 17.6}{20}$
$= 4224$ N
So $T > W$ and the climber will bounce back up again.

(c) In equilibrium, the forces on the climber must balance.

$\Rightarrow T = mg$, giving $\dfrac{4800x}{20} = 40 \times 9.8$

and $x = 1.6$ m

In parts (a) and (b) we have assumed that air resistance can be neglected. In (c) we assume that air resistance and other factors prevent the climber from bouncing up and down indefinitely.

Exercise 11.2

Take g as 9.8 m s^{-2} where necessary.

A1 A particle of mass 0.8 kg is attached to one end of a light elastic string of natural length 2 m and modulus of elasticity 40 N. The other end is attached to a fixed point O on a smooth horizontal table. The particle is projected away from O along the table with a speed of 6 m s^{-1}. How far will the particle travel before it comes to rest for the first time?

A2 A particle of mass 0.5 kg is attached to one end of a light string of natural length 1.5 m. The other end is attached to a fixed point on a smooth horizontal table. The particle is projected along the table from O with a speed of 10 m s^{-1}. If it travels 2 m before coming to rest for the first time calculate the modulus of elasticity of the string.

A3 A catapult is to be fired horizontally. The natural length of the elastic is 20 cm and

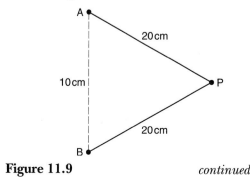

Figure 11.9

continued

the modulus of elasticity is 80 N. A bead of mass 20 g is placed at the midpoint of the elastic and pulled to the point P, as shown in Figure 11.9, before release. What is the energy stored in the elastic? Find the speed of the bead as it leaves the catapult.

A4 The spring on a pinball machine has natural length 15 cm and modulus of elasticity 150 N. It is compressed by 5 cm in order to fire a ball of mass 30 g. What is the speed of the ball on release?

A5 A toy gun fires table tennis balls of mass 10 g using a compressed spring firing mechanism. Before firing the spring of natural length 20 cm and modulus of elasticity 30 N is compressed by 12 cm. Find the speed of a ball on release.

B1 A particle of mass 0.2 kg is attached to a fixed point O by a light elastic string of natural length 1 m. The particle is released from rest at O and falls under gravity. The particle first comes to rest at a point B 1.5 m below O. Find:

  (a) the loss in GPE as the particle moves from O to B

  (b) the modulus of elasticity of the string.

B2 A toy of mass 0.5 kg is attached to one end of an elastic string of natural length 1 m which is hanging vertically with the other end attached to a fixed point O. The modulus of elasticity of the string is 8 N.

  (a) How far below O will the toy hang in equilibrium?

  (b) If the toy is released at rest from O, how far will it fall before coming to rest for the first time?

B3 One end of a string of natural length 1 m and modulus of elasticity 200 N is attached to a fixed point O. The other end is attached to a particle of mass 10 kg which is

released from rest at a point 0.8 m below O. Find:

  (a) the speed when the particle has fallen 0.2 m

  (b) the speed when the particle has fallen 0.5 m

  (c) how far the particle falls before coming to rest.

B4 A particle of mass 2 kg is suspended by a vertical elastic string with its other end attached to a fixed point O. The natural length of the string is 80 cm and in equilibrium the length of the string is 1 m.

  (a) Find in terms of g the modulus of elasticity of the string.

The particle is now pulled down a further 10 cm and released.

  (b) How high will it rise before it comes to rest for the first time?

  (c) In terms of g, what will be the tension in the string be at this point?

B5 Repeat (b) and (c) in question **B4** if the particle is pulled down a further distance of 30 cm. (Hint: does the string become slack?)

B6 A climber of mass 70 kg has a rope of length 50 m attached to him. The other end is attached to a point 20 m below him on a rock face. The modulus of elasticity of the rope is 1500 N. If he falls off the face, find how far he drops before coming to rest for the first time.

B7 A particle of mass m is attached to one end of an elastic string of natural length l and modulus $4mg$. The other end is attached to a fixed point O. Show that the particle will hang in equilibrium at a depth $5l/4$ below O. The particle is released at rest from O. Show that the lowest point it reaches is $2l$ below O.

Revision questions

Take g as 9.8 m s^{-2} where necessary.

C1 In a car safety test a car of mass 0.5 t is driven at 20 m s^{-1} into a buffer which can be modelled by an elastic spring of natural length 1.5 m.

In stopping the car the buffer is compressed by 50 cm. Ignoring all other resistances, calculate the modulus of elasticity of the spring. Find the compression of the spring if the car had an initial speed of:

(a) 10 m s^{-1} (b) 30 m s^{-1}.

C2 A particle of mass 3 kg is attached to one end of an elastic string of length 1.5 m and modulus of elasticity 60 N. The other end of the string is attached to a fixed point O on a rough horizontal table, and the coefficient of friction between the particle and the table is 0.4. The particle is projected from O along the table with a speed of 4 m s^{-1}.
   (a) Find the work done by friction on the particle before the string becomes taut.
   (b) Hence, find the speed of the particle when the string becomes taut.
   (c) How far does the particle travel from O before it comes to rest?

C3 A climber of mass 60 kg is testing a new rope of natural length 30 m. When she hangs freely in equilibrium the rope is stretched by 1 m. Calculate the modulus of elasticity of the rope. She now climbs a high tower, fixes the free end of the rope and releases herself to fall vertically.

   (a) Find the extension of the rope when she comes instantaneously to rest.
   (b) Find her greatest speed during her fall. (Hint: what will her acceleration be at this point?)

C4 A particle of mass 3 kg rests on a rough horizontal plane. The coefficient of friction μ between the particle and the plane is 0.5. The particle is attached to one end of a light elastic string of natural length 1.5 m and modulus of elasticity 20 N. The free end is slowly pulled horizontally.

   (a) What is the tension in the string when the particle starts to move?
   (b) What is the length of the string when the particle starts to move?

C5 A light elastic string of modulus 48 N and natural length 1.2 m has one end attached to a fixed point O. A particle of mass 0.6 kg is attached to the other end and released from rest from O.
   (a) Show that, when the extension is x, the EPE in the string is $20x^2$.
   (b) Calculate the value of x when the particle first comes to rest.
   (c) Calculate the speed of the particle when it is 1.5 m below O.

C6 A ball of mass 0.2 kg is attached to one end of a light elastic string of natural length 1.5 m and modulus of elasticity 60 N which is hanging vertically. The other end is attached to a fixed point O. In equilibrium the ball is at E. Find the depth of E below O.

The ball is released at rest from O. What assumptions are made in order to apply the principle of conservation of energy in the subsequent motion? Find:
   (a) the speed of the ball as it passes E
   (b) the maximum depth of the ball below O.

C7 One end of a light elastic string of natural length l and modulus of elasticity $2mg$ is attached to the point O of a smooth plane inclined at 30° to the horizontal. The other end is fastened to a particle of mass m, which is held at O and then released. Show that the particle first comes to rest a distance $2l$ from O.

C8 The ends of a light elastic string of natural length $6l$ and modulus of elasticity λ are attached to two points A and B where AB is horizontal and AB = $8l$. A particle of mass m is attached to the midpoint of AB. It is held at rest with the string horizontal and then released. It falls a distance of $3l$ before coming instantaneously to rest.
   (a) Show that $\lambda = 3mg$.
   (b) Find in terms of g the magnitude of the acceleration of the particle when it first comes to rest.

Chapter 12

MOMENTUM AND IMPULSE (2)

12.1 Impact of a particle with a fixed plane

Key points

Newton's experimental law of impact states:

> **When two bodies collide, their relative velocity of separation is proportional to their relative velocity of approach.**

The constant of proportionality is denoted by the letter e and is called the coefficient of restitution where
- the value of e lies between 0 and 1
- if $e = 1$, the collision is perfectly elastic
- if $e = 0$, the collision is perfectly inelastic.

The value of e is dependent on the two bodies in contact.

Example 1

A ball drops onto hard ground with a speed of 5 m s^{-1} and rebounds with a speed of 3 m s^{-1}. Find the coefficient of restitution for the collision.

Solution

Since there is an external impulse on the ball from the ground, conservation of momentum will not apply.

Using Newton's law of impact:

velocity of separation $= e \times$ velocity of approach

Thus $3 = e \times 5$, giving $e = 0.6$.

Example 2

A particle of mass 0.5 kg strikes a smooth plane at an angle of 30° to the plane at a speed of 3 m s^{-1}. It rebounds at an angle of 20°. Find the speed with which it rebounds and the value of the coefficient of restitution for the impact.

Solution

See Figure 12.1.

Since the plane is smooth the impulse on the particle is perpendicular to the plane. The component of momentum (and hence the velocity) is conserved parallel to the plane, giving:

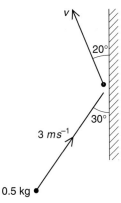

Figure 12.1   0.5 kg

$$v \cos 20° = 3 \cos 30° \tag{1}$$

Newton's law of impact perpendicular to the plane gives:

$$v \sin 20° = e(3 \sin 30°) \tag{2}$$

From (1) $v = \dfrac{3 \cos 30°}{\cos 20°} = 2.76$

Dividing equation (2) by equation (1) gives

$$\tan 20° = e(3 \tan 30°) \Rightarrow \quad e = \dfrac{\tan 20°}{\tan 30°} \approx 0.2$$

Exercise 12.1

Take g as 9.8 m s^{-2} where necessary.

A1 A ball of mass 5 kg is dropped onto the ground from a height h and takes 5 s to land. Find:

  (a) the value of h

  (b) the speed with which the ball reaches the ground.

If the coefficient of restitution between the ball and the ground is 0.7, find:

  (c) the height to which the ball rises

  (d) the time taken to reach the highest point after impact with the ground.

A2 A marble of mass 0.25 kg is thrown downwards to the ground from a height of 5 m. If it hits the ground with a speed of 15 m s^{-1}, find:

  (a) its initial speed

  (b) the time taken to reach the ground.

If the coefficient of restitution between the marble and the ground is 0.9, find:

  (c) the speed of the marble after impact

  (d) the time taken to reach its maximum height.

A3 A ball takes 1.5 s to fall to the ground from rest and 0.8 s to rebound to its maximum height after impact with the horizontal ground. Find:

  (a) the coefficient of restitution between the ball and the ground

  (b) the initial and final heights of the ball.

A4 A ball is dropped to the ground from a height h m. It takes a total of 2 s to rebound to its new maximum height. If the coefficient of restitution between the ball and the ground is 0.9, find:

continued **147**

Exercise 12.1 *continued*

(a) the value of h

(b) the maximum height of the ball after the first bounce.

A5 A ball of mass 0.5 kg is dropped from a height 2 m onto a floor. It rebounds at 4 m s^{-1}. Find:

(a) the coefficient of restitution between the ball and the floor

(b) how high the ball will rise after the second bounce.

A6 A ball of mass 0.3 kg is thrown onto the ground with an initial speed of 2 m s^{-1} from a height of 3 m. If the coefficient of restitution between the ball and the ground is 0.8, find:

(a) the speed with which the ball first hits the ground

(b) the height to which it rebounds.

(c) How many bounces will be needed before the ball fails to reach a height of 1 m? (Use a trial and error method.)

A7 A ball is thrown vertically downwards with a speed of $u \text{ m s}^{-1}$ from point 2 m above the ground. It strikes the floor and just reaches its original height after one bounce. If the coefficient of restitution for the impact is 0.7, find the value of u.

A8 Find the value of u in question **A7** if the ball just reaches its original height after two bounces.

B1 A ball A is placed midway between two vertical parallel walls which are 3 m apart and is lying on a smooth floor. Initially A is projected towards one wall at right angles to it, with velocity 2 m s^{-1}. The coefficient of restitution for the impact at the first wall is 0.4. Find:

(a) the speed with which the ball rebounds and moves towards the other wall

(b) the time that elapses before it hits the other wall.

The coefficient of restitution for the collision with the second wall is 0.5. Find:

(c) the speed with which the ball rebounds from this wall

(d) after how long its speed will have reduced to less than 0.1 m s^{-1} and how far it will then have travelled.

B2 A ball is projected upwards with a speed of 5 m s^{-1} from a point 2 m above the ground. It hits a ceiling which is 1 m above it and rebounds. The coefficient of restitution for the collision is 0.9. Find the speed with which it rebounds. The ball then falls to the ground and rebounds. If the coefficient of restitution for the collision at the floor is 0.7, find:

(a) the height to which the ball then rises

(b) at what speed the ball would have to be first thrown upwards in order to hit the ceiling again after one bounce on the floor.

B3 A ball travelling at 4 m s^{-1} strikes a smooth wall at an angle of $50°$ and rebounds at an angle of $35°$. Calculate the speed with which the ball rebounds and the coefficient of restitution for the impact.

B4 A particle of mass m is dropped from a height h onto a horizontal surface. The coefficient of restitution for the impact is e. Find in terms of e and h the height to which it will rebound.

B5 A billiard ball hits a smooth cushion at an angle $30°$ to the normal. If the ball is deflected through a right angle, find the coefficient of restitution for the impact.

B6 A billiard ball is moving near the corner of a billiard table. Show that after striking two adjacent cushions it will be moving back parallel to its original path, assuming the collisions are smooth.

B7 A girl throws a ball horizontally near the corner of a room to hit one wall at an angle of $50°$ at a distance of 2 m from the corner of the room. The ball rebounds and hits the adjacent wall 1.5 m from the corner. The mass of the ball is 100 g and its initial speed is 8 m s^{-1}. Assuming that all the

Exercise 12.1 *continued*

collisions are smooth and that the walls are at right angles, find:

(a)   the coefficient of restitution between the ball and the first wall

(b)   the magnitude of the impulse on the first wall.

B8   A ball drops from a height of 1 m onto the ground. If the coefficient of restitution between the ball and the ground is 0.5, find the total distance travelled by the ball just before:

(a)   the second bounce,

(b)   the 3rd bounce.

How far will it travel in total. (Hint: you will need to use the formula for the infinite sum of a Geometric Progression).

12.2 Direct impact of two particles

Key points

Care needs to be taken when finding the relative velocities of approach and separation of two moving objects, and clearly labelled diagrams are very important. Two cases are used to illustrate this.

(i)   The particles pursue each other in the same straight line (Figure 12.2).

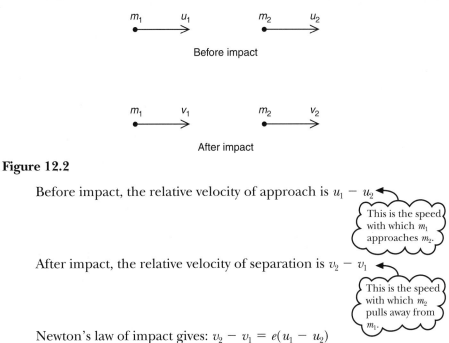

Before impact

After impact

Figure 12.2

Before impact, the relative velocity of approach is $u_1 - u_2$

> This is the speed with which m_1 approaches m_2.

After impact, the relative velocity of separation is $v_2 - v_1$

> This is the speed with which m_2 pulls away from m_1.

Newton's law of impact gives: $v_2 - v_1 = e(u_1 - u_2)$

(ii)   The particles approach each other and rebound after impact (Figure 12.3).

Before impact, the relative velocity of approach is $u_1 - (-u_2) = u_1 + u_2$

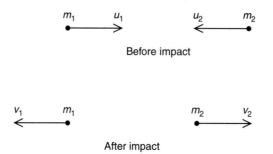

Before impact

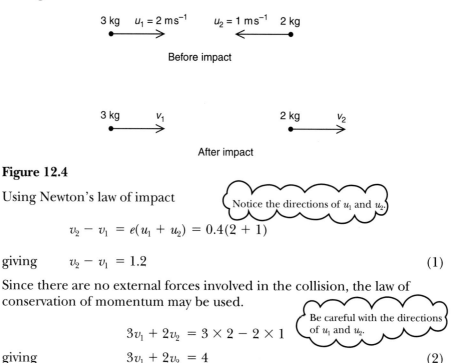

Figure 12.3

After impact, the relative velocity of separation is $v_2 - (-v_1) = v_2 + v_1$

Newton's law of impact gives $\qquad v_2 + v_1 = e(u_1 + u_2)$

Note: the term relative velocity is commonly used even though the equations we write in one dimension involve speeds. In such cases, positive and negative signs are used to indicate directions.

Example 1

A particle of mass 3 kg moving at 2 m s^{-1} strikes a mass of 2 kg moving at 1 m s^{-1} towards it. If the coefficient of restitution for the collision is 0.4, find the velocities of the particles after the collision.

Solution

See Figure 12.4.

3 kg $\quad u_1 = 2\,\text{ms}^{-1} \quad u_2 = 1\,\text{ms}^{-1}$ 2 kg

Before impact

3 kg $\quad v_1 \qquad\qquad$ 2 kg $\quad v_2$

After impact

Figure 12.4

Using Newton's law of impact $\qquad$ *Notice the directions of u_1 and u_2.*

$$v_2 - v_1 = e(u_1 + u_2) = 0.4(2 + 1)$$

giving $\qquad v_2 - v_1 = 1.2 \qquad\qquad\qquad\qquad\qquad (1)$

Since there are no external forces involved in the collision, the law of conservation of momentum may be used.

Be careful with the directions of u_1 and u_2.

$$3v_1 + 2v_2 = 3 \times 2 - 2 \times 1$$

giving $\qquad 3v_1 + 2v_2 = 4 \qquad\qquad\qquad\qquad\qquad (2)$

Multiplying equation (1) by 3 and adding to equation (2),

$5 v_2 = 7.6$, therefore $v_2 = 1.52$ m s^{-1}

Substituting in equation (1)

$1.52 - v_1 = 1.2$, giving $v_1 = 0.32$ m s^{-1}.

> Note: if we had assumed that the 3 kg mass rebounded after the collision and labelled its speed v_1 to the left in Figure 12.4 we would have found $v_1 = -0.32$ m s^{-1}.

Example 2

Three spheres A, B and C of masses m, $2m$ and $3m$ respectively lie in a straight line on a smooth horizontal table with B between A and C. The coefficient of restitution is 0.5 for all collisions. The sphere A is projected towards B with speed u. Describe what happens subsequently.

Solution

See Figure 12.5.

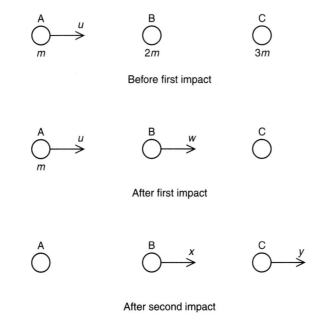

Figure 12.5

For the first impact,

using the principle of conservation of momentum

$$mv + 2mw = mu \Rightarrow v + 2w = u \qquad (1)$$

From Newton's law of impact

$$w - v = e u \qquad (2)$$

Adding equations (1) and (2)

$$3w = u(1 + e) \Rightarrow w = \frac{u}{3} \times \frac{3}{2} = \frac{u}{2}$$

Substituting in equation (1) $v = u - 2w = 0$

Sphere A comes to rest after the first impact.

For the second impact,

using the principle of conservation of momentum

$$2m(0.5\,u) = 2mx + 3my \Rightarrow u = 2x + 3y \qquad (3)$$

From Newton's law of impact

$$y - x = e(0.5u) \Rightarrow 0.25u = y - x \qquad (4)$$

Multiplying equation (4) by 2 and adding to equation (3) gives

$$5y = 3u/2 \Rightarrow y = 0.3u$$

Substituting in equation (4) gives $\quad x = 0.3u - 0.25u = 0.05u.$

Since the speed of B is in the positive direction it will not collide with A again, nor will it hit C, so there will be no further collisions.

Exercise 12.2

In questions **A1** to **A5**:

   (a)   state the velocity of approach of the two particles

   (b)   state the velocity of separation of the two particles

   (c)   find the coefficient of restitution for the collision

   (d)   show that the total momentum before and after impact is constant

   (e)   find the loss of energy as a result of the collision.

A1 See Figure 12.6.

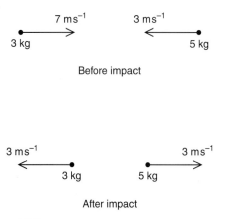

Before impact

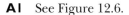

After impact

Figure 12.6

A2 See Figure 12.7.

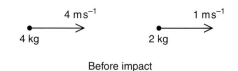

Before impact

After impact

Figure 12.7

A3 See Figure 12.8.

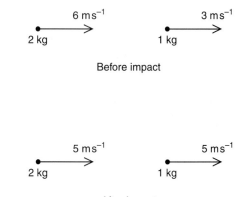

Before impact

After impact

Figure 12.8

Exercise 12.2 *continued*

A4 See Figure 12.9.

6 ms^{-1} 3 ms^{-1}

2 kg   3 kg

Before impact

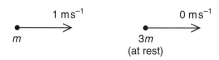

3 ms^{-1} 5 ms^{-1}

2 kg   3 kg

After impact

Figure 12.9

A5 See Figure 12.10.

1 ms^{-1} 0 ms^{-1}

m $3m$
             (at rest)

Before impact

0.1 ms^{-1} 0.3 ms^{-1}

m $3m$

After impact

Figure 12.10

A6 A particle of mass 3 kg is moving at 2 m s^{-1} when it strikes a second particle of mass 2 kg moving directly towards it at 1 m s^{-1}. If the coefficient of restitution for the collision is 0.5, find the velocities of the particles after the collision.

B1 A particle of mass m moving with speed $3u$ hits a particle of mass $3m$ moving with speed $2u$ in the opposite direction. After the collision the particle of mass $3m$ is brought to rest. Find:

(a) the speed of the particle of mass m after the collision

(b) the coefficient of restitution for the collision

(c) the loss of energy due to the collision in terms of m and u.

B2 A particle of mass m hits a particle of mass $2m$ which is at rest. After the collision the ratios of their speeds is 2:3. Find:

(a) the coefficient of restitution for the collision

(b) the loss of energy due to the collision in terms of m and u.

B3 Two marbles A and B of equal mass lie in a smooth horizontal circular groove at opposite ends of a diameter. A is projected along the groove and hits B after time t. When will the next collision occur, assuming the coefficient of restitution for the collision is e?

B4 Three spheres A, B and C of masses m, $2m$ and $4m$ respectively lie in a straight line on a smooth horizontal table with B between A and C. The coefficient of restitution for all collisions is e. A is projected towards B with speed 4 m s^{-1} and C moves with speed 1 m s^{-1} after being struck by B. Prove that A and B are at rest after the final collision and find the value of e.

B5 Two coins each of mass 90 g are at rest on a smooth horizontal table and a coin of mass 10 g is moving along the line of centres between them with velocity 3 m s^{-1}. If all the collisions are perfectly elastic, how many collisions will there be?

B6 Three discs A, B and C of masses 10 g, 20 g and 30 g lie in order in a straight line on a smooth horizontal table. The coefficient of restitution for all collisions is 0.5. If A is projected towards B with speed 2 m s^{-1}, how many collisions will there be?

12.3 Oblique impact

Key points

The following points are worth remembering when solving problems involving the oblique impact of two smooth objects:

- Newton's law of impact is applied to the common normal at the point of contact, e.g. along the line of centres in the case of collisions between spheres or discs.
- The total momentum for the system as a whole is conserved in any direction.
- Since the impulse acts along the line of centres, momentum is conserved for individual particles perpendicular to the line of centres.

Example 1

A sphere A of mass 2 kg is moving with a speed 5 m s^{-1} when it strikes a stationary sphere B of mass 1.5 kg at an angle of 60°. After the collision B moves as shown in Figure 12.11.

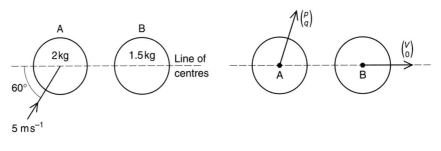

Before impact   After impact

Figure 12.11

Find the speed of B after impact and the speed and direction of A if the coefficient of restitution for the collision is 0.5.

Solution

Let the velocity of A after impact be $\mathbf{v}_A = \begin{pmatrix} p \\ q \end{pmatrix}$ and the velocity of B after

impact be $\mathbf{v}_B = \begin{pmatrix} v \\ 0 \end{pmatrix}$, as shown in Figure 12.11.

The momentum of A is conserved perpendicular to the line of centres:

$2 \times 5 \times \sin 60° = 2 \times q \Rightarrow q = 4.33.$

Total momentum is conserved along the line of centres

$2 \times 5 \times \cos 60° = 2p + 1.5v$

$\Rightarrow \qquad 2p + 1.5v = 5$ (1)

Newton's law of impact along the line of centres

$(v - p) = 0.5(5 \cos 60°) \Rightarrow v - p = 1.25$ (2)

Solving (1) and (2) gives $v = 2.14$ and $p = 0.89$.

The speed of B after impact is 1.5 m s^{-1}. The velocity of A is

$\begin{pmatrix} 0.89 \\ 4.33 \end{pmatrix}$ m s^{-1}, giving A a speed of 4.42 m s^{-1} and a direction of

$\tan^{-1}(4.33/0.89) \approx 78°$ with the line of centres.

Exercise 12.3

A1 Two uniform spheres A and B of equal radius have masses 100 g and 200 g respectively. Initially B is at rest and A is moving at a speed of 3 m s^{-1}. They collide and immediately before impact A makes an angle of 20° with their line of centres AB. After the collision A turns through 70°. Find:

  (a) the speed of B immediately after the impact

  (b) the coefficient of restitution of the collision.

A2 Two coins A and B lie at rest in contact on a smooth horizontal table. A third coin C strikes A and B simultaneously with a speed of 2 m s^{-1} perpendicular to their line of centres. C is at rest after the collision. If all the coins are identical, find the coefficient of restitution and the speeds of A and B after the collision.

A3 Two spheres A and B of masses $2m$ and $3m$ respectively are on a smooth horizontal table. Sphere B is at rest when sphere A is projected towards it with a speed of 4 m s^{-1} at an angle of 45° to their line of centres AB. If A is deflected through 45°, find the speeds of each sphere after the impact and the coefficient of restitution.

A4 Two billiard balls A and B each have mass 0.2 kg. Initially B is at rest on a smooth horizontal table and A moves with a speed of 3 m s^{-1} until it collides with B. At the instant of collision the line through the centres of A and B makes an angle of 30° with the direction of A's motion. After the collision A is deflected through 30°. Find:

  (a) the speed of B after the collision

  (b) the coefficient of restitution for the collision

  (c) the magnitude and direction of the impulse on A in the collision.

A5 Figure 12.12 shows a shot attempted by a

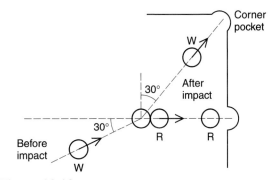

Figure 12.12

billiards player. If the balls have the same mass, find the coefficient of restitution for the impact if the ball labelled W falls into the corner pocket.

B1 Two balls B and C of equal mass are situated on a billiard table at two corners of an equilateral triangle of side $2a$. A third ball, A, of the same mass is projected towards B with speed 5 m s^{-1}, as shown in Figure 12.13. If the coefficient of restitution for all collisions is 0.8, find the direction in which A should be hit in order for it to hit C. In this case find the speeds of B and C after they have been hit by A.

continued

155

Exercise 12.3 *continued*

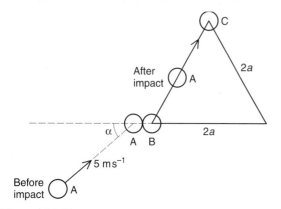

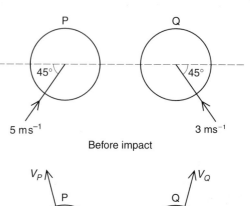

Before impact

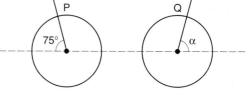

After impact

Figure 12.13

Figure 12.14

B2 Two spheres of masses m and $2m$ are approaching each other with speeds $2u$ and u along parallel lines. When they meet the direction of motion of the lighter one makes an angle of $\alpha°$ with their line of centres. If they move off at right angles to the original direction, prove that the coefficient of restitution for the collision is $\tan^2\alpha$.

B3 Two spheres P and Q of equal masses are approaching each other at right angles at speeds of 5 m s^{-1} and 3 m s^{-1} respectively, as shown in Figure 12.14. After the collision P is turned through 60°. Find the coefficient of restitution for the collision and the speeds of the spheres after they collide.

B4 Two spheres A and B of masses $2m$ and $3m$ respectively are moving on a smooth horizontal table. A is moving at 3 m s^{-1} and B is moving at 2 m s^{-1}, so that when they collide A makes an angle of 60° and B an

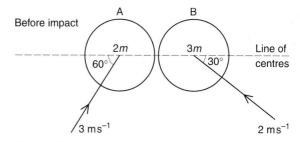

Figure 12.15

angle of 30° with their line of centres, as shown in Figure 12.15. The coefficient of restitution for the collision is 0.5.

Find the speeds and directions of both particles after the collision.

Revision questions

Take g as 9.8 m s^{-2} where necessary.

C1 Two uniform spheres A and B are of equal size and have masses $5m$ and $4m$ respectively. They are moving in a straight line towards each other each with speed u, and A is brought to rest by the collision. Find:

    (a) the coefficient of restitution for the collision

    (b) the loss in kinetic energy due to the impact in terms of m and u.

C2 Two particles A and B of masses m and $2m$ are initially moving in the same direction with speeds $4u$ and $3u$ respectively. They collide, the coefficient of restitution for the collision being e.

(a)   Find in terms of e and u the speed of A and B after the collision.

(b)   Show that whatever the value of e, the speed of B cannot exceed

$$\frac{11u}{3}.$$

(c)   Find the impulse on B in terms of m, u and e.

C3   A snooker ball hits a smooth cushion with a speed u at an angle of $60°$. The coefficient of restitution for the collision is $\frac{1}{3}$. Find the angle at which the ball leaves the cushion and show that it will have lost two thirds of its kinetic energy at the collision.

C4   Two balls P and Q of masses m and $2m$ respectively lie on a smooth horizontal table in a line at right angles to a vertical wall against which the table rests. P is projected towards Q with a speed of 3 m s^{-1}.

(a)   Find the speed of Q after the collision.

(b)   If P is then brought to rest, find the value of e, the coefficient of restitution.

(c)   Find the speed with which Q rebounds from the wall, if the coefficient of restitution for this collision is the same as in (a).

(d)   If Q then strikes P again, what are the speeds of P and Q after this collision?

C5   Two particles P and Q of masses $4m$ and $5m$ respectively are at rest on a smooth horizontal floor. P is projected towards Q with a speed of 2 m s^{-1}.

(a)   Find the minimum value of the coefficient of restitution in order that P will reverse its direction after the impact.

(b)   For this minimum value of e, find the speed of Q after impact.

(c)   Find the loss of KE as a result of the collision with this value of e.

C6   A particle A of mass m and speed u strikes a particle B of mass $2m$ which is at rest. The coefficient of restitution for the collision is $\frac{3}{4}$. Particle B then strikes a wall at right angles, the coefficient of restitution for this collision being e. Show that particle B will subsequently catch up with A provided $e > \frac{2}{7}$.

C7   A particle A of mass $2m$ moving with speed u on a smooth horizontal table strikes a particle B of mass $3m$ which is at rest a distance d from a vertical wall. The coefficient of restitution for the collision is $\frac{1}{2}$ and subsequently particle B strikes the wall at right angles and rebounds. The coefficient of restitution for the collision between particle B and the wall is $\frac{2}{3}$. Find, in terms of d, the distance of the particles from the wall and the time at which particle B collides with particle A for the second time.

C8   Two unit masses are moving in the same straight line with speeds u_1 and u_2 respectively, as shown in Figure 12.16, with $u_1 > u_2$. After the collision they move off with speeds v_1 and v_2 respectively.

Before impact   After impact

Figure 12.16

If the coefficient of restitution for the collision is e, find:

(a)   the loss in KE at the collision

(b)   the values of e for which the energy loss is a maximum and a minimum.

(c)   For these values of e, find expressions for v_1 and v_2 in terms of u_1 and u_2.

What do you notice in each case?

C9   A particle is dropped from a height of 0.5 m onto a fixed plane which is inclined at an angle of $15°$ to the horizontal. If the coefficient of restitution for the collision is 0.7, find the distance down the plane to the next bounce.

Chapter 13

STATICS (2)

Key points

A **rigid body** is an object made up of particles all of which are fixed distances from each other.

A **lamina** is a two-dimensional shape (has negligible thickness).

The centre of mass (COM) of a body is the point where the mass of the body appears to act. The centre of gravity (COG) is where the weight of the body appears to act.

For all the bodies under our consideration the COM and the COG will be at the same point, usually denoted by the letter G. For simple shapes the position of G may be determined by symmetry:

Object	Position of G
Uniform rod	Centre of rod
Triangular lamina	Intersection of medians
Uniform cuboid	Centre of cuboid
Circular hoop/disc	Centre of hoop/disc
Uniform cylinder	Midpoint of the axis of symmetry

If the forces acting on a body do not act through a common point we have to consider whether the forces will produce a rotation as well as a translation.

The rotational effect of a force is known as its **moment**.

> **The moment of a force about a point X is the product of the magnitude of the force and the perpendicular distance from X to the line of action of the force.**

The unit of moment is the newton metre (N m).

Notes:

(1) The moment is a function of the position of X.

(2) The moment about X may be positive (anticlockwise) or negative (clockwise).

(3) If X lies on the line of action of F, then the moment of F about X is zero.

In Figure 13.1 the anticlockwise moment of the force F about the point X is Fd.

If a rigid body is in equilibrium, the following two conditions must hold:

(1) The resultant external force is zero.

(2) The sum of the moments about any point must be zero (this is often referred to as the principle of moments).

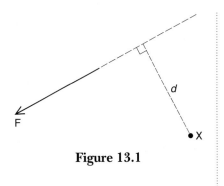

Figure 13.1

Example I

A uniform bar is 3 m long and has a mass of 2 kg. Masses of 3 kg and 4 kg are suspended from its ends A and D respectively. At which point must the bar be supported so that it rests horizontally in equilibrium?

Solution

Suppose that the bar is supported at C where $CD = x$. Figure 13.2 shows all the forces acting on the bar, including the weight force of the bar at B (the midpoint) and the vertical contact force at C (which clearly has magnitude $9g$).

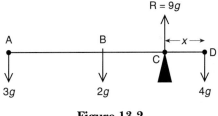

Figure 13.2

Taking moments about C

$$\text{total positive moment} = \text{total negative moment}$$

$$3g(3 - x) + 2g(1.5 - x) = 4gx$$

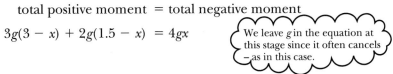

> We leave g in the equation at this stage since it often cancels – as in this case.

giving $x = 1\frac{1}{3}$. The bar is supported $1\frac{1}{3}$ m from C.

Example 2

A light rod AB 5 m long is suspended at A and B by two vertical strings. Weights of 4 N, 6 N, 8 N and 10 N are hung from the rod at distances of 1 m, 2 m, 3 m and 4 m from A. Find the tensions in the strings at A and B.

Solution

Let S and T be the tensions in the strings at A and B. Figure 13.3 shows all the forces acting on the rod. Since the resultant force is zero:

$$S + T = 4 + 6 + 8 + 10 \Rightarrow S + T = 28 \tag{1}$$

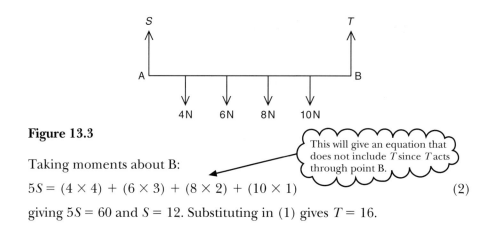

Figure 13.3

This will give an equation that does not include T since T acts through point B.

Taking moments about B:

$$5S = (4 \times 4) + (6 \times 3) + (8 \times 2) + (10 \times 1) \qquad (2)$$

giving $5S = 60$ and $S = 12$. Substituting in (1) gives $T = 16$.

Exercise 13.1

Take g as 9.8 m s^{-2} where necessary.

A1 Find the moment of the given force about the point X in each of the cases in Figure 13.4 (Note anticlockwise is positive).

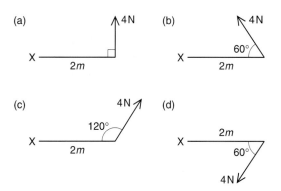

Figure 13.4

A2 ABCD is a square of side 2 m. Forces act in the directions shown in Figure 13.5. Find

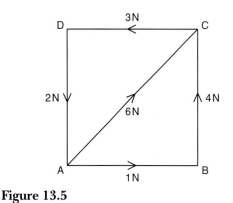

Figure 13.5

the resultant moment of all the forces about:

(a) A (b) B (c) C (d) D.

A3 A light rod of length 4 m carries masses of 6 kg and 10 kg at its ends A and B respectively. It rests in equilibrium on a single support at a point C in the rod. Find the distance of C from the end A.

A4 A uniform horizontal beam of mass 4 kg and length 2 m rests on vertical supports at its ends. The beam has a mass of 2 kg attached 0.8 m from one end. Find the forces of the supports on the beam.

A5 Masses of 1 kg, 2 kg, 3 kg and 4 kg are suspended from a uniform rod AB of length 5 m at distances of 1 m, 2 m, 3 m and 4 m respectively from A. The mass of the rod is 4 kg. The rod rests horizontally and in equilibrium on a single support C. Find the distance CA.

A6 A heavy uniform beam AB 5 m long and with a mass of 10 kg is supported at a point 2 m from A. A mass of 6 kg is placed at the end A of the rod and a mass m is placed at the end B. The rod rests horizontally in equilibrium. Find m.

A7 A boy and a man carry a uniform horizontal ladder 8 m long of mass 50 kg. The boy supports one end with a force of 200 N. How far from the centre does the man support the ladder?

Exercise 13.1   *continued*

B1 The side of a square ABCD is 1 m. Forces of 4 N, 3 N, 2 N and 5 N act along the sides CD, BA, DA and the diagonal DB. Find the total moment about C.

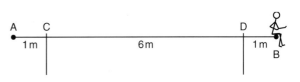

Figure 13.7

B2 A light rectangular plate ABCD has a force of 6 N acting along AD, as shown in Figure 13.6. AD = 2 m and AB = 3 m.

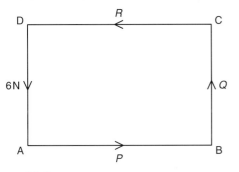

Figure 13.6

If the system is in equilibrium, find the values of *P*, *Q* and *R*.

B3 A light rectangular plate ABCD has force 5 N acting along each of AB and CD. Given that AB = 2.5 m and AD = 3 m, what forces acting along AD and CB will keep the plate in equilibrium?

B4 Forces of 5 N, 5 N, 5 N and 10 N act along the sides AB, BC, CD and DA respectively of a square ABCD of side 2 m. Find:

(a) the magnitude and direction of the resultant force

(b) the total moment of the forces about A.

B5 Figure 13.7 shows a heavy plank AB of length 8 m and mass 20 kg resting on supports at C and D. A girl of mass 45 kg stands on the end B of the plank. Find the contact forces at C and D. What is the maximum mass that can be placed at B before the plank starts to tip? (Hint: when this happens, the contact force at C will be zero.)

B6 A uniform bar AB 3 m long and of mass 5 kg rests on the ground. If a mass of 20 kg is placed on the rod 1 m from B, find the vertical force needed at A which will just lift that end. (Hint: as A is about to lift the bar is turning about point B.)

What would be the minimum force required to lift the end B?

B7 Figure 13.8 shows a crane 15 m long with a mass 20 t at one end 10 m from the cabin. What is the mass of the counterpoise required if the system is to remain in equilibrium?

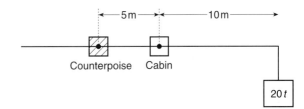

Figure 13.8

If the counterpoise remains of fixed mass and the load is doubled, how far must the counterpoise be pulled from the cabin to maintain equilibrium?

13.2 Equilibrium of a body under coplanar forces

Key points

In solving problems to determine the values of unknown forces we use the conditions for equilibrium and proceed as follows.

Set the components of external forces equal to zero in two perpendicular directions. These are usually either
- vertically and horizontally or
- parallel and perpendicular to a line or surface.

Set the total moment of external forces to zero about suitably chosen points.

Smooth hinges

When a body is said to be smoothly hinged the action of the hinge on the body is a single force acting through the centre of the hinge. It is often convenient to resolve this force into two perpendicular components.

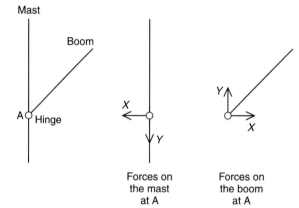

Figure 13.9

Figure 13.9 shows a boom on a yacht hinged, to a mast at A. The forces on the mast and the boom are shown separately with the hinge 'exploded'.

Smooth pegs

If a rod is in contact with a smooth peg, then the contact force from the peg is perpendicular to the rod.

Example 1

A farmyard gate PQRS is modelled by a uniform lamina of mass 150 kg (Figure 13.10). PQ = 1.5 m, QR = 3 m and there are smooth hinges at P and Q. The force at Q is always horizontal. A girl of mass 40 kg sits on the

Figure 13.10

gate at R. Find the magnitude of the forces on the gate at P and Q.
Take g as 9.8 m s^{-2}.

Solution

Figure 13.11 shows all the forces acting on the gate.

> Notice that the only horizontal forces are at P and Q. Since these must balance they are both labelled with the same letter X (acting in opposite directions).

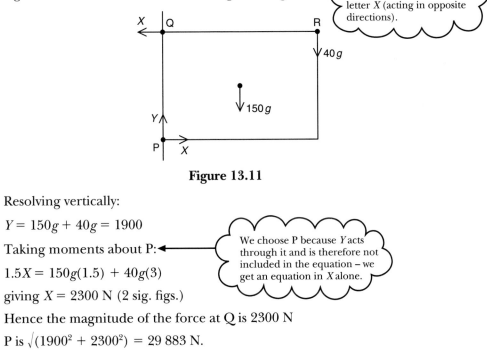

Figure 13.11

Resolving vertically:

$Y = 150g + 40g = 1900$

Taking moments about P:

> We choose P because Y acts through it and is therefore not included in the equation – we get an equation in X alone.

$1.5X = 150g(1.5) + 40g(3)$

giving $X = 2300$ N (2 sig. figs.)

Hence the magnitude of the force at Q is 2300 N

P is $\sqrt{(1900^2 + 2300^2)} = 29\,883$ N.

The magnitude of the force at P is 3000 N (2 sig. figs.)

Example 2

A uniform rod of length 3 m and mass 20 kg is smoothly hinged to a vertical wall at A and passes over a smooth peg P where AP = 1 m. The rod makes an angle of 40° with the downward vertical. Find:

(a)   the contact force at P

(b)   the magnitude of the reaction at A.

Take g as 9.8 m s^{-2}.

Solution

Let S be the normal contact force on the rod from the peg and let Q and R be the components of the reaction perpendicular and parallel to the rod at A.

Taking moments about A:

> These are useful directions since they lead to simple equations in one unknown.

$S \times 1 = 20\,g \sin 40° \times 1.5$

giving $S = 190$ N (2 sig. figs.)

Resolving parallel to the rod:

$R = 20g \cos 40° = 153.2$, giving R as 150 N. (2 sig. figs.)

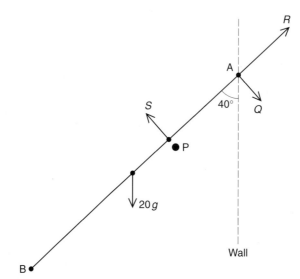

Figure 13.12

Resolving perpendicular to the rod

$Q = S - 20g \sin 40° = 63$

The magnitude of the reaction at A $= \sqrt{(Q^2 + R^2)} = 160$

Alternatively, we could have taken horizontal and vertical components of the reaction at A. If X is the horizontal component and Y is the vertical component, resolving horizontally and vertically gives $X = 146$ and $Y = 74$ so that the magnitude of the reaction is $\sqrt{(X^2 + Y^2)} = 160$ as before.

Exercise 13.2

Take g as 9.8 m s^{-2} where necessary.

A1 A uniform rod AB of mass 2 kg is smoothly hinged at A and is held horizontally by a string of length 0.8 m attached to the free end B and to a point C, 0.6 m above the hinge, as shown in Figure 13.13. Find the

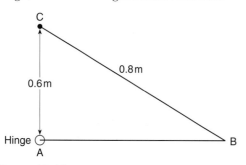

Figure 13.13

tension in the string and the magnitude of the reaction at the hinge.

A2 A uniform mast of length 8 m and mass 40 kg is inclined at 15° to the vertical. It is smoothly hinged at the lower end and is supported by a horizontal wire at the top. Calculate the tension in the wire and the magnitude of the reaction at the hinge.

A3 A uniform rod of length 1.3 m and mass 3 kg is hinged at its lower end A. The upper end B rests against a smooth vertical wall 0.5 m from A. Find the magnitude of the forces on the rod at A and B.

A4 A uniform rod of mass 6 kg and length 2 m is smoothly hinged at its lower end A. It is inclined at an angle 2θ to the vertical and passes over a smooth peg P. Find the magnitude of the contact force at P in terms of θ when AP is:

(a) 1.5 m (b) 0.5 m.

Exercise 13.2   *continued*

A5 A uniform rod of length 6 m and weight W is hinged at its upper end A. It hangs at an angle of 30° to the vertical and passes over a smooth peg P where AP = 2 m. Find in terms of W the contact force at P and the magnitude of the reaction at the hinge.

B1 A uniform rectangular gate is supported by two hinges in a vertical line 0.9 m apart. The gate is 1.5 m wide and has a mass of 40 kg. The upper hinge exerts a horizontal force up to a maximum of 500 N before breaking. A boy of mass 30 kg sits on the top of the gate. What is the maximum distance he can sit from the line of the hinges before the gate breaks?

B2 A uniform horizontal beam AB is 6 m long and is smoothly hinged at A. The mass of the beam is 100 kg and it carries a load of 300 kg at B. It is supported by a rope attached to a point on the beam 4 m from A and to a point 3 m vertically above A. Find the tension in the rope and the magnitude of the reaction at the hinge.

B3 The end A of a uniform rod AB of length 1 m is smoothly hinged and the rod is kept in equilibrium by a horizontal string attached at B. The weight of the rod is 40 N and the tension in the string is 25 N. If the angle of the string with the downward vertical is α, prove that $\tan\alpha = \frac{5}{4}$ and find the magnitude of the reaction at the hinge.

B4 A uniform rod of weight W can freely turn about a hinge at its upper end. The lower end is pulled aside by a horizontal force. Find the inclination of the rod to the vertical if the magnitude of the horizontal force is:

(a) $W/2$ (b) $3W/4$.

B5 A uniform rod AB is freely hinged at its lower end A and is held at an angle θ to the vertical by a string attached at B. Find in terms of W and θ the minimum possible tension in the string and the magnitude of the corresponding reaction at the hinge.

B6 A uniform rod AB of weight W and length $2l$ is smoothly hinged at its lower end A. A horizontal force of 50 N at the upper end B keeps the rod in equilibrium inclined at an angle θ to the horizontal where $\tan\theta = 3$. Find:

(a)   the mass of the rod AB

(b)   the magnitude and direction of the force exerted by the hinge on the rod.

13.3 Problems involving friction

Key points

We use the inequality $\dfrac{F}{R} \leq \mu$ (see Chapter 4) for rough contact to determine the conditions for equilibrium.

Concurrency condition

Sometimes it is possible to reduce the total number of forces acting on a body to three, and in this case we can use the **concurrency condition** for equilibrium, which states:

> **If three forces are not all parallel and are in equilibrium then their lines of action are concurrent.**

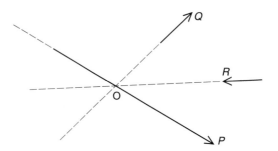

Figure 13.14

We can deduce this rule easily as follows.

Consider three forces P, Q and R acting as shown in Figure 13.14. If they are not all parallel, the lines of action of P and Q will meet in a point, O, say. P and Q have no moment about O and for equilibrium R must also have no moment about O. Therefore the line of action of R must pass through O and all forces are concurrent.

One particular case where the number of forces acting can be reduced occurs when friction is present.

We can combine the friction F and the normal contact force R to give a resultant called the rough reaction R_F.

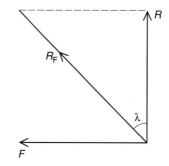

Figure 13.15

When friction is limiting, this force makes an angle λ with the normal contact force.

λ is called the **angle of friction** and is defined by $F/R = \tan \lambda = \mu$.

Example I

A uniform ladder of length 6 m and weight W rests in equilibrium with its foot on horizontal ground and its upper end resting against a smooth vertical wall. Contact with the ground is rough and the coefficient of friction is $\frac{1}{4}$. Find the maximum value of θ, the angle between the ladder and the wall, before the ladder starts to slip.

Solution

Figure 13.15 shows the forces acting.

Resolving vertically $R = W$

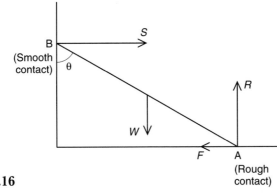

Figure 13.16

Resolving horizontally $\qquad S = F$

Taking moments about A:

$$(S\cos\theta) \times 6 = (W\sin\theta) \times 3$$

Hence $\qquad\qquad S = F = \tfrac{1}{2}W\tan\theta$

giving $F/R = \tfrac{1}{2}\tan\theta$, and since $\dfrac{F}{R} \le \mu$, $\tfrac{1}{2}\tan\theta \le \tfrac{1}{4}$

$\Rightarrow \tan\theta \le \tfrac{1}{2}$ and $\theta \le 26.6°$.

Example 2

Solve Example 1 using the concurrency condition.

Solution

In limiting equilibrium the rough action R_F makes an angle λ with the

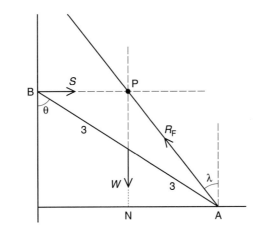

Figure 13.17

vertical, as shown in Figure 13.17. There are three forces S, W and R_F in equilibrium, and from the concurrency condition, their lines of action must pass through the same point. The lines of W and S must pass through the point P, therefore the line of action of R_F must also pass through P.

Now, $\tan\lambda = \mu = \tfrac{1}{4}$

Also, $PN = 6\cos\theta$ and $\dfrac{NA}{PN} = \tan\lambda$, where $NA = 3\sin\theta$

Hence, $\dfrac{3\sin\theta}{6\cos\theta} = \frac{1}{4}$, giving $\tan\theta = \frac{1}{2}$ and $\theta = 26.6°$ as before.

Example 3

A uniform rod AB of mass m and length l is smoothly jointed at A to a fixed horizontal wire AC. The end B is attached to one end of a string of length l. The other end of the string is attached to a bead of mass m at P, which can slide on the wire. The coefficient of friction between the bead and the wire is μ. If the system is in equilibrium with the rod inclined at an angle θ to the horizontal, find the tension in the string in terms of m and θ and

show that $\tan\theta \geq \dfrac{1}{5\mu}$.

Solution

Figure 13.18 shows the forces acting on the rod and the bead.

Notice that triangle ABC is isosceles so that we can identify the angles as shown.

Taking moments about the rod at A:

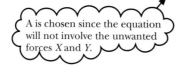

A is chosen since the equation will not involve the unwanted forces X and Y.

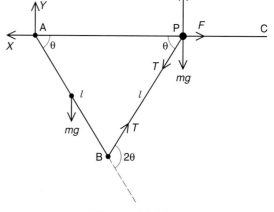

Figure 13.18

$mg\cos\theta\,(l/2) = T\sin 2\theta\,(l)$

$\Rightarrow \qquad T = \dfrac{mg\cos\theta}{3 \times 2\sin\theta\cos\theta} = \dfrac{mg}{4\sin\theta}$

Resolving forces on the bead,

vertically $\qquad R = T\sin\theta + mg = \dfrac{5mg}{4}$

horizontally $\qquad F = T\cos\theta = \dfrac{mg\cos\theta}{4\sin\theta} = \dfrac{mg}{4\tan\theta}$

Thus $\dfrac{F}{R} = \dfrac{1}{5\tan\theta} \leq \mu$, giving $\tan\theta > 1/5\mu$, as required.

Exercise 13.3

A1 A uniform ladder of length 4 m and weight W rests in equilibrium against a smooth vertical wall with its foot on rough horizontal ground. The coefficient of friction between the ladder and the ground is $\frac{1}{3}$. Find the angle between the ladder and the wall when the ladder is on the point of slipping.

Exercise 13.3 *continued*

A2 A uniform ladder of length 8 m and weight *W* rests against a smooth vertical wall and rough horizontal ground. The ladder will rest in limiting equilibrium when the angle between the ladder and the wall is 42°. Find the coefficient of friction for contact between the ladder and the ground.

A3 A uniform ladder of weight *W* and length 2*a* will just rest in equilibrium inclined at an angle θ to a smooth vertical wall with the lower end on rough horizontal ground. Find an expression for $\tan \theta$ in terms of μ, the coefficient of friction for contact between the ladder and the ground.

A4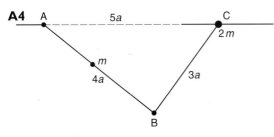

Figure 13.19

Figure 13.19 shows a uniform rod AB of mass *m* and length 4*a* freely hinged at A connected by an inextensible string of length 3*a* to a bead of mass 2*m* at C. AC = 5*a* and the bead is threaded on a rough horizontal wire. Find the tension in the string and the magnitude of the reaction at the hinge A in terms of *m* and *g*. If equilibrium is limiting, find the coefficient of friction for the contact between the bead and the wire.

A5 A uniform ladder AB of weight *W* rests in limiting equilibrium with A on rough horizontal ground and B against a smooth vertical wall. The coefficient of friction between the ladder and the ground is 0.3. Find, in terms of *W*, the contact force between the ladder and the wall and the magnitude of the resultant force between the ladder and the ground. Find also the angle of inclination of the ladder to the wall.

Questions **B1** to **B4** refer to a uniform ladder AB of mass 40 kg and length 6 m leaning at an angle of 50° to the horizontal in contact with rough horizontal ground at A and a vertical wall at B.

B1 If contact at B is smooth, what is the minimum coefficient of friction required at A for equilibrium?

B2 If the coefficient of friction for contact at B is 0.2, find the new minimum coefficient of friction for contact at A required for equilibrium.

B3 If the coefficient of friction for contact at A is 0.35, calculate the minimum value of the coefficient of friction required at B for equilibrium.

B4 If the coefficient of friction at A is 0.5, contact at B is smooth, and a man of 70 kg begins to climb the ladder, how far up will he get before the ladder slips? Take *g* as 10 m s^{-2}.

B5 A uniform rod is in limiting equilibrium with one end on rough horizontal ground. The upper end is supported by a string which is at right angles to the rod. If the rod is inclined at an angle θ to the horizontal and the coefficient of friction is μ, find an expression for μ in terms of θ.

B6 A uniform ladder of weight *W* and length 2*a* rests at an angle of 60° to the horizontal with one end on rough horizontal ground and the other end against a smooth vertical wall. A child of weight 4*W* climbs the ladder and just reaches the top before the ladder starts to slip. Find the coefficient of friction for contact between the ladder and the ground.

Revision questions

Take g as 9.8 m s^{-2} where necessary.

C1 A soccer crossbar AB is 7 m long and has a mass of 10 kg. It is supported by two vertical posts at its ends A and B. A goalkeeper of mass 80 kg hangs from the bar 2 m from the end A. Find the magnitude of the reactions at A and B.

C2 A uniform rod AB of length $4l$ and weight W is smoothly hinged at A. The upper end B is supported by a horizontal wire and a particle of weight $2W$ is attached to the rod at C, where AC = $3l$. The rod is inclined at an angle of 30° to the vertical. Find in terms of W:

   (a) the tension in the wire

   (b) the magnitude and direction of the force exerted on the rod by the hinge.

C3 A uniform beam AB of mass 80 kg rests in equilibrium at an angle θ to the horizontal where $\cos \theta = \frac{4}{5}$. The lower end A is on rough horizontal ground and a horizontal string is attached to the end B. Given that the frictional force is limiting, calculate the tension in the string and the coefficient of friction between the beam and the ground.

C4 A ladder of mass 30 kg rests at an angle of 50° to the horizontal with its upper end against a smooth vertical wall. The lower end is joined by a string to the junction of the wall and the floor, which is smooth. Find the tension in the string.

A boy of mass 60 kg now climbs three-quarters of the way up the ladder. Find the new tension in the string.

C5 Figure 13.20 shows a uniform ladder AB of mass 20 kg and length 10 m, whose lower end rests on rough horizontal ground. The ladder is inclined at 60° to the horizontal and is supported by a smooth rail at C where AC = 8 m. Find:

   (a) the force exerted on the rod at C

   (b) the vertical and horizontal components of the contact forces between the rod and the ground.

If the ladder is in limiting equilibrium, find the coefficient of friction for contact between the lower end of the ladder and the ground.

C6 A uniform rod AB has mass 2 kg and length 80 cm. The lower end, A, is smoothly hinged and the upper end is supported by a string at right angles to the rod. The rod is in equilibrium inclined at an angle of 20° to the horizontal. Calculate the tension in the string and the magnitude of the reaction at the hinge.

C7 A uniform ladder of mass 10 kg and length 6 m rests against a smooth vertical wall at an angle of 60° to the horizontal. The foot of the ladder is on rough horizontal ground. Find the contact force between the ladder and the ground when a man of mass 70 kg climbs 5 m up the ladder. Find the least value of μ to prevent slipping in this position.

C8 Figure 13.21 shows one half of a drawbridge which can be modelled by a uniform rod AB of length 10 m and mass 7 t smoothly hinged at B and supported at A by a cable fixed to a point 10 m vertically above B. The breaking strain of the cable is 8.5×10^4 N.

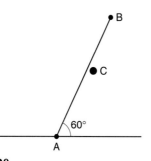

Figure 13.20

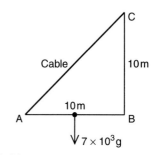

Figure 13.21

Find the maximum mass of a vehicle that can cross the bridge. (Hint: model the vehicle as a particle.)

C9 A uniform rod AB rests in equilibrium with its upper end resting against a smooth vertical wall. The rod is held at 60° to the horizontal by a string attached to the lower end B and to a point C on the wall vertically above A. Prove that $CA = \dfrac{\sqrt{3}}{2} AB$.

Chapter 14

STATICS (3)

14.1 Centre of mass of composite bodies

Key points

For a collection of particles of mass m_1, m_2, m_3, . . . , m_n in a plane at points with coordinates (x_1,y_1), (x_2,y_2), . . . , (x_n,y_n), the coordinates (x_G,y_G) of the centre of mass are given by:

$$Mx_G = \sum_1^n m_i x_i, \quad My_G = \sum_1^n m_i y_i, \text{ where } M = \sum_1^n m_i$$

In two dimensions a uniform body is one which has a constant surface density (mass per unit area). We use σ to represent the surface density, so that the mass M is given by $M = \sigma A$ where A is the area.

A simple composite body is one which is made up of uniform bodies whose COMs are known. The combined COM is found by treating the separate parts as particles concentrated at their COM.

In this chapter all bodies will be assumed to be uniform.

For uniform three-dimensional shapes we use ρ to represent the density (mass per unit volume), so that the mass M is given by $M = \rho V$ where V is the volume. The following two results will be useful.

Solid	Position of COM
Cone, height h	On the axis of symmetry $\frac{1}{4}h$ from the base
Hemisphere, radius a	On the axis of symmetry $\frac{3}{8}a$ from the circular base

Example 1

Find the position of the COM of the trapezium shown in Figure 14.1.

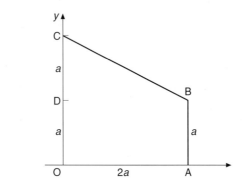

Figure 14.1

Solution

Let the surface density be σ.

It is often helpful to set out the working in a table:

Figure	Mass	x coordinate of COM	y coordinate of COM
Rectangle OABD	$2a^2\sigma$	a	$\frac{1}{2}a$
Triangle DBC	$a^2\sigma$	$\frac{1}{3}(2a)$	$\frac{1}{3}(a + a + 2a)$
Trapezium OABC	$3a^2\sigma$	x_G	y_G

Therefore $\quad 3a^2\sigma x_G = (2a^2\sigma)a + (a^2\sigma)(\frac{2}{3}a)$

giving $\qquad\qquad x_G = \frac{8}{9}a$

Similarly $\quad 3a^2\sigma y_G = (2a^2\sigma)\frac{1}{2}a + (a^2\sigma)\frac{4}{3}a$

giving $\qquad\qquad y_G = \frac{7}{9}a$

> The centre of mass of a triangular lamina with vertices $(x_1, y_1), (x_2, y_2), (x_3, y_3)$ is $\frac{1}{3}(x_1 + x_2 + x_3, y_1 + y_2 + y_3)$.

Example 2

The base of a lampshade is made in the shape of a frustum of height h with base radius $2a$ and upper radius a (Figure 14.2(a)). Find the height of the COM above the base.

Figure 14.2a

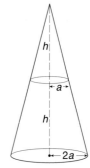

Figure 14.2b

Solution

The frustum is formed by removing a cone of height h base radius a from a cone of height $2h$, base radius $2a$ as shown in Figure 14.2(b).

Let the density be ρ. As before we set out the calculation in a table.

Solid	Mass	Height of COM above base of large cone
Large cone	$\frac{1}{3}\pi(2a)^2 2h\rho = \frac{8}{3}\pi a^2\rho$	$\frac{1}{4}(2h) = h/2$
Small cone	$\frac{1}{3}\pi(a)^2 h\rho = \frac{1}{3}\pi a^2\rho$	$h + \frac{1}{4}h = \frac{5}{4}h$
Frustum	$\frac{7}{3}\pi a^2\rho$	y_G

Therefore $\quad (\frac{7}{3}\pi a^2\rho)y_G + (\frac{1}{3}\pi a^2\rho)(\frac{5}{4}h) = (\frac{8}{3}\pi a^2\rho)h/2$

giving $\qquad\qquad\qquad \frac{7}{3}y_G + \frac{5}{12}h = \frac{4}{3}h$

and $\qquad\qquad\qquad\qquad y_G = \frac{11}{28}h$

Exercise 14.1

A1 Find the coordinates of the COM of each of the systems of particles in Figure 14.3.

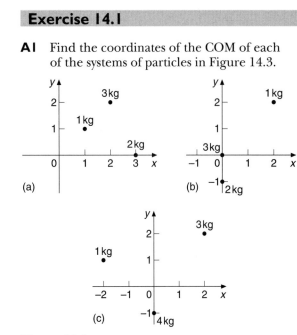

(a)

(b)

(c)

Figure 14.3

A2 The framework of a kite is made from a series of uniform rods, as shown in Figure 14.4. Each rod has mass *m* per unit length. Find the distance of the COM from O.

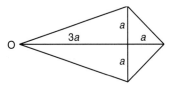

Figure 14.4

A3 A squash racket of mass 200 g and total length 70 cm consists of a handle of mass 150 g whose centre of mass is 20 cm from the end and a frame whose centre of mass is 55 cm from the end. Find the distance of the centre of mass of the racket from the end of the handle.

A4 Find the *x* and *y* coordinates of the centres of mass of the shapes shown in Figure 14.5.

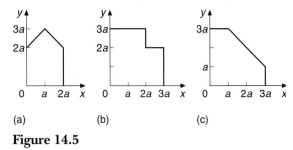

(a)　　　　(b)　　　　(c)

Figure 14.5

A5 Two particles of masses 2 kg and 3 kg are placed at the ends of a uniform rod AB of length 2 m and mass 1 kg. Find the distance of the COM from the end A of the rod.

A6 Figure 14.6 shows a lampbase of uniform density. Find the height of the centre of mass above the base.

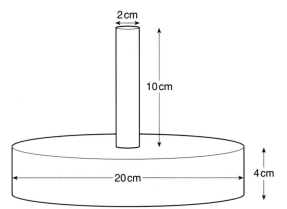

Figure 14.6

A7 Figure 14.7 shows a uniform lamina formed by removing a square of side *a* from the square of side 3*a*. Find the distance of the COM from AB.

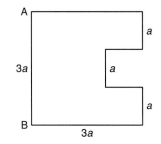

Figure 14.7

A8 Figure 14.8 shows a uniform lamina in the shape of a kite. Find the distance of the COM from the point A.

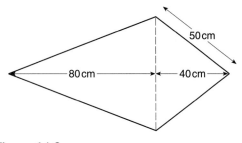

Figure 14.8

Exercise 14.1   *continued*

B1   An ear-ring is made by removing a circle of radius 3 cm from a circle of radius 4 cm, as shown in Figure 14.9. Find the *x* coordinate of the COM of the ear-ring.

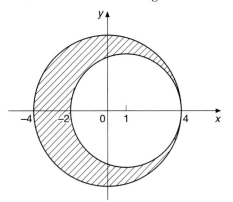

Figure 14.9

B2   The solid in Figure 14.10 is made by fixing a cylinder of height *h* and radius *a* to the top of a frustum of the same material. Find the height of the COM above the base in terms of *h*.

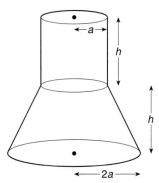

Figure 14.10

B3   A hemispherical bowl has outer radius 10 cm and thickness 1 cm, as shown in Figure 14.11. Find the height of the COM above the circular base.

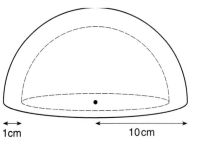

Figure 14.11

B4   Figure 14.12 shows a child's toy which consists of a cone of height *a* and base radius *a* fixed on to a hemisphere of radius *a*. Find the distance of the COM from O.

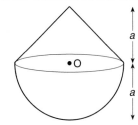

Figure 14.12

B5   Figure 14.13 shows a uniform lamina in the shape of an isosceles trapezium. Find the distance of the COM from AB.

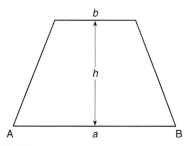

Figure 14.13

B6   A rectangular lamina ABCD is folded along EF and GF, as shown in Figure 14.14. Find the distance of the COM of the resulting figure from AB.

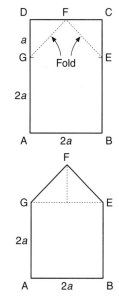

Figure 14.14

14.2 Use of integration to find Centres of Mass

Key points

Laminas

The coordinates (x_G, y_G) of the centre of mass (COM) of the lamina in figure 14.15 are given by:

$$x_G = \frac{\int_a^b xy\,dx}{\int_a^b y\,dx} \qquad y_G = \frac{\int_a^b \frac{1}{2}y^2\,dx}{\int_a^b y\,dx}$$

Notice that σ has been excluded since it cancels out.

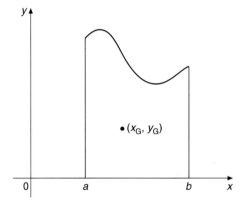

Figure 14.15

Volumes of revolution

The centre of mass of the solid shown in Figure 14.16 lies on the axis of symmetry, and if this is the *x*-axis, the *x* coordinate of the COM is given by:

$$x_G = \frac{\int_a^b xy^2\,dx}{\int_a^b y^2\,dx}$$

Notice that ρ and π have been omitted since they cancel out.

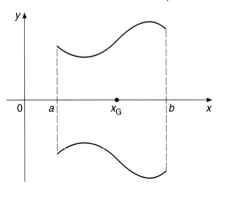

Figure 14.16

Example 1

The rudder of a boat is in the shape of the curve $y = 16 - x^4$, as shown in Figure 14.17. Find the position of the COM.

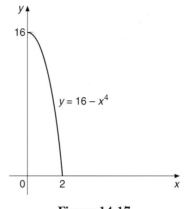

$y = 16 - x^4$

Figure 14.17

Solution

Treating the rudder as a uniform lamina:

$$\int_0^2 y\,dx = \int_0^2 (16 - x^4)\,dx$$

$$= [16x - x^5/5]_0^2 = 128/5$$

$$\int_0^2 xy\,dx = \int_0^2 (16x - x^5)\,dx$$

$$= [8x^2 - x^6/6]_0^2 = 64/3$$

giving $\quad x_G = \dfrac{64/3}{128/5} = 5/6$

$$\int_0^2 \frac{y^2}{2}\,dx = \int_0^2 (128 - 16x^4 + x^8/2)\,dx = [128x - 16x^5/5 + x^9/18]_0^2$$

$$= 8192/45$$

Therefore $y_G = \dfrac{8192/45}{128/5} = 64/9$

Example 2

A solid paperweight is made by rotating the curve $y = \sqrt{x}$ through 4 right angles about the x-axis between $x = 0$ and $x = 4$ (Figure 14.18). Find the distance of the COM from O.

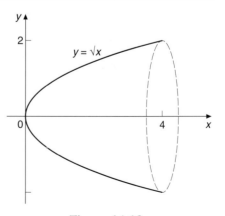

$y = \sqrt{x}$

Figure 14.18

Solution

$$\int_0^4 y^2\,dx = \int_0^4 x\,dx = \left[\frac{x^2}{2}\right]_0^4 = 8$$

$$\int_0^4 xy^2\,dx = \int_0^4 x^2\,dx = \left[\frac{x^3}{3}\right]_0^4 = 64/3$$

$$\Rightarrow x_G = \frac{64/3}{8} = 8/3$$

Exercise 14.2

A1 Find the coordinates of the COM of the uniform lamina formed by the curve $y = x^2$ and the lines $x = 1$ and $y = 0$.

A2 Find the coordinates of the COM of the uniform lamina bounded by the curve $y = \sqrt{x}$ and the lines $x = 1$ and $y = 0$.

A3 Find the coordinates of the COM of the uniform lamina bounded between the curves $y = x^2$ and $y = \sqrt{x}$.

A4 Find the coordinates of the COM of the uniform lamina formed between the curve $y = 4 - x^2$ and the positive x and y axes.

A5 Prove that the COM of a uniform solid hemisphere of radius a is $3a/8$ above the centre of the base.

A6 Prove that the COM of a uniform solid cone of height h is $h/4$ above the centre of the base.

In questions **A7** to **A10** find the coordinates of the COM of the uniform solid formed when each of the regions with the given boundaries is rotated through $360°$ about the x-axis.

A7 $y = x^2$, $x = 1$ and $y = 0$.

A8 $y = x$, $x = 1$ and $y = 0$.

A9 $y = \sqrt{(a^2 - x^2)}$, $x = 0$ and $y = 0$.

A10 $y = 4 - x^2$, $x = 0$ and $y = 0$.

B1 Find the coordinates of the COM of the uniform lamina between the curve $y = 8 - x^3$ and the positive x and y axes.

B2 Find the coordinates of the COM of a uniform semicircular lamina contained between the curve $y = \sqrt{(a^2 - x^2)}$ and the x-axis.

B3 Find the coordinates of the centroid of the uniform lamina in the shape of a quadrant contained between the curve $y = \sqrt{(a^2 - x^2)}$ and the positive x and y axes.

B4 Find the coordinates of the COM of the region enclosed between the curve $y = 1/x$ and the lines $y = 0$, $x = 1$ and $x = 2$.

B5 Find the coordinates of the COM of the region contained between the curve $y = \sin x$ and the x-axis between $x = 0$ and $x = \pi$.

B6 A paperweight is made by rotating the curve $y = \sin x$ through 2π radians about the x-axis between $x = 0$ and $x = \pi/2$. Find the x coordinate of the COM.

14.3 The equilibrium of a freely suspended body

Key points

If a body is freely suspended, it rests in equilibrium under the action of its weight force W acting downwards through the centre of gravity and the tension T in the supporting string (see Figure 14.19). These two forces must be equal and opposite and act in the same line. Therefore the centre of gravity (and the centre of mass) will be vertically below the point of suspension.

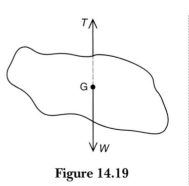

Figure 14.19

Example 1

Figure 14.20(a) shows a uniform rectangular sheet ABCD where
AB = 6 cm, BC = 4 cm and a square of edge 2 cm has been removed from
the corner at A. The sheet is suspended by means of a string attached at
C. Find the angle that CB makes with the vertical in equilibrium.

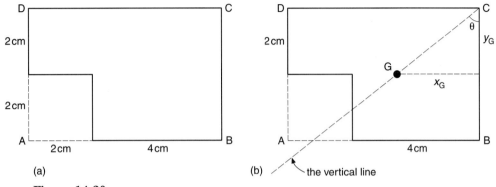

(a)   (b)

Figure 14.20

Solution

If G is the COM of the body, the angle we want is BCG = θ, since CG will
be vertical. Let x_G be the distance of G from BC and let y_G be the distance
of G from CD, as shown in Figure 14.20(b).

Let the surface density be σ.

Shape	Mass	Distance of COM from CB	Distance of COM from DC
ABCD	24σ	3	2
APQR	4σ	5	3
PBCDRQ	20σ	x_G	y_G

Therefore $(20\sigma)x_G + (4\sigma)5 = (24\sigma)3$

giving $20x_G + 20 = 72$

and $x_G = 2.6$

Similarly $(20\sigma)y_G + (4\sigma)3 = (24\sigma)2$

gives $y_G = 1.8$

and $\tan\theta = x_G/y_G$ giving $\theta = 55.3°$

Example 2

Two uniform rods AB and BC each of mass M and length $2a$ are rigidly
joined at B where ABC = 90°. The system hangs in equilibrium from A.

(a) Show that AB makes an angle α with the vertical, where $\tan\alpha = \frac{1}{3}$.

(b) If a mass m is attached at C, AB makes an angle β with the vertical,
where $\tan\beta = \frac{1}{2}$. Find m in terms of M.

Solution

(a) By symmetry, the centre of mass G in Figure 14.21(a) is at the midpoint of PQ, where P and Q are the positions of the COM of the rods. In equilibrium AG is vertical and

$$\tan \alpha = \frac{a/2}{3a/2} = \tfrac{1}{3}$$

(b) In this case AQ must be vertical and in Figure 14.21(b),

$$\tan \beta = \frac{a}{2a} = \tfrac{1}{2}$$

In equilibrium, taking moments about AQ

$$Md_1 = md_2$$

$$\Rightarrow \quad Ma \sin \beta = ma \cos \beta$$

and $\quad m = M \tan \beta$

$$\Rightarrow \quad m = \frac{M}{2}$$

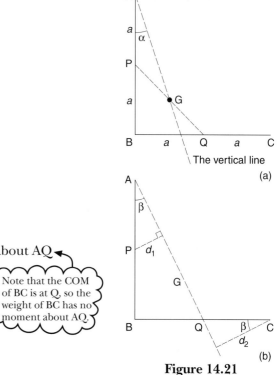

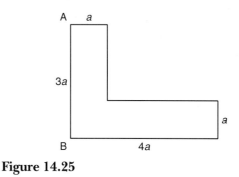

Note that the COM of BC is at Q, so the weight of BC has no moment about AQ.

Figure 14.21

Exercise 14.3

In each of questions **A1** to **A6** a uniform lamina is freely suspended from point A. Find the inclination of AB to the vertical in equilibrium.

A1 See Figure 14.22.

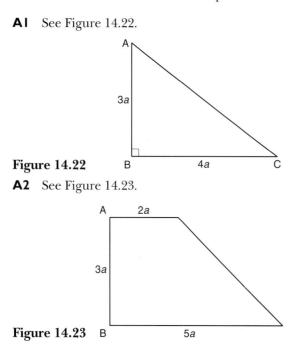

Figure 14.22

A2 See Figure 14.23.

Figure 14.23

A3 See Figure 14.24.

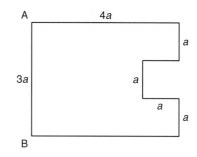

Figure 14.24

A4 See Figure 14.25.

Figure 14.25

Exercise 14.3 *continued*

A5 See Figure 14.26.

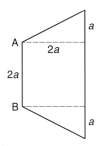

Figure 14.26

A6 See Figure 14.27.

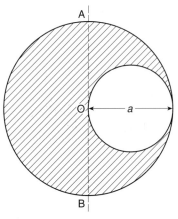

Figure 14.27

B1 The frustum in Example 2 of Section 14.1 is freely suspended from a point A on the rim of the upper circular face. Find the angle of inclination of this face to the vertical in terms of a and h.

B2 A uniform rod 13 cm long of weight W is suspended from a fixed point by two strings fastened to its ends. The lengths of the strings are 5 cm and 12 cm. Find:

(a) the inclination of the rod to the vertical

(b) the tensions in the two strings in terms of W.

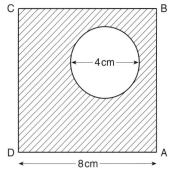

Figure 14.28

B3 A circular hole of radius 2 cm is cut from a uniform square lamina, as shown in Figure 14.28.
The centre of the hole is 3 cm from AB and BC. The lamina is freely suspended from A. Find the inclination of AB to the vertical.

B4 A uniform L-shaped wire ABC is suspended from A. If AB:BC = 3:4, find the inclination of AB to the vertical.

B5 Figure 14.29 shows a uniform circular lamina of radius 12 cm with two circular holes cut from it. One is of radius 3 cm with its centre 8 cm along OA, the other is of radius 4 cm with its centre at the midpoint of OB where OA is perpendicular to OB. The lamina is freely suspended from A. Find the inclination of OA to the vertical.

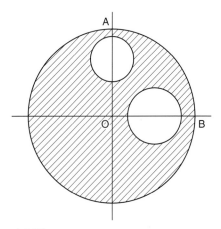

Figure 14.29

14.4 Sliding and toppling

Key points

Figure 14.30 shows three bodies resting on a horizontal plane.

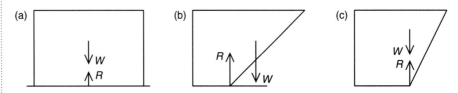

Figure 14.30

The body in Figure 14.30(a) is in equilibrium under the action of the weight force and the normal contact force.

The body in Figure 14.30(b) cannot remain in equilibrium. Since the line of action of W is outside the area of contact of the body with the plane, it will topple over.

The position in Figure 14.30(c) is the case of limiting equilibrium, where the line of action of W just passes through the edge of the area of contact of the body with the plane.

Example 1

A lampbase consists of a uniform cylinder of height $40r$ and radius r attached to a disc of the same material of radius $8r$ and thickness $2r$. It stands on a plane inclined at an angle α to the horizontal which is sufficiently rough to prevent slipping. Show that the body will topple if $\tan \alpha > \frac{4}{3}$.

Figure 14.31

Solution

If G is the COM of the body, equilibrium will be limiting when the vertical line through G passes through the edge of the base, as shown in Figure 14.31. We need to find the height of G above the bottom of the base.

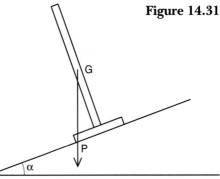

Object	Volume	Height of COM above PQ
Disc	$\pi(8r)^2 2r = 128\pi r^3$	r
Rod	$\pi r^2 .40r = 40\pi r^3$	$22r$
Lampbase	$168\pi r^3$	y_G

Thus, $168 y_G = 128r + 880r$ giving $y_G = 1008r/168 = 6r$

On the point of toppling, $\tan \alpha = \dfrac{8r}{6r} = \frac{4}{3}$

Thus, the object will topple if $\tan \alpha > \frac{4}{3}$.

If the plane had not been sufficiently rough equilibrium could have been broken by sliding before toppling occurred.

Example 2

A cuboid of height ka has a square base of side a in contact with a rough inclined plane. The inclination of the plane is gradually increased. Show that the cuboid will slide before it topples if $\mu < \dfrac{1}{k}$, where μ is the coefficient of friction for contact between the cuboid and the plane.

Solution

Suppose the cuboid does not topple. Consider the forces on the block shown in Figure 14.32(a).

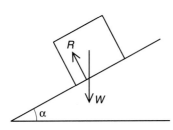

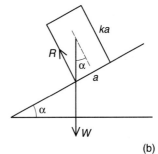

Figure 14.32 (a) (b)

Resolving up the plane $F = W \sin \alpha$

Perpendicular to the plane $R = W \cos \alpha$

Thus $F/R = \tan \alpha \le \mu$

Hence sliding will not occur provided $\tan \alpha \le \mu$.

If the cuboid does not slide, it will be on the point of toppling in the position shown in Figure 14.32(b).

In this case, $\tan \alpha = \dfrac{a/2}{ka/2} = \dfrac{1}{k}$

Toppling will not occur provided $\tan \alpha \le \dfrac{1}{k}$

Hence, sliding occurs before toppling if $\mu < \dfrac{1}{k}$.

Exercise 14.4

A1 A uniform cube rests in equilibrium with one face in contact with a rough horizontal plane. The plane is gradually tilted. Find whether the cube slides before it topples, if the coefficient of friction between the cube and the plane is

(a) $\frac{1}{2}$ (b) $\frac{4}{5}$.

A2 A uniform equilateral triangular lamina rests vertically with one edge on a rough horizontal plane. A horizontal force is applied to the upper vertex parallel to the base and is gradually increased. Find the minimum value of the coefficient of friction between the lamina and the plane if it topples before it slides.

B1 A lamina is formed by removing an isosceles triangle from the bottom corner of a square of side $2a$, as shown in Figure 14.33. Find, in terms of a, the maximum value of x for which the lamina will stand in equilibrium on the plane.

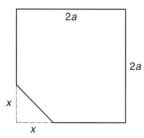

Figure 14.33

B2 A uniform cuboid of square base of side a and height $4a$ is at rest on a rough horizontal plane inclined at an angle α to

the horizontal. The coefficient of friction between the cuboid and the ramp is μ. Find the minimum values for μ and α for which the cuboid will topple rather than slide.

B3 A uniform isosceles triangular prism of base 12 cm and vertical height 8 cm rests on a rough horizontal table, as shown in Figure 14.34. A horizontal force P is applied to the top of the prism and is

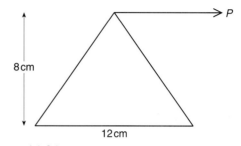

Figure 14.34

increased gradually. The coefficient of friction between the prism and the plane is $\frac{1}{2}$. Will equilibrium be broken by sliding or toppling?

B4 A uniform solid cylinder has height 10 cm and base radius 6 cm. It stands on its circular base on a rough plane inclined at an angle α to the horizontal, and the coefficient of friction between the cylinder and the plane is μ. Determine whether the cylinder topples, slides or remains in equilibrium in the following cases:

(a) $\mu = \frac{1}{3}$, $\tan \alpha = \frac{1}{2}$

(b) $\mu = \frac{5}{6}$, $\tan \alpha = \frac{4}{5}$.

Revision questions

C1 A uniform square plate ABCD has mass $10M$. Particles of mass M, $2M$, $3M$ and $4M$ are attached at A, B, C and D respectively and the system hangs freely from D. Find the inclination of DA with the vertical.

C2 Figure 14.35 shows a uniform solid made by fixing a cone of height h on top of a cylinder of the same base radius and height $2h/3$. When the solid is freely suspended

from B, the line AB is horizontal.

Prove that $\tan \alpha = \sqrt{5}/6$.

C3 Three uniform rods, AB, BC and CA of lengths $3a$, $5a$ and $4a$ are smoothly hinged together to form a triangle. Each rod has mass m per unit length and the frame is freely suspended from A. A particle of mass km is attached at B and, in equilibrium, BC is horizontal. Show that $k = 4$.

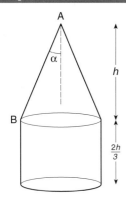

Figure 14.35

C4 Figure 14.36 shows a frustum of height h cut from a cone of height $2h$. It rests on a rough horizontal plane. Prove that it will not topple provided $\cos^2 \theta > 28/45$.

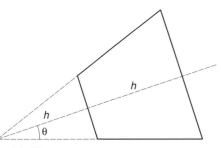

Figure 14.36

C5 A uniform lamina ABC is suspended from A, as shown in Figure 14.37. The mass of the lamina is M and a mass m is attached at B so that, in equilibrium, BC is horizontal. Find m in terms of M.

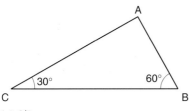

Figure 14.37

C6 Figure 14.38 shows a uniform lamina which is a square of side $2a$ with a square of side a removed from one corner. The plane is sufficiently rough to prevent sliding. What is the maximum value of α, if the lamina does not topple over?

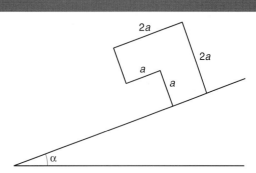

Figure 14.38

C7 A uniform hemispherical bowl has an inner radius a and an outer radius $2a$. AOB is a diameter of the flat surface, as shown in Figure 14.39. Show that the COM is $45a/56$ below O. If the bowl is suspended freely from A, find the angle that AB makes with the vertical.

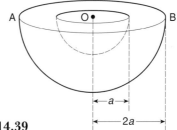

Figure 14.39

C8 Figure 14.40 shows a uniform lamina of surface density σ. Find the height of the COM above OA.

The lamina is suspended freely from O and a particle of mass $k\sigma a^2$ is attached at A. The system hangs in equilibrium with OB vertical. Find the value of k.

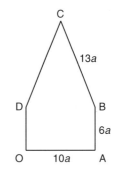

Figure 14.40

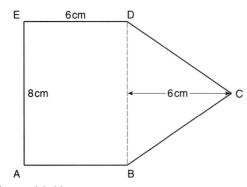

Figure 14.41

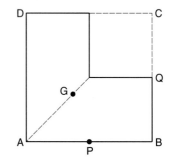

Figure 14.42

C9 Figure 14.41 shows a uniform lamina ABCDE of mass M, where BCD is an isosceles triangle. Find the distance of the COM from AE. When the lamina is freely suspended from D with a particle of mass m attached at C, DB is vertical. Prove that $m = 2M/9$.

C10 ABCD is a uniform square lamina of side $2a$ and mass $4M$ with a square side a removed from the corner at C (see Figure 14.42). G is the COM of the lamina.

(a) Prove that $AG = \frac{5}{6}a\sqrt{2}$.

(b) The lamina is suspended freely from P, the midpoint of AB. Find the angle AB makes with the vertical.

(c) When a particle of mass m is attached to point Q, the system hangs freely from P with AB horizontal. Find m in terms of M.

Chapter 15

SIMPLE HARMONIC MOTION

Key points

Simple Harmonic Motion (SHM) occurs when a particle moves in a straight line under the influence of a force which attracts it to a fixed point, such that the magnitude of the force is proportional to the displacement from the fixed point.

In Figure 15.1, SHM will occur if $F = kx$, where x is the distance of a particle P from the fixed point O.

Figure 15.1

Applying N2 to the particle: $F = m\ddot{x} = -kx$

Writing the acceleration, $\ddot{x}$, in the form $v\dfrac{dv}{dx}$, we get $\quad v\dfrac{dv}{dx} = -\omega^2 x$

where $\omega^2 = k/m$

Separating the variables and integrating this equation with respect to x with the condition that $v = 0$ when $x = a$, we get

$$v^2 = \omega^2(a^2 - x^2)$$

Thus, $v = \dfrac{dx}{dt} = \omega\sqrt{(a^2 - x^2)}$

Separating the variables and integrating, we obtain

$$x = a\cos(\omega t + \epsilon) \text{ or } x = a\sin(\omega t + \epsilon)$$

where ϵ is a constant of integration determined by the initial conditions and is sometimes referred to as the **phase angle**.

Either form may be used, and our choice usually depends on the initial conditions given.

The **period of periodic time** (the time for a complete oscillation) is given

by: $T = \dfrac{2\pi}{\omega}$ and its **amplitude** (maximum distance from O) is given by a.

Summary of SHM

Basic equation	$\ddot{x} = -\omega^2 x$
Periodic time	$T = \dfrac{2\pi}{\omega}$
General displacement	$x = a\sin(\omega t + \epsilon)$ or $x = a\cos(\omega t + \epsilon)$ where a is the amplitude and ϵ is called the phase angle.
Speed	$v^2 = \omega^2(a^2 - x^2)$

Example 1

A particle is moving with SHM in a straight line about a fixed point O. When it is 3 m from O its speed is 4 m s^{-1} and the magnitude of its acceleration is 10 m s^{-2}. Calculate:

(a)   the amplitude and period of the motion

(b)   the maximum speed of the particle during the motion.

> Note that this applies both when the particle is moving towards and away from O since v is squared in the equation.

Solution

(a)   Since $v = 4$ when $x = 3$, we can use the equation $v^2 = \omega^2(a^2 - x^2)$ to
      give $16 = \omega^2(a^2 - 9)$ \hfill (1)

The magnitude of the acceleration is $\omega^2 x$.

Therefore $10 = \omega^2 \times 3$, giving $\omega = 1.83$ \hfill (2)

Substituting for ω^2 in equation (1) $(a^2 - 9) = 4.8$, so $a^2 = 13.8$

Hence, the amplitude a is 3.71 m and the period $T = \dfrac{2\pi}{\omega} = 3.44$ s.

(b)   The particle reaches its maximum speed when the acceleration is zero, which occurs at O, when $x = 0$.

Hence $v_{max} = a\omega = (1.83 \times 3.71) = 6.78$.

The maximum speed is 6.78 m s^{-1}.

Exercise 15.1

A1   A particle performs SHM about a point O. When the particle is 2 m away from O its speed is 6 m s^{-1} and its acceleration is 10 m s^{-2}. Calculate the amplitude, period and maximum speed of the particle.

A2   A particle starts at a point O, performing SHM of amplitude 0.3 m, centre O and period $\frac{1}{4}\pi$ s. Calculate the time taken:

(a)   to reach a point 0.2 m from O

(b)   to reduce its speed to half its maximum value.

Exercise 15.1 *continued*

A3 A particle performs SHM at a rate of 4 oscillations per second and its greatest acceleration is 25 m s^{-2}. Calculate the amplitude of the motion.

A4 A particle moves with SHM so that its greatest speed is 5 m s^{-1} and its greatest acceleration is 8 m s^{-2}. Calculate the period and amplitude of the motion.

A5 A particle is moving with SHM about a fixed point O. The period is 3π s and it passes through a point A, 2.5 m from O, with speed 4 m s^{-1} away from O. Calculate the time that elapses before it is next at A.

A6 A particle makes 8 oscillations per second and has an amplitude of 6 cm. Calculate the maximum acceleration of the particle.

B1 A particle performs SHM about a point O and its displacement, x, is related to the time, t, by the equation $x = \sin \omega t$. If the speed at time t is v and the acceleration is a, draw graphs of:

(a) x against t (b) v against t
(c) a against t (d) v against x
(e) a against x.

B2 A particle moves with SHM along the x-axis. The end points are at $x = a$ and

$x = b$. The maximum speed during the motion is u. Show that the period is given by

$$\frac{\pi(b - a)}{u}.$$

B3 A particle of mass m is moving in a straight line under the action of a force $F = 8x$ directed towards a fixed point O, where x is the distance from O. If the speed of the particle is zero when $x = a$, use the work–energy equation to deduce the speed of the particle at O in terms of a.

B4 A particle of mass 0.5 kg moves along the x-axis under the influence of a force which is directed towards O and has magnitude $\omega^2 x$. The amplitude of the motion is a. When $x = \frac{1}{2}a\sqrt{3}$ and the particle is moving away from O, it receives an impulse $\omega^2 a$ in the positive x direction. Show that the new motion is SHM about O with amplitude $a\sqrt{3}$.

B5 A particle moves in a straight line with simple harmonic motion of period 8 s about a fixed point O on the line. At a certain time it is at a distance 2 m from O and 2 s later it is still on the same side of O but is now 5 m from O.

(a) Find the amplitude of the motion.

(b) Find the displacement and speed of the particle after a further 2 sec.

15.2 Oscillatory systems

Example 1

The upper end of an elastic string of natural length 30 cm is attached to a fixed point O. When a particle of mass 2 kg is attached to it, it extends by a length of 10 cm and hangs in equilibrium. If the mass is pulled down a further 5 cm and released, prove that the motion is simple harmonic and find its period. Take g as 10 m s^{-2}.

Solution

Suppose the mass is in equilibrium at the point E in Figure 15.2(a) and let the modulus of elasticity of the string be λ. ON is the natural length of the string. Using N2 and Hooke's law, we get

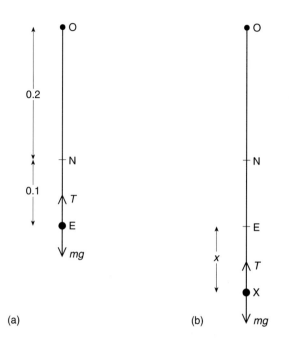

(a)   (b)

Figure 15.2

$$T = \lambda \frac{0.1}{0.3} = 2\,g$$

giving $\lambda = 60$

Suppose the particle is at a distance x below E, as shown in Figure 15.2(b).

Using N2, $m\ddot{x} = mg - T$

giving $\qquad 2\ddot{x} = 2g - \dfrac{6g}{0.3}(x + 0.1)$

and $\ddot{x} = -100x$, which is the equation for SHM.

Since the particle is released from rest, i.e. $\dot{x} = 0$ when $t = 0$, we choose the form of solution $x = a\cos(\omega t + \epsilon)$, where $\omega^2 = 100$.

So, $\dot{x} = a\cos(10t + \epsilon)$ and $\dot{x} = -10a\sin(10t + \epsilon)$

Since $\dot{x} = 0$ when $t = 0$, $10a\sin\epsilon = 0$, and as $a \neq 0$, $\epsilon = 0$, giving

$\dot{x} = a\cos 10t$

The second initial condition is $x = 0.05$ when $t = 0$, giving $a = 0.05$ and leading to the solution $x = 0.05\cos 10t$

Now, the minimum value of x is -0.05 when $\cos 10t = -1$, and the minimum length of the string is $0.4 - 0.05 = 0.35 > 0.3$.

Thus, the particle does not reach N and the string remains taut

throughout the motion, which is simple harmonic with period $\dfrac{2\pi}{\omega} = \dfrac{\pi}{5}$.

Example 2

If the mass in Example 1 is pulled down a distance 20 cm below the equilibrium position and released, find:

(a) the time taken between the particle being released and the string first becoming slack

(b) how high the particle rises

(c) the time for a complete oscillation.

Take g as 10 m s^{-2}.

Solution

(a) As in Example 1 we obtain the equation: $\ddot{x} = -100x$

So x is given by $x = a \cos(\omega t + \epsilon)$, where $\omega^2 = 100$.

The initial conditions are $t = 0$ when $x = 0.2$ and $\dot{x} = 0$, which lead to $a = 0.2$ and $\epsilon = 0$.

Therefore $x = 0.2 \cos 10t$

The equation of motion and the formula for x hold for as long as the string remains stretched, i.e. for $x > -0.1$.

When the string becomes slack: $-0.1 = 0.2 \cos 10t$

giving

$$t = \frac{1}{10} \cos^{-1}\left(-\frac{1}{2}\right)$$

Hence the string becomes slack when $t = \dfrac{1}{10}\left[\pi - \dfrac{1}{3}\pi\right] = \dfrac{1}{15}\pi$

(b) Suppose the particle rises to a point H, as shown in Figure 15.3.

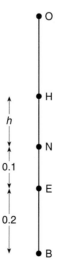

Figure 15.3

Between the lowest point, B, and the natural length position, N, the motion is SHM, so we may apply the equation $v^2 = \omega^2(a^2 - x^2)$, where $a = 0.2$ and $\omega^2 = 100$.

At N, $x = -0.1$ and we obtain $v^2 = 3$.

The motion from N to H is free motion under gravity.

Using $v^2 = u^2 - 2gh$, with $v = 0$ and $u^2 = 3$, we get $h = 3/20$.

The particle rises to a height of 15 cm above N.

(c) The time for the motion from N to H is given by $v = u - gt$ which leads to $t = 0.1\sqrt{3}$

Thus the total time from B to H is $\pi/15 + 0.1\sqrt{3} \approx 0.382$

The motion will be symmetrical, so the time for a complete oscillation will be 0.764 s.

Example 3

A particle of mass 0.5 kg is attached to one end of an elastic string of natural length 2 m and modulus of elasticity 16 N. The other end of the string is attached to a fixed point O on a smooth horizontal table. The particle is projected from O along the table with a speed of 3 m s^{-1}. Find:

(a) the maximum length of the string

(b) the time taken for the particle to come to instantaneous rest for the first time.

Solution

(a) Suppose e is the extension when the particle comes to rest, as shown in Figure 15.4. Using the energy equation $KE_O = EPE_P$

Figure 15.4

$$\frac{1}{2}0.5 \times 3^2 = \frac{16e^2}{2 \times 2}$$

giving $e = \frac{3}{4}$

Hence the maximum length of the string is $2\frac{3}{4}$ m.

(b) The time from O to N is $\frac{2}{3}$ s, since the speed is constant.

Consider the motion from N to P.

Using N2 on the particle at point X,　$0.5\ddot{x} = \dfrac{-16x}{2}$

leading to $\ddot{x} = -16x$, which is the equation for SHM.

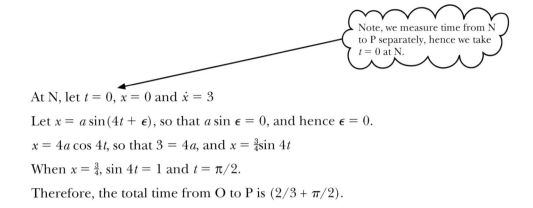

At N, let $t = 0$, $x = 0$ and $\dot{x} = 3$

Let $x = a \sin(4t + \epsilon)$, so that $a \sin \epsilon = 0$, and hence $\epsilon = 0$.

$x = 4a \cos 4t$, so that $3 = 4a$, and $x = \frac{3}{4}\sin 4t$

When $x = \frac{3}{4}$, $\sin 4t = 1$ and $t = \pi/2$.

Therefore, the total time from O to P is $(2/3 + \pi/2)$.

Example 4

Two identical elastic strings each of natural length 10 cm and modulus of elasticity 4 N are fastened to a particle of mass 100 g. Their other ends are attached to two fixed points P and Q which are 40 cm apart and are at rest on a smooth horizontal table. The particle is pulled aside from O, the midpoint of PQ, to a point R where PR = 15 cm. The particle is then released.

(a) Show that the motion is simple harmonic and find its period and amplitude.

(b) When the particle is at O and moving towards Q the string OQ is cut. Find how far the particle moves towards Q before first coming to rest.

Solution

(a) Let x be the displacement to the left of O at time t, as shown in Figure 15.5(a). Let the tensions in the two strings be T_1 and T_2.

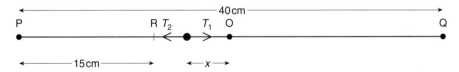

Figure 15.5a

Applying N2 to the particle $m\ddot{x} = T_2 - T_1$

Applying Hooke's law to the strings

$$T_1 = \frac{4}{0.1}(x + 0.1) = 40(x + 0.1)$$

$$T_2 = \frac{4}{0.1}(0.1 - x) = 40(0.1 - x)$$

So

$0.1\ddot{x} = 40(0.1 - x) - 40(x + 0.1)$

giving $\ddot{x} = -800x$

Since both strings are taut at R, they will remain so throughout the motion, which is SHM. So

$x = a \cos (\omega t + \epsilon)$ with $\omega^2 = 800$

Initially, $x = 0.05$, $\dot{x} = 0$ when $t = 0$, giving $a = 0.05$ and $\epsilon = 0$

Therefore $x = 0.05 \cos \sqrt{800}\, t$

The period is $\dfrac{2\pi}{\omega} = \dfrac{\pi}{\sqrt{200}} = \dfrac{\pi}{10\sqrt{2}}$

(b)   If v is the speed at O, $v = a\omega = 0.05 \times \sqrt{800} = \sqrt{2}$

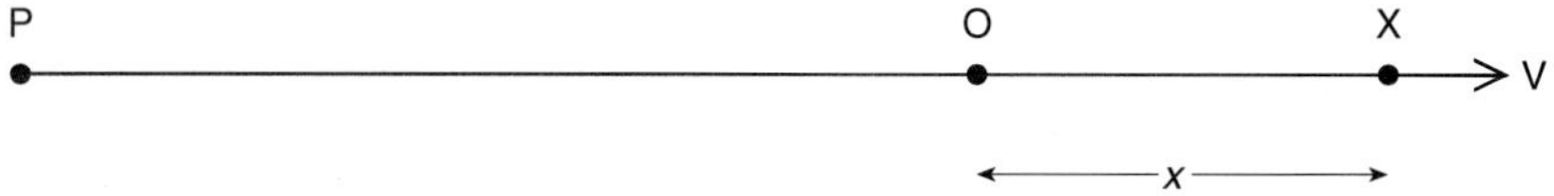

Figure 15.5b

After the string OQ is cut, the speed v at the point X in Figure 15.5(b) can be found using the energy equation, since the table is smooth.

$$KE_O + EPE_O = KE_X + EPE_X$$

$$\frac{1}{2}(0.1)2 + \frac{1}{2}\frac{4}{0.1}\,0.1^2 = \frac{1}{2}\,0.1v^2 + \frac{1}{2}\frac{4}{0.1}\,(0.1 + x)^2$$

The particle first comes to rest when $v = 0$, which leads to

$$0.3 = 20\,(0.2 + x)^2$$

giving $x = 0.0225$, i.e. the particle moves approximately 2 cm from O towards Q.

Exercise 15.2

Take g as 10 m s^{-2} where necessary.

A1   One end of an elastic string of natural length 1.5 m and modulus of elasticity 15 N is attached to a fixed point O and the other is attached to a particle of mass 400 g. Find the extension in the string when it is hanging vertically in equilibrium. The particle is pulled down a further 20 cm. Find:

(a)   the time taken for it to return to its initial position

(b)   the greatest speed it attains.

A2   An elastic string of natural length 0.5 m and modulus of elasticity 20 N is stretched between two points A and B on a smooth horizontal table. AB = 1 m, and a particle of mass 0.4 kg is fastened to the middle of the string. The particle is pulled towards A to a point P, where AP = 0.25 cm, and is then released. Show that the subsequent motion is simple harmonic. Find the period and the greatest speed of the particle during the motion.

A3   A light spring of length l and modulus λ lies on a smooth horizontal table. One end

Exercise 15.2 *continued*

of the spring is fixed to a point O and the other end is attached to a particle of mass m. The spring is compressed to a length $\frac{1}{2}l$ and released.

(a) Show that the motion is simple harmonic with period $2\pi\sqrt{\dfrac{ml}{\lambda}}$

(b) Find the speed of the particle when the length of the spring is $5l/4$.

A4 A particle P of mass 0.2 kg moves on a smooth horizontal table. It is attached to one end of a light elastic string of natural length 0.5 m and modulus of elasticity 60 N, the other end of which is attached to a fixed point O on the table. The particle is released from rest when it is 1.3 m from O. Ignoring all resistances, calculate the speed of the particle when the string becomes slack. Find the time from release to reaching the point O.

B1 An elastic string of natural length $3l$ and modulus of elasticity λ is attached to two points A and B on a smooth horizontal table where AB = $3a(>3l)$. A particle of mass m is attached to a point P of the string where AP = a. It is pulled towards A a distance $d(d < a{-}l)$ and released. Show that the motion is simple harmonic with period

$$\frac{2\pi}{3}\sqrt{\frac{6ml}{\lambda}}.$$

B2 A particle of mass 2 kg is on a smooth horizontal table and is attached to one end

A of an elastic string of natural length 1.5 m and modulus of elasticity 12 N. The other end is fixed to a point O on the table. The particle is released when it is at a point B, where OB = 2 m. Find the time taken for the particle to reach O.

B3 One end of an elastic string of natural length 200 cm and modulus of elasticity 50 N is fixed to a point O on a smooth horizontal table. The other end is attached to a particle of mass 0.3 kg, which is lying on the table. The particle is pulled aside to a point P such that OP = 400 cm and is then released from rest. Find the time taken for the particle to return to O.

B4 A horizontal table is oscillating horizontally with SHM with period 2 s and maximum speed 4 m s^{-1}. Show that a heavy particle on the table will not slide if the coefficient of friction is greater than $2\pi/5$.

If the coefficient of friction is $\pi/10$ and the particle is placed on the table, when its acceleration is zero, calculate the speed of the table when the particle starts to slide.

B5 A particle of mass m is attached to one end of a light elastic string of natural length a, the other end of which is fixed to a point O. The particle is released from rest at O and falls a depth $2a$ before coming to rest.

(a) Prove that the tension in the string at the lowest point is $4mg$.

(b) Find the time for the particle to reach the lowest point.

15.3 Approximate SHM

Key points

There are many physical situations in which the motion of a system is approximately SHM, which the following example of the simple pendulum illustrates.

When other systems are found to perform SHM, they are often described by quoting the length of the equivalent simple pendulum which has the same period.

Example 1

A particle of mass m is suspended at the end of a light inelastic string of length l. The particle is pulled to one side through a small distance. Show that the subsequent motion is approximately simple harmonic.

Solution

Suppose that at time t the string makes an angle of θ radians with the downward vertical, as shown in Figure 15.6, where θ is small.

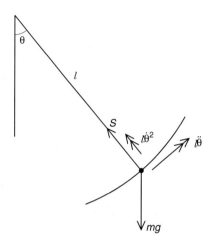

Figure 15.6

Applying N2 to the particle:

towards O $\quad S - mg\cos\theta = ml\dot\theta^2$ $\hspace{3cm}$ (1)

where S is the tension in the string,

tangentially $\quad -mg\sin\theta = ml\ddot\theta$ $\hspace{3cm}$ (2)

From (2) we obtain $\quad \ddot\theta = -\dfrac{g}{l}\sin\theta$

When θ is small, $\sin\theta \approx \theta$, so that $\ddot\theta \approx -\dfrac{g}{l}\theta$

This is the equation of SHM for θ, for which the period is $2\pi\sqrt{\dfrac{l}{g}}$ which we note is independent of the mass, m.

This is called a **simple pendulum**.

Exercise 15.3

B1 In a grandfather clock the pendulum takes 1 second for half a complete oscillation, i.e. to swing from one extreme to the other. Estimate the length of the pendulum, taking the value of g to be 9.812 m s^{-2}.

If the value of g is estimated to be 10 m s^{-2}, will this give a longer or shorter pendulum? If a pendulum is made to this size, how much will it lose or gain in a week compared with the one made with g taken as 9.812 m s^{-2}?

B2 A particle hanging in equilibrium at the end of a light spring stretches it by a distance d. Prove that for vertical oscillations about the equilibrium position, the length of the equivalent simple pendulum is d.

B3 A smooth circular wire of radius 0.8 m is fixed in a vertical plane. A light string of length 0.8 and modulus of elasticity 5 N has one end fixed to a point of the wire which is vertically above the centre and the other end is attached to a particle of mass 1 kg which is threaded on the wire. Show that the bead will perform approximate SHM about the lowest point on the wire and find its period. Take g as 10 m s^{-2}.

B4 Suppose the smooth circular wire in question **B3** has radius a and the string has modulus of elasticity λ with the bead having mass m. Show that the bead will perform approximate SHM provided $\lambda < 2mg$, and that the period is given by

$$2\pi\sqrt{\frac{2am}{2mg - \lambda}}.$$

Revision questions

Take g as 10 m s^{-2} where necessary.

C1 A particle P is moving in SHM in a straight line with centre O and amplitude 5 m. Given that the speed of P when $OP = 2$ m is 3 m s^{-1}, find the period of the motion.

C2 A horizontal platform performs SHM vertically with centre O amplitude 0.1 m and period 0.5 s. A particle is placed on the platform when it is at rest 0.1 m below O. Show that the particle will lose contact with the platform when the platform is 0.0633 m above O, correct to 3 significant figures. Find the speed of the particle at this instant, correct to 3 significant figures.

C3 On a certain day the depth of water at low tide at 7.00 a.m. is 5 m. At the following high tide at 1.15 p.m. the depth is 15 m. Assuming that the rise and fall of the water level is simple harmonic, find:

(a) the earliest time a ship can enter the harbour if a minimum depth of 12.5 m is required

(b) the rate at which the water is rising at that time. Give your answer in metres per minute.

C4 A particle of mass m on a smooth horizontal table is performing SHM with period T and amplitude a under the action of a force towards O. It collides with a similar particle of mass m, which is initially at rest at O. After the collision the particles coalesce. If the force is unchanged, show that the subsequent motion is simple harmonic and find the new period and amplitude in terms of T and a.

C5 The ends of a light elastic string of natural length $2l$ and modulus of elasticity $3mg$ are attached to two fixed points A and B on a smooth horizontal table where $AB = 6l$. A particle P of mass m is attached to the midpoint and is projected towards A with a speed of $\sqrt{\dfrac{2gl}{3}}$. Prove that the motion is simple harmonic with period $2\pi\sqrt{\dfrac{l}{6g}}$.

Find the amplitude of the motion in terms of l.

C6 Two elastic strings of natural length l and modulus $4mg$ are attached to two points A and B on a smooth horizontal table where $AB = 4l$. A particle of mass m is attached to the midpoint of AB. It is pulled to a point at a distance l from A and released from rest. Prove that the motion is simple harmonic with period $2\pi\sqrt{\dfrac{l}{2g}}$. When the particle passes through O the string OB is cut. Find how far from A the particle travels before it first comes instantaneously to rest.

C7 A particle P of mass m lies on a smooth horizontal table. It is attached to a point A on the table by a string of natural length $3a$ and modulus of elasticity λ and to a point B by a string of natural length $2a$ and modulus of elasticity 2λ. If $AB = 7a$ prove that in equilibrium $AP = 9a/2$. The particle is released from rest at a point P where $AP = 5a$. Prove that the subsequent motion is simple harmonic with period $\pi\sqrt{\dfrac{3ma}{\lambda}}$.

C8 A fixed point A is vertically above another fixed point B where $AB = 3$ m. A particle of mass m is joined to A by a string of natural length 1 m and modulus of elasticity $4mg$. It is joined to B by a string of natural length 1 m and modulus of elasticity $5mg$.

(a) Show that in equilibrium the particle rests at a depth $\frac{1}{6}$ m below the midpoint of AB.

(b) The particle is pulled down a further distance of $\frac{1}{3}$ m and released from rest. Prove that the subsequent motion is SHM with period $\dfrac{2\pi}{3\sqrt{g}}$.

(c) Suppose instead that the particle is given a downwards impulse I from its equilibrium position. Find in terms of m the maximum value of I if both strings are to remain taut during the subsequent motion.

ANSWERS

Chapter 1

Exercise 1.1
A1 100 m min^{-1}
A2 8 m s^{-1} 55 m
A3 0.5 m s^{-2} 11.25 m
A4 a) $t = 2$ b) 6 m s^{-1} c) 15 m
A5 153.5 m
A6 1.25 m s^{-2} 8 s
A7 a) 4.8 s   b) 72 m

B1 a) 166.25 s   b) 2.7 m s^{-1}
   c) -0.9 m s^{-1}
B2 2 m s^{-2}
B3 After 6 s. 27 m
B4 a) OA: 6 m s^{-1} AB: 5 m s^{-1} BC: at rest
   CD: 10 m s^{-1} DE: 10 m s^{-1}
   b) 3.3 m s^{-1} c) -1.67 m s^{-1}
B5 13.8 m s^{-1} 1.5 m s^{-1}
B6 1.15 m s^{-1}
B7 a) 30 s   b) 2000 m

Exercise 1.2
A1 20.4 m
A2 3.02 s
A3 3 m s^{-2}, 150 m
A4 0.087 m s^{-2}
A5 a) 1.53 m   b) 22.8 m s^{-1}
A6 0.25 m s^{-2}, 80 s
A7 1 m s^{-2} 200 m
A8 4.4 m s^{-1} -3.9 m s^{-2}

B1 28.3 m s^{-1}
B2 1 m s^{-2} 8.5 m s^{-1}
B3 2.45 m
B4 1/2, 2/3
B5 2.5 km, 3.33 km
B6 100 m
B8 10 m s^{-1} 15.5 s
B9 b) $^6/_7$
B10 24.5 s, 4 s

Revision questions
C1 42 m
C2 a) 18.97 m s^{-1} b) 378 m   c) 10.6 s
   d) 86.9 m s^{-1}
C3 $T = 10. 1 \text{ m s}^{-2}$
C5 8275 m
C6 b) 1440 m   c) 120 s   d) $1/30 \text{ m s}^{-2}$
C7 9.2 m
C8 $^7/_4$ s, apple going down, orange moving up.
C9 a) $+2 \text{ m s}^{-1}$, -1 m s^{-1}, $+2 \text{ m s}^{-1}$, -2 m s^{-1}
   b) 1 m s^{-1} c) decelerating, not uniformly, from rest to -2 m s^{-1}, between $t = 6$ and $t = 10$, then at constant speed to $t = 12$.
C10 a) 4 m s^{-1} b) 1.5 m s^{-2} c) 118 m

Chapter 2

Exercise 2.1
A1 10.20 m s^{-1}, $011.3°$
A2 3.24 m, 206.2°
A3 3.85 m, 23.3°
A4 10.62 m, 94.7°
A5 30.26 m s^{-1}, 344.6°
A6 17.32, 10
A7 2.82, 1.5
A8 0.87, 4.92
A9 1, 1.73
A10 East: -60.6 km. North: 197.7 km

B1 6.05 knots. 214.6°. 18 nautical miles off course
B2 148.3°
B3 16.7 m
B4 7.57 m s^{-1}. 200 m
B5 48.1 °
B6 304.8 °
B7 AB: 116.7°. 197 s
   BC: 83.3 s
   CA: 211.1°. 124.4 s
   No wind: 375 s

Exercise 2.2
A1 15.0, bearing 062°
A2 $P = 8.85$ N, $Q = 2.01$ N

A3 Magnitude: 9.43 N. Bearing 062°
A5 Parallel to 38 N force
A6 397 N
A7 Magnitude: $\sqrt{58}$. Direction: 156.8° with **i** direction
A8 Q = 4.48 N. R = 3.66 N
A9 Magnitude: $\sqrt{52}$ N. Bearing: 110°
A10 a) F = 13, α = 157°
   b) F = 7.81, α = 154°
   c) r = 3, α = 120°

B1 F = 1.74 N. α = 22.7°
B2 a) 6.28 N. 133° with 7 N force
   b) 10.99 N. 19.5° with direction of 3 N force
B3 12.8 N. 204.7° with **i** direction. $y = 0.46x$
B4 7.14 N. 90.9° with **i** direction
B5 4.29 N. 234° with **i** direction
B6 $x = 5, y = -8$. Resultant: $-6\mathbf{i} + 10\,\mathbf{j}$

Revision questions
C1 7.62 N. 111.9° with 7 N force
C2 12.28 N. 79.2° anti-clockwise from line BC
C3 9.06 N. 39.1° with AB
C4 35.13 N. 15.8° with 45 N force
C5 b) P = 367 N.   c) as b)
C6 13.1 knots. 063.9°

Chapter 3

Exercise 3.1

A1 a) $\begin{pmatrix} -5 \\ -0 \end{pmatrix}$ m s^{-2}

   b) $\begin{pmatrix} -2 \\ -4 \end{pmatrix}$ m s^{-2}

   c) $^1/_9\begin{pmatrix} -30 \\ -20 \end{pmatrix}$ m s^{-2}

A2 a) $\begin{pmatrix} -2.5 \\ -2.5 \end{pmatrix}$ m s^{-2}

   b) $\begin{pmatrix} 0 \\ -2 \end{pmatrix}$ m s^{-2}

   c) $\begin{pmatrix} 0 \\ 0 \end{pmatrix}$ m s^{-2}

A3 a) $\mathbf{i} - 2\mathbf{j}$ b) $9\mathbf{i}$ c) $8\mathbf{i} + 2\mathbf{j}$
   d) $4\mathbf{i} + \mathbf{j}$ e) $4\mathbf{i} + (2t - 3)\mathbf{j}$ f) $4\mathbf{i} + \mathbf{j}$
A4 a) $16\mathbf{i} + 11\mathbf{j}$ b) $54\mathbf{i} + 26\mathbf{j}$
   c) $\sqrt{(38^2 + 14^2)} = 40.5$ d) $3t^{1/2}\mathbf{i} + 3t\mathbf{j}$
   e) $^3/_2t^{-1/2}\mathbf{i}$

A5 a)

t	1	2	3	4	6
r	$3\mathbf{i} + 4\mathbf{j}$	$6\mathbf{i} + 2\mathbf{j}$	$9\mathbf{i} + ^4/_3\mathbf{j}$	$12\mathbf{i} + \mathbf{j}$	$18\mathbf{i} + ^2/_3\mathbf{j}$

   c) $xy = 12$ d) $\mathbf{v} = 3\mathbf{i} - ^4/_{t^2}\mathbf{j}$

   e) $a = \dfrac{8}{t^2}\mathbf{j}$

A6 a) $\mathbf{v} = 6t\mathbf{i} + 12t^{-1/2}\mathbf{j}$, $|\mathbf{v}| = \sqrt{(t^2 + 4/t)}$
   b) $t = 4$ c) $\mathbf{a} = 6\mathbf{i} + 6t^{-t/3}\mathbf{j}$

B1 a) $6\mathbf{i} - 3\mathbf{j}$ b) $(t^3 + 1)\mathbf{i} + (4t^{3/2} - 1)\mathbf{j}$
   c) $2\mathbf{i} + 3\mathbf{j}$ d) $\sqrt{17}$
B2 a) $\mathbf{v} = (2t^2 + 1)\mathbf{i} + (2 - 3t)\mathbf{j}$
   b) $\mathbf{r} = (^2/_3t^3 + t - 3)\mathbf{i} + (2t - 3t^2 + 2)\mathbf{j}$
   c) $\mathbf{r} = 18\mathbf{i} - 19\mathbf{j}$, speed $= \sqrt{410}$

B3 a) $\mathbf{v} = \begin{pmatrix} 6t - 4 \\ 2t \end{pmatrix}$

   b) $t = 2$ c) $\mathbf{a} = \begin{pmatrix} 6 \\ 2 \end{pmatrix}$ $|\mathbf{a}| = \sqrt{40}$

B4 a) $-^1/_3\mathbf{j}, 6\mathbf{i} - ^1/_{12}\mathbf{j}, 12\mathbf{i} - ^1/_{27}\mathbf{j}$

   b) $\mathbf{r} = t^2\mathbf{i} + \dfrac{3}{(t + 3)}\mathbf{j}$

   c) $\mathbf{a} = 2\mathbf{i} - \dfrac{6}{(t + 3)^3}\mathbf{j}$

   d) $\mathbf{a} \to 2\,\mathbf{i}, \mathbf{v} \to 2t\,\mathbf{i}, \mathbf{r} \to t^2\mathbf{i}$

B5 b) $2\mathbf{i} - \mathbf{j}$ c) $\mathbf{j}$ d) $2\mathbf{i} - \mathbf{j}$
B6 $t = 3$
B7 $\mathbf{v} = 0$ when $t = 6$. When $t = 6$,
   $\mathbf{r} = -30\mathbf{i} - 36\mathbf{j}, \mathbf{a} = 2\mathbf{i} + 6\mathbf{j}$
B8 a) 52   b) 14.2
B9 3.35 s

Exercise 3.2

A1 a) $\mathbf{v} = \begin{pmatrix} 18 \\ -9 \end{pmatrix}$

   b) $\mathbf{r} = \begin{pmatrix} 12 \\ -6 \end{pmatrix}$

A2 a) $\mathbf{v} = (3 - t)\mathbf{i} + (5 - 2t)\mathbf{j}$ b) 2.5 s
   c) 3 s

A3 $\mathbf{v} = \begin{pmatrix} 18 \\ 1 \end{pmatrix}$ $\mathbf{r} = \begin{pmatrix} 7 \\ -0.5 \end{pmatrix}$

A4 a) $\begin{pmatrix} 0.5 \\ -1 \end{pmatrix}$ b) $\begin{pmatrix} 5.5 \\ 0 \end{pmatrix}$

A5 a) $\mathbf{a} = \begin{pmatrix} 0 \\ 6 \end{pmatrix}$ (constant)

B1 When $t = 4$ $\mathbf{r} = \begin{pmatrix} 28 \\ 8 \end{pmatrix}$

B2 a) $\mathbf{a} = \begin{pmatrix} -2 \\ 1 \end{pmatrix}$ b) $\mathbf{v} = \begin{pmatrix} 0 \\ 5 \end{pmatrix}$

c) At $t = 5$, $\mathbf{r} = \begin{pmatrix} -4 \\ 14.5 \end{pmatrix}$

B3 a) $\sqrt{38}$
b) $\mathbf{v}_A = 2t\mathbf{i} - 3\mathbf{j}$, $\mathbf{v}_B = 3\mathbf{i} + 2t\mathbf{j}$. Hence $\mathbf{v}_A.\mathbf{v}_B = 0$

B4 a) $\mathbf{r}_A = \begin{pmatrix} t \\ t - t^2 + 3 \end{pmatrix}$

$\mathbf{r}_B = \begin{pmatrix} t^2 \\ t^2/2 - t \end{pmatrix}$

b) No c) $t = 1$ d) $t = 0.21, 4.79$

Exercise 3.3
A1 a) 3 s b) 36 m c) 11.75 m
A2 a) 93.7 m b) 4.33 s c) 216.5 m
d) $v^2 = 1700 \Rightarrow v \approx 41.2$ m s^{-1}
A3 The ball goes straight into the goal
A4 Time to goal line = 2.79 s, the ball clears the bar by 14 m (!) and the speed as the ball crosses the bar is 16.28 m s^{-1}
A5 a) $25\sqrt{2}$ m s^{-1} b) 22.5 m
A6 a) B
A7 a) 80 m b) $10\sqrt{17}$ m s^{-1} c) $2\sqrt{3}$ s
d) Yes
A8 a) $\sin^{-1}(1/3) \approx 19.47°$ b) 4 s
c) 226.3 m

B1 a) 13.98 m s^{-1} b) t = 3.34 s
c) 25.73 m
B2 a) $\theta = 17.83°$ b) 4.9 s c) 373 m
B3 a) 5.7 m b) 7.2 m
B4 a) 3.38 s b) 15.9 m c) 26.2 m s^{-1}
B5 a) 42.15 m b) i) 42.4 m ii) 41.3 m, 44°
B6 a) 4.47 s b) 447 m c) 109.5 m s^{-1}
d) Vertically above B

B7 a) $\begin{pmatrix} 3/5 ut \\ 4/5 ut - 5t^2 \end{pmatrix}$

b) $\mathbf{h} = 120 - 5t^2$
c) $\mathbf{u} \geq 75/\sqrt{6}$ (30.6 m s^{-1})

B8 a) 68.2° b) 53.85 m s^{-1} c) 22.4 m s^{-1}

Revision questions
C1 a) $\mathbf{v} = \begin{pmatrix} 2t \\ 3t^2 - 1 \end{pmatrix}$ $\mathbf{a} = \begin{pmatrix} 2 \\ 6t \end{pmatrix}$ b) $t = 1/\sqrt{3}$

C2 a) $\sqrt{41}$ b) $t = 1$
c) $\mathbf{v}_1 = \begin{pmatrix} 2t \\ 2 \end{pmatrix}$ $\mathbf{v}_2 = \begin{pmatrix} -1 \\ 2t \end{pmatrix}$
$|\mathbf{v}_1| \neq |\mathbf{v}_2|$ for any value of t.

C3 a) $\mathbf{AB} = \begin{pmatrix} t^3 - 2t \\ 3t - t^2 - 2 \end{pmatrix}$

$\mathbf{AB} \neq \begin{pmatrix} 0 \\ 0 \end{pmatrix}$ for any value of t.

b) $\sqrt{445}$ c) AB = 1

C4 a) 28.8 m b) 1.07 s c) 2.65 s
d) 34.9 m s^{-1}
C5 a) 1.8 m b) 8.78 m
C6 29.4 m s^{-1}
C7 a) 1.55 s b) 1.67 m

C8 a) $\mathbf{v} = \begin{pmatrix} -\pi \sin \pi t \\ \pi \cos \pi t \end{pmatrix}$

b) $\mathbf{a} = \begin{pmatrix} -\pi \cos \pi t \\ -\pi^2 \sin \pi t \end{pmatrix}$

The magnitude of the acceleration is constant.

C9 a) $\mathbf{v} = \begin{pmatrix} e^t + e^{-t} \\ e^t - e^{-t} \end{pmatrix}$

$\mathbf{a} = \begin{pmatrix} e^t - e^{-t} \\ e^t + e^{-t} \end{pmatrix}$ b) $y^2 - x^2 = 4$

Chapter 4

Exercise 4.1
A1 a) 470 N b) 290 N c) 0 N
A2 T = 9.8, S = 16.97
A3 a) T = 67.2. b) m = 8.4 kg
A4 S = 1043 N. T = 357 N
A5 a) T = 2.86 N b) $\theta = 71°$
A6 a) 1194 N b) −1104 N
A7 T = 13.4 N. S = 19.6 N

B1 a) P = 36.6 N b) R = 86.5 N
B2 a) 31.5 N b) 30.4 N
B3 a) 392 N
b) S = 34.3 N T = 278 N
B4 a) 19.6 N, 29.4 N
b) $\alpha = 46.6°$, $\beta = 29°$

B5 a) $T = 159.5$ N, $S = 130$ N
　　 b) AB under tension. AC under
　　 compression
B6 a) $T = 357$ N　 b) $S = 350$ N
B7 112 N

Exercise 4.2
A1 a) 0.51　 b) 3.75 N
A2 47.1 N

A3 a) 3/8　 b) $\dfrac{mg}{16} (8 - 3\sqrt{3})$

A4 0.7
A5 116 N
A6 a) 0.28　 b) 1190 N
A7 a) 29.6 N　 b) 136 N
A8 a) $m > 0.85$　 b) $m < 2.15$

B2 a) 35.3 N　 b) 66.4 N
B3 a) 5.2 N　 b) 35.8 N　 c) 1.18 N
B4 a) 0.17　 b) 20.7 N
B5 a) 9.13 N　 b) 29.6 N
B6 0.49. Since $0.49 < \tan 30°$, if 40 N force is
　　 removed, particle will slide down the plane.

Revision questions
C1 26 N, 32 N
C2 81 N, 36°
C3 0.58
C4 a) $P = 2/11\ mg$　 b) $P = 5\ mg$
C5 a) 5/9　 b) 2.76

Chapter 5

Exercise 5.1
A1 13.5 N
A2 180 N
A3 140 m s^{-2}　 3.5 N
A4 5.4 N
A5 3.78 m s^{-2} on a bearing of 113°
A6 14.9 N on a bearing of 129°
A7 1.05 m s^{-2}　 18.4 ° below the x-axis
A8 5.75 m s^{-2}. 12.8 m s^{-1}. 244 m
A9 5.19 m s^{-2}

B1 5.12 N. At an angle of 24.9° with the 10 N
　　 force
B2 5.23 m s^{-2}. 2.73 m s^{-2}
B3 a) 64 N, 47 N　 b) 128 N, 94 N
B4 0.42 m s^{-2}. 59.9°
B5 0.41 m s^{-2}. 7.97°
B6 0.59 m s^{-2}. Lift force is 7.58×10^5 N
B7 6.72 m s^{-2}. 16.6 m s^{-1}　 46.6 m
B8 0.52 m s^{-2}

Exercise 5.2
A1 12900 N. 312 N
A2 a) 9800 N　 b) 430 N　 c) 15.6 N
　　 d) 9790 N　 e) 9800 N
A3 a) 848 N, 7630 N　 b) 623 N, 561 N
A4 a) 10600 N, 834 N　 b) 12300 N, 960 N
　　 c) 9020 N, 706 N
A5 a) 0.51 m s^{-2}　 b) 15.5 m　 c) 7.84 s

B1 40 s, 500 m,
B2 151 km h^{-1}
B3 8.8°
B4 a) 17.1 N　 b) 17.7 N
B5 a) 0.51 m s^{-2}　 b) 2.92 s
　　 c) 11 m, 2.28 m

Revision questions
C1 2.28 m s^{-2}. 322°
C2 1.56 m s^{-2}. 7.81×10^5 N
C3 215.6 N, 0.82 m s^{-2}
C4 -3.04 m s^{-2}. 3.29 m s^{-1}
C5 a) 2450 N
　　 b) i) 0.41 m s^{-2} ii) 12.2 m s^{-1}
　　 c) i) -0.425 m s^{-2} ii) 1.7 m s^{-1}
C6 a) 8720 N　 b) 0.6 s　 c) $n \leq 6$
C7 $2P = 3.16$ m　 a) 5.92 s　 b) 11.2 m
C8 49.5 N, 2790 N

Chapter 6

Exercise 6.1
A1 a) 0.5 m s^{-2}　 b) 4000 N
A2 a) $2/3$ m s^{-2}　 b) 10/3 N
A3 a) $20/13$ m s^{-2}　 b) 154 N
A4 a) 1.43 m s^{-2}　 b) 1071 N
A5 a) 345 N, 225 N　 b) 5600 N, 2480 N
A6 a) 210 N, 90 N　 b) 0.075 m s^{-2}, 2670 m

B1 a) 382 N　 b) 114 N
B2 i) 1.33 m s^{-2} ii) 0.48 m s^{-2}
B3 a) 2.02 m s^{-2}　 b) 2390 N
B4 a) 3×10^4 N　 b) 5000 N
　　 c) 0.014 m s^{-2}　 d) 4.5 km
B5 a) i) 5.36×10^4 N
　　 ii) 2.29×10^5 N　 b) i) 909 N
　　 ii) 3410 N
B6 a) 1.04 m s^{-2}　 b) 504 N　 c) 1.60 m s^{-2}.
　　 115 m

Exercise 6.2 (NB $g = 10$ so final numerical answers should be given to 1 sig. fig.)
A1 $T = 8g/3$ N　 $a = g/3$ m s^{-2}
A2 $a = 7g/12$ m s^{-2}
A3 $a = g/12$ m s^{-2}. $13g/3$ N, $55g/12$ N

A4 a) $a = g/5$ m s^{-2} b) $T = 0.36g$ N
A5 $a = g/6$ m s^{-2}
A6 $a = 4g/7$ m s^{-2}

B1 $T = 2.32g$ N $a = 0.82g$ m s^{-2} $\alpha = 48.6°$
B2 $T = 1.652g$ N $a = 0.026g$ m s^{-2}
B3 $a = 7g/16$ m s^{-2} $T = 45g/16$ N
B4 $T = 20$ N $a = 1.5$ m s^{-2} increase to 59°
B5 a) $a = 0.18g$ m s^{-2} b) $T = 1.68g$ N
B6 a) $T = 2.93g$ N
        b) $a = 0.27g$ m s^{-2} 1.15 m

Exercise 6.3
A1 $\mu = 0.74$
A2 41 N
A3 a) $F = 2.0$ N 10.0 m s^{-2} b) $F = 0$ N,
        $a = 0$ m s^{-2} c) $F = 4$ N, $a = 2.2$ m s^{-2}
A4 15 m
A5 1.7 m s^{-2}. 10 N
A6 2.9 m s^{-2}. 14 N

B1 16 m
B2 a) 0.36 b) 0.66
B3 1.62 m s^{-2}, 4.0 m s^{-1}
B4 1.5 m s^{-2}, 25 N
B5 a) 6.1 m s^{-2} b) 2.1 m c) 0.82 s
        d) 0.06 m s^{-2} e) 0.5 m s^{-1} f) 9.1 s
B6 a) $1.8g$ N b) 0.26 c) $2.55g$ N

Revision questions
C1 a) 0.75 m s^{-1} b) 1.6 s c) 0.008 s
C2 a) $T = 10g/9$ N $a = 2g/7$ b) 15 N
        c) 0.2 kg
C3 a) 1.9 m s^{-2}
        b) 3.8 m s^{-1} 4.5 m
C4 $K = 0.144$. On train 260 N. On car 110 N
        a) 1.4 m s^{-2} down slope b) 13 m
C5 a) $4/150$ m s^{-2} b) First: 3.4×10^4 N.
        Last: 1.3×10^4 N
        c) 6.8×10^4 N d) 4.1 km
C6 $4mg/5$, $a = g/2$
C7 a) $a = g/5$ m s^{-2}, $T_1 = 24g/5$ N,
        $T_2 = 12g/5$ N b) $a = g/3$ m s^{-2}.
        $T_1 = 4g$ N, $T_2 = 2g$ N, accelerations of
        masses hanging from the moving pulley:
        $g/2$ and $g/6$

Chapter 7

Exercise 7.1
A1 a) 288 b) 1600 c) 62.5
A2 a) 468.75 kJ b) 180 kJ
        c) 8.35×10^{-14} J d) 2.25×10^{-3} kJ

A3 1.69 N
A4 1.67×10^4 N
A5 25.6 m
A6 15.4 kg

B1 a) 5760 J b) 112 N
B2 6.2 m s^{-1}
B3 3.5 m s^{-1}
B4 a) 4.9 N b) 49 J c) 10 m

Exercise 7.2
A1 8160 J, 14.3 m s^{-1}
A2 6.97 m s^{-1}
A3 0.705 N, 13.5 m s^{-1}
A4 a) 10 N b) 12.6 N
A5 4.48 m s^{-1} 1.02 m

B1 a) 12.5 m s^{-1} b) 11.8 m s^{-1}
B2 2320 N
B3 a) 1.07 m b) 3.2 m s^{-1}
B4 239000 N

Exercise 7.3
A1 60 kW
A2 4.5 kW
A3 750 N
A4 710 N
A5 a) 30 m s^{-1} b) 17 m s^{-1} c) 47 m s^{-1}
A6 a) 500 kW b) 6.25 m s^{-1}
        c) 3.16 m s^{-1}

B1 20 kW
B2 19 kW 0.49 m s^{-2}
B3 (a) 50 kW (b) 36 kW (c) 12 m s^{-1}
B4 (a) 120 kW (b) 0.027 m s^{-2}
        (c) $\sin \alpha = 0.03$
B5 36 kW. 29 m s^{-1}
B6 $A = 2.125$. $a = 1.15$ m s^{-2}

Exercise 7c
C1 (a) 4250 J (b) 9000 J
C2 (a) 1500 J (b) 6750 J (c) 160 N
        (d) 42 m
C3 (a) 0.74 m (b) 1.63 m s^{-1}
C4 400 kW
C5 (a) 144 km h^{-1} (b) 55 km h^{-1}
C6 77 kW
C7 8.4 kW
C8 40 m s^{-1} 15 m s^{-1}

Chapter 8

Exercise 8.1
A1 (a) 17000   (b) 2.25   (c) 2.7
A2 17000 N s
A3 1.5 N s, 1.5 Ns
A4 0.8 N s away from the cushion
A5 1.3 m s^{-1}
A6 8.25 N s
A7 6.94 N s
A8 9000 N s, 19.1 m s^{-1}
A9 (a) 2.7 N s   (b) 0
     (c) Weight force: $t = 1.8$ s
A10 (a) 30 N   (b) 6 N

B1 1.7 Ns
B2 0.67 N s. Contact not smooth
B3 2.74 N s. 15.6° to normal
B4 1.46 N s, 16.7° to normal
B5 Deflection: 138.5° 25.2 m s^{-1}.
B6 (a) 1.03 m s^{-1} (b) 0 N s
B7 9.6 m s^{-1}, 51.3° to the original direction
B8 21.7 m s^{-1}, 14° to the wall
B9 11.1 N s, 16° to the normal
B10 17519 N s, 11.6° to the normal

Exercise 8.2
A1 (1) 2 m s^{-1} (b) 1.6 m s^{-1}
A2 (1) (a) 13.8 m s^{-1} (b) 7/8 m s^{-1}
     (2) (a) 2.75 m s^{-1} (b) 0.25 m s^{-1}
     (3) (a) 2.28 m s^{-1} (b) 0.5 m s^{-1}
A3 0.083 m s^{-1}
A4 3 m s^{-1}
A5 (a) 3 m s^{-1} (b) 6750 J   (c) 3000 J
     lost.
A6 (a) 0.3 N s   (b) 1.5 m s^{-1} (c) 0.525 J
A7 (a) 13.3 km h^{-1} (b) 7.8 × 10^{3} J
A8 (a) 0.1 m s^{-1} (b) 150 N   (c) −225 J

B1 (a) 3.26 m s^{-1}, 45°   (b) 8.87 J
B2 (a) $v = 2.95$ m s^{-1}, $w = 1.95$ m s^{-1}
     (b) 0.375 J
B3 (a) 3.89 m s^{-1}. 1322 J   (b) 2.78 m s^{-1}. -
     1137 J   (c) 2.0 m s^{-1} −16350 J
B4 2.55 m s^{-1}. 0.65°. 0.2185 J
B5 1.35 m s^{-1}. 17.6°
B6 1.62 m s^{-1}. 5.37 m s^{-1}

Exercise 8.3
A1 (a) 2 m s^{-1} (b) 4 N s   (c) 12 J
A2 (a) 4 m s^{-1} (b) 4 N s   (c) 12 J
A3 (a) u (b) 4 mμ (c) 10 mμ^2
A4 (a) 4u (b) 4 mμ (c) 10 mμ^2
A5 0.23 m s^{-1}. 6.42 J

A6 0.235 m s^{-1}, 2.35 m. Approx 25 sec
A7 2500 N s

B1 (a) $-u$ (b) 3 mμ^2/2, 27 mμ^2/2
B2 (a) 4000 m s^{-1} (b) 1500 m kJ
B3 (a) 2.67 m s^{-1} (b) 21.3 kJ loss
     (c) 69.3 kJ gain
B4 (a) 4.36 m s^{-1} (b) 3273 N s   (c) 17 kJ
B5 9.5 m s^{-1}. 4200 N s
B6 136.9 N s. 37.2° to the slope. 780 J

Exercise 8C
C1 (a) 2 m s^{-1} (b) 5000 J
C2 (a) 8 m s^{-1}, 12 m s^{-1} (b) 60 J
C3 (a) 8.39 m s^{-1} (b) 0.04 N s
     (c) 0.045 J
C4 (a) 8400 N s   (b) 42000 N

C5 (a) $\left(\dfrac{-4}{8}\right)$m s^{-1} (b) $\left(\dfrac{-15}{15}\right)$N s

     (c) 120 J loss
C6 (a) 0.5 kg at 143° to direction of 2 kg
     piece.   (b) Yes   (c) gain of 536 J
C7 (a) 3.62 m s^{-1} (b) 185 N s
C8 2.17 m s^{-1}. 0.0375 N s 0.007 J
C9 (a) 141 N s   (b) 3.54 m s^{-1}. They would
     be unchanged
C10 (a) 0.433 rad s^{-1} (b) 75 N s

Chapter 9

Exercise 9.1
A1 $v = 65$ $x = 68$
A2 $v = 12$ $x = 13.5$
A3 $v = 3.75$ $x = 7$
A4 $v = 24$ $x = 57.6$
A5 $v = 6$ $x = 25^{1}/_{3}$
A6 27 m s^{-1} 46 m

B1 $v = 1 + \sin t$ $x = 3 + t - \cos t$

B2 $v = 2 \cos \dfrac{1}{2} t$ $x = 4 \sin \dfrac{1}{2} t$

B3 $v = \dfrac{1}{t + 1}$ $x = \ln (t + 1)$

B4 $v = 3(t + e^{-t})$

     $x = 3 + 3\left(\dfrac{t^2}{2} - e^{-t}\right)$

B5 21.1 m
B6 13.9 km. 3.24 h

Exercise 9.2
A1 10.6
A2 5
A3 $\sqrt{21} \approx 4.58$
A4 9.71
A5 $21^1/_3$
A8 9 m

B1 a) 2 m s^{-1} b) 5 m from O
B2 a) $^2/_3$ m
B5 a) 10 h   b) 10.5 km
B6 $^\pi/_6$ s

Exercise 9.3
A2 a) 50 m s^{-1} b) 2.55 s   c) 27.7 m

A4 $v = u\dfrac{(e^{20t/u} - 1)}{(e^{20t/u} + 1)}$.

As $t \to \infty$, $v \to u$

B1 $45 \ln\left(\dfrac{13}{9}\right) \approx 16.5$ m, 17 m s^{-1}

B3 Last part: max. speed is 40 m s^{-1}. 1.15 s

B4 a) $v = \dfrac{1}{2}(2e^{-2t} - 1)$

b) $v \to -^1/_2$

c) $x = \dfrac{1}{4} - \dfrac{v}{2} + \dfrac{1}{2}\ln\dfrac{2v + 1}{2}$

Revision questions

C1 b) $x = \dfrac{t}{4} + \dfrac{1}{4}e^{-2t} - \dfrac{1}{4}$

C3 b) P ultimately moves away from O approaching a speed of $\sqrt{30}$ m s^{-1}
C4 a) 1.6×10^5 km   b) 6.45×10^3 km
C6 a) 8 m s^{-1} b) 0.458 m s^{-2}
c) 1.74 s
C7 a) 7.9×10^3 m s^{-1} b) 1.12×10^4 m s^{-1}

C8 $x = \dfrac{2u^{3/2}}{k}(u^{1/2} - v^{1/2})$

Chapter 10

Exercise 10.1
A1 0.45 m s^{-2}
A2 $v = 988$ m s^{-1} $a = 1.98 \times 10^{-3}$ m s^{-2}
A3 40 rad s^{-1}
A4 1.5 s 10.5 rad s^{-1}
A5 4.4×10^{-4} rad s^{-1}
A6 $v = 3.9$ m s^{-1} $a = 3.08$ m s^{-2}

B1 a) $(x + 2)^2 + (y - 3)^2 = 16$
b) $v = 12\cos 3t\mathbf{i} - 12\sin 3t\mathbf{j}$.
$a = -36\sin 3t\mathbf{i} - 36\cos 3t\mathbf{j}$.   c) $|v| = 12$
and $|a| = 36$
B2 a) $v = 15t^2$ along the tangent
a has two components: $75t^4$ towards O and $30t$ along the tangent
b) a has magnitude 6076 m s^{-2} and is directed at an angle of 89.2° to the tangent
B3 Small pulley: 50 rad s^{-1}
Large pulley: 25 rad s^{-1}
B4 6.7 rad s^{-1}
B5 a) 0.75 m s^{-1} b) 7.5 rad s^{-1}, 15 rad s^{-1}
B6 a) 16.7 rad s^{-1} b) 10 m s^{-1}

Exercise 10.2
A1 10°
A2 18 m s^{-1}
A3 120 m s^{-1}
A4 5.3 rad s^{-1}
A5 a) 0.37 N   b) 37°
A6 9.8 cm

B1 2 cm, 22 rad s^{-1}
B2 2.5 N   5.7 rad s^{-1}
B3 a) 0.52 m s^{-1}
b) 0.089 N, 0.49 N   49 rpm

B4 $\omega^2 = \dfrac{g\cot\theta}{(r + l\cos\theta)}$

B5 a) $T = m(g\cos\alpha + l\omega^2\sin^2\alpha)$,
$R = m\sin\alpha(g - l\omega^2\cos\alpha)$

Exercise 10.3
A1 a) 3.56 m s^{-1} b) 0.646 m
A2 51.9°, 2.42 m s^{-1}
A3 a) 6.44 m s^{-1} b) 2.11 m
A4 a) 0.203 m   b) 0.459 m
A5 a) 6.11 N   b) 1.12 m
A6 a) 1.94 m s^{-1} b) 0.123 N towards O

B1 0.240 N
B2 5.42 m s^{-1}. Yes
B3 a) $v^2 = 4.17 - 3.92\cos\alpha$
b) $R = 2.94\cos\alpha - 2.09$ c) 44.8°
B4 3.63 m s^{-1}, 0.342 N outwards
B5 a) 4.54 m s^{-1} b) 7.11 N   c) 0.968 m
B6 a) 2.61 m s^{-1} b) 1.30 m s^{-1}
c) 0.260 m below O

Exercise 10.4
A1 a) 0.45 m   b) 5 m (string becomes slack)   c) 6 m (completes circles)
A2 a) $u^2 \leq 2ag$ b) $2ag < u^2 < 4ag$
c) $u^2 \leq 4ag$

A3 1 m
A4 5 m s^{-1}, 0 N
A5 3 m s^{-1}
A6 0.3 m

B1 a) $\cos^{-1}(^2/_3) \approx 48.2°$
b) $\sqrt{(2g)} \approx 4.47$ m s^{-1} c) 0.4 m
B2 a) $v^2 = 10.04 - 10\cos\alpha$
b) $3\cos\alpha - 2.008$ c) approx 48°
d) approx 1.83 m s^{-1} at 48° to horizontal
e) approx 0.73 m
B3 a) 0.4 m above A b) 1 m s^{-1}
c) 0.04 m
B4 a) approx 126° b) 3 m s^{-1} c) 1 m
B5 b) $\alpha = \sin^{-1}(^1/_3)$ $v = 4/\sqrt{3}$ m s^{-1}

Revision questions
C1 a) $u = \sqrt{(40d)}$ b) $v^2 = 20d(1 - \cos\theta)$
c) $R = 10m(3\cos\theta - 2)$ d) $\cos^{-1}(^2/_3)$
C2 4 rad s^{-1}
C3 approx 13 N, 15 rad s^{-1}
C4 $\tan^{-1}(^5/_3)$, $\tan^{-1}(2)$

C6 a) $\dfrac{13mg}{12}$ b) $5m\left(a\omega^2 - \dfrac{g}{12}\right)$

c) $\sqrt{\dfrac{g}{12a}}$

C7 0.9 rad s^{-1}. Assumptions: treat child + seat as particle, wires light, inextensible, no air resistance etc.

Chapter 11

Exercise 11.1
A1 15250 N
A2 10 N
A3 0.38 kg
A4 a) 2.78 J b) 11.1 J 8.41 J
A5 a) 480 N b) 4 J
A6 a) 1600 b) 2 J c) 6 J
A7 a) 0.8 J b) 3.6 J c) 2.8 J

B1 10 N 1.9 kg 0.34 J
B2 a) 8.3 N b) 0.42 J
B3 85 N
B4 a) 45 J b) 3.0 kg
B5 a) $5a/4$ b) $mga/16$

Exercise 11.2
A1 3.2 m
A2 300 N
A3 8 J 28.3 m s^{-1}

A4 9.13 m s^{-1}
A5 14.7 m s^{-1}

B1 a) 2.9 J b) 24 N
B2 a) 1.6 m b) 2.9 m
B3 a) 2.0 m s^{-1} b) 2.8 m s^{-1} c) 3.2 m
B4 a) $8g$ N b) 20 cm c) g N
B5 0.625 m – the string is slack
B6 150 m

Revision questions
C1 $\lambda = 1.2 \times 10^6$ N a) 25 cm b) 75 cm
C2 a) 17.64 J b) 2.06 m s^{-1} c) 1.84 m
C3 a) 8.8 m b) 24 m s^{-1}
C4 a) 15 N b) 2.6 m
C5 b) 0.76 m c) 3.0 m s^{-1}
C6 1.549 m (1.5 m to 2 sig. fig.) a) 5.5 m s^{-1}
b) 0.44 m
C8 b) $7g/5$

Chapter 12

Exercise 12.1
A1 a) 120 m b) 49 m s^{-1} c) 60.0 m
d) 3.5 s
A2 a) 11 m s^{-1} b) 0.38 s c) 10 m s^{-1}
d) 1.0 s
A3 a) 0.53 b) 11 m, 3.1 m
A4 a) 5.4 m b) 4.4 m
A5 a) 0.64 b) 0.33 m
A6 a) 7.92 m s^{-1} b) 2.04 m c) 3
A7 6.4 m s^{-1}
A8 11 m s^{-1}

B1 a) 0.8 m s^{-1} b) 4.5 s c) 0.4 m s^{-1}
d) 30.75 s, 10.5 m
B2 a) 1.6 m b) 9.8 m s^{-1}
B3 3.1 m s^{-1}. 0.59
B4 e^2h
B5 $^1/_3$
B7 a) 0.63 b) 0.23 N s
B8 a) 1.5 m
b) 1.656 m (1.7 m to 2 sig. fig.)
1.667 (1.7 m to 2 sig. fig.)

Exercise 12.2
A1 a) 10 m s^{-1} b) 6 m s^{-1} c) 0.6
e) 60 J
A2 a) 3 m s^{-1} b) 1.5 m s^{-1} c) 0.5
e) 16.5 J
A3 a) 3 m s^{-1} b) 0 m s^{-1} c) 0 e) 3 J
A4 a) 3 m s^{-1} b) 2 m s^{-1} c) $^2/_3$ e) 3 J
A5 a) 1 m s^{-1} b) 0.2 m s^{-1} c) 0.2
e) 0.36 m

A6 0.2 m s^{-1}, 1.7 m s^{-1}

B1 a) $3u$ b) 0.6 c) $6mu^2$

B2 a) $^1/_8$ b) $\dfrac{21mu^2}{64}$

B3 $\dfrac{2t}{e}$

B4 0.5
B5 3
B6 2

Exercise 12.3
A1 a) 1.41 m s^{-1} b) 0.5
A2 $e = {}^2/_3$, $\mathbf{v} = {}^2/_{\sqrt{3}}$ (both)
A3 Small sphere: $2\sqrt{2}$ m s^{-1}, large sphere $4\sqrt{2}/3$ m s^{-1}. $e = 2/3$
A4 a) $\sqrt{3}$ m s^{-1} b) $^1/_3$
   c) 0.35 N s along the line of centres
A5 $e = 1/3$

B1 $\alpha = 9.83°$ 4.43 m s^{-1}, 0.887 m s^{-1}
B3 $e = 0.58$ $v_P = 3.66$ m s^{-1}, $v_Q = 3.17$ m s^{-1}
B4 Sphere A: 2.96 m s^{-1} at 61.5° to line of centres
   Sphere B: 1.02 m s^{-1} at 78° to line of centres

Revision questions
C1 a) $^1/_8$ b) $\dfrac{35mu^2}{8}$

C2 a) $v_A = \dfrac{(10 + e)u}{3}$, $v_B = \dfrac{(10 + 2e)u}{3}$

   c) $2mu\dfrac{(10 + e)}{3}$

C3 30°
C4 a) 1.5 m s^{-1} b) 0.5 c) 0.75 m s^{-1}
   d) 0.75 m s^{-1}, 0.375 m s^{-1}
C5 a) 0.8 b) 1.6 m s^{-1} c) 6.4 m J

C7 $\dfrac{2d}{3}$

C8 a) $\dfrac{(1 - e^2)(u_1 - u_2)^2}{4}$

   b) 1, 0 c) When $e = 1$, $v_1 = u_2$;
   when $e = 0$, $v_2 = v_1 = {}^1/_2(u_1 + u_2)$
C9 0.58 m

Chapter 13

Exercise 13.1
A1 a) 8 N m b) 6.93 N m c) 6.93 N m
   d) -6.93 N m
A2 a) 14 N m b) 1.51 N m c) 6 N m
   d) 18.49 N m
A3 2.5 m
A4 27 N, 31 N
A5 2.86 m
A6 $^7/_3$ kg
A7 $^8/_3$ m

B1 2.54 N m
B2 -4 N, 6 N, -4 N
B3 6 N
B4 a) 5 N in direction DA b) 10 N m
B5 25 N, 613 N. 60 kg
B6 90 N, 160 N
B7 40 t. A further 5 m

Exercise 13.2
A1 13 N. 13 N
A2 53 N. 400 N
A3 30 N. 6.1 N
A4 a) $4g\sin 2\theta$ b) $12g\sin 2\theta$
A5 $\dfrac{3W}{4}$. $\dfrac{W\sqrt{13}}{4}$

B1 0.53 m
B2 8600 N. 7000 N
B3 47 N
B4 a) 45° b) 56°
B5 $\dfrac{W\sin\theta}{2}$.

   $\dfrac{W\sqrt{(4\cos^2\theta + \sin^2\theta)}}{2}$

B6 a) 31 kg
   b) 300 N at 81° to the horizontal

Exercise 13.3
A1 $\tan^{-1}({}^2/_3) \approx 33.7°$
A2 0.45
A3 $\tan\theta = 2\mu$
A4 $T = 2mg/5$. $mg\sqrt{13}/5$. $\mu = {}^3/_{29}$
A5 0.3 W, 1.04 W, 31°

B1 0.42
B2 0.39
B3 0.47
B4 2.1 m

B5 $\mu = \dfrac{\sin\theta\cos\theta}{1+\sin^2\theta}$

B6 0.52

Revision questions
C1 610 N   270 N

C2 a) $\dfrac{2W}{\sqrt{3}}$

 b) $W\sqrt{\dfrac{31}{3}}$ at 69° to horizontal

C3 T = 520 N $\mu = {}^2/_3$
C4 120 N, 490 N
C5 a) 61 N   b) 170 N, 53 N $\mu = 0.32$
C6 9.4 N, 11.7 N
C7 Horizontal: 360 N. Vertical 780 N   0.46
C8 2.5 t

Chapter 14

Exercise 14.1
A1 a) $(13/6, 7/6)$ b) $(1/3, 0)$
 c) $(1/2, 3/8)$
A2 $2.2a$
A3 28.75 cm
A4 a) $(a, 19a/15)$ b) $(11a/8, 11a/8)$
 c) $(53a/42, 53a/42)$
A5 ${}^7/_6$ m
A6 2.17 cm
A7 $11a/8$
A8 200/3 cm

B1 $-9/7$

B2 $\dfrac{29h}{40}$

B3 5.35 cm
B4 $a/6$ (below O)

B5 $\dfrac{h(a+2b)}{3(a+b)}$

B6 $13a/9$

Exercise 14.2
A1 $(3/4, 3/10)$
A2 $(3/5, 3/8)$
A3 $(9/20, 9/20)$
A4 $(3/4, 8/5)$
A7 5/6
A8 3/4
A9 $3a/8$
A10 5/8

B1 $(0.8, 3.43)$
B2 $(0, 4a/3\pi)$
B3 $(4a/3\pi, 4a/3\pi)$
B4 $(1.44, 0.36)$
B5 $(\pi/2, \pi/8)$

B6 $\dfrac{\pi}{4} + \dfrac{1}{\pi} \approx 1.1$

Exercise 14.3
A1 $\tan^{-1}(2/3) \approx 33.7°$
A2 $\tan^{-1}(83/12) \approx 47.3°$
A3 $\tan^{-1}(41/33) \approx 51.1°$
A4 $\tan^{-1}(5/2) \approx 68.2°$
A5 $\tan^{-1}(10/9) \approx 48.0°$
A6 $\tan^{-1}(2/3) \approx 33.7°$

B1 $\tan^{-1}\left(\dfrac{17h}{14a}\right)$

B2 a) $45.2°$

 b) $\dfrac{12W}{13}, \dfrac{5W}{13}$

B3 48.5°
B4 $\tan^{-1}(16/33) = 25.9°$
B5 $\tan^{-1}(4/3) = 53.1°$

Exercise 14.4
A1 a) slides   b) slides

A2 $\dfrac{1}{\sqrt{3}}$

B1 $1.12a$ approximately: it is the solution of the cubic equation

$$4a^3 = 4a^2x - \dfrac{1}{3}x^3$$

B2 $\mu = 1/4$ $\alpha = \tan^{-1}(1/4) \approx 14°$
B3 Sliding
B4 a) slides   b) topples

Revision questions
C1 39.8°
C5 $m = 2M/3$
C6 $\tan^{-1}(4/7) \approx 29.7°$
C7 $\tan^{-1}(45/112) = 21.9°$
C8 $13a/2$ $k = 35/3$
C9 $3a/2$
C10 b) $\tan^{-1}5 = 78.7°$ c) $m = M/6$

Chapter 15

Exercise 15.1

A1 Amplitude is 3.35 m, Period is 2.18 s.
Max speed = 7.48 m s^{-1}

A2 a) 0.09 s   b) 0.13 s

A3 0.04 m

A4 Period is 3.93 s.   Amplitude is 25/8 m

A5 3.53 s

A6 152 m s^{-2}

B3 $2a \sqrt{\dfrac{2}{m}}$

B5 a) 6.72 m   b) -2 m, 4.24 m s^{-1}

Exercise 15.2

A1 0.4 m   a) 0.3 s   b) 1 m s^{-1}

A2 Period is 0.44 s. Max speed = 1.77 m s^{-1}

A3 b) $\dfrac{1}{4} \sqrt{\dfrac{3l}{m}}$

A4 19.6 m s^{-1}. 0.071 s

B2 $\left(\dfrac{\pi}{4} + \dfrac{3}{2} \right)$ s ≈ 2.29 s

B3 0.282 s

B4 $\sqrt{15}$ m s^{-1}

B5 b) $\sqrt{\dfrac{a}{4g}} \left(2\sqrt{2} + \pi - \cos^{-1} \dfrac{1}{3} \right)$

Exercise 15.3

B1 0.994 m. Longer. It will lose just over $1^1/_2$ hours in a week

B3 $2\pi \sqrt{\dfrac{8}{75}}$

Revision questions

C1 $2\pi \dfrac{\sqrt{21}}{3}$

C2 0.997 m s^{-1}

C3 a) 11.10 a.m.   b) 0.036 m min^{-1}

C4 New period = $\sqrt{2}T$. New amplitude = $a/\sqrt{2}$

C5 $l/3$

C6 $l(1 + \sqrt{3}) \approx 2.73l$

C9 c) $m\sqrt{g}$

INDEX